Test Bank

for
Tan's

Applied Calculus for the Managerial, Life, and Social Sciences

Sixth Edition

Tracy Wang
Curry College

Australia • Canada • Mexico • Singapore • Spain • United Kingdom • United States

Printed in the United States of America
1 2 3 4 5 6 7 08 07 06 05 04

Printer: West Group

ISBN: 0-534-46504-8

Thomson Brooks/Cole
10 Davis Drive
Belmont, CA 94002-3098
USA

Asia
Thomson Learning
5 Shenton Way #01-01
UIC Building
Singapore 068808

Australia/New Zealand
Thomson Learning
102 Dodds Street
Southbank, Victoria 3006
Australia

Canada
Nelson
1120 Birchmount Road
Toronto, Ontario M1K 5G4
Canada

Europe/Middle East/South Africa
Thomson Learning
High Holborn House
50/51 Bedford Row
London WC1R 4LR
United Kingdom

Latin America
Thomson Learning
Seneca, 53
Colonia Polanco
11560 Mexico D.F.
Mexico

Spain/Portugal
Paraninfo
Calle/Magallanes, 25
28015 Madrid, Spain

TABLE OF CONTENTS

Chapter 1 ■ Preliminaries

Section 1.1

1. Determine whether the statement $\frac{4}{5} < \frac{2}{3}$ is true or false.
   Answer: False

2. Determine whether the statement $-3 \le -3$ is true or false.
   Answer: True

3. Show the interval $(-4,3]$ on a number line.
   Answer:

4. Show the interval $(-\infty,5]$ on a number line.
   Answer:

5. Find the values of x that satisfy the inequality $2x+3<11$.
   Answer: $x<4$

6. Find the values of x that satisfy the inequalities $2 \le x-1 \le 7$.
   Answer: $3 \le x \le 8$

7. Find the values of x that satisfy the inequalities $2 \le 2-2x \le 8$.
   Answer: $[-3,0]$

8. Find the values of x that satisfy the inequalities $x-2<4$ and $x+1 \ge 3$.
   Answer: $2 \le x < 6$

9. Find the values of x that satisfy the inequalities $3x-2<4$ or $x+1 \ge 7$.
   Answer: $(-\infty,2) \cup [6,\infty)$

10. Evaluate the expression $|-4+3|$.
    Answer: 1

11. Evaluate the expression $2-|2-4|$.
    Answer: 0

12. Evaluate the expression $|\pi-4|-3$.
    Answer: $1-\pi$

13. Evaluate the expression $\left|2-\sqrt{5}\right|-\left|6-2\sqrt{5}\right|$.

Answer: $-8+3\sqrt{5}$

14. Suppose that a and b are positive real numbers and that $a > b$. State whether the given inequalities are true or false.

(a) $b-a<0$

Answer: True

(b) $\frac{a}{b}<1$

Answer: False

(c) $-a>-b$

Answer: False

15. Suppose that a and b are positive real numbers and that $a > b$. State whether the given inequalities are true or false.

(a) $\frac{1}{a}<\frac{1}{b}$

Answer: True

(b) $a^2<b^2$

Answer: False

(c) $\frac{b}{a}>0$

Answer: True

16. Evaluate $64^{2/3}$

Answer: 16

17. Evaluate $\left[\left(\frac{1}{4}\right)^{1/2}\right]^{-1}$

Answer: 2

18. Evaluate $\left(\frac{1}{4}\right)^{-3/2}$

Answer: 8

19. Evaluate $\sqrt[3]{\frac{-1}{64}}$

Answer: $\frac{-1}{4}$

20. Evaluate $\left(\dfrac{3^{1.1}\cdot 3^{0.9}}{3^2}\right)^{1/2}$

Answer: 1

21. Rewrite the expression $(xy)^{-3}$ using positive exponents only.

Answer: $\dfrac{1}{(xy)^3}$

22. Rewrite the expression $\sqrt{x^{-3}}\sqrt{9x^4}$ using positive exponents only.

Answer: $3x^{1/2}$

23. Simplify the expression $(x^3y^{-2})(x^4y^{-5})$.

Answer: $\dfrac{x^7}{y^7}$

24. Simplify the expression $\dfrac{x^{5/3}}{x^{-1}}$.

Answer: $x^{8/3}$

25. Simplify the expression $\left(\dfrac{e^{x+1}}{e^{x-3}}\right)^{3/2}$.

Answer: e^6

26. Simplify the expression $\sqrt[3]{x^{-4}}\cdot\sqrt{9x^3}$.

Answer: $3x^{1/6}$

27. Simplify the expression $\sqrt{64x^2y^{-8}}$.

Answer: $\dfrac{8x}{y^4}$

28. Rationalize the denominator of the expression $\dfrac{4}{3\sqrt{2x}}$.

Answer: $\dfrac{2\sqrt{2x}}{3x}$

29. Rationalize the denominator of the expression $\sqrt{\dfrac{3x}{2y}}$.

Answer: $\dfrac{\sqrt{6xy}}{2y}$

30. Rationalize the numerator of the expression $\dfrac{2\sqrt{x}}{3y}$.

Answer: $\dfrac{2x}{3y\sqrt{x}}$

31. Rationalize the numerator of the expression $\dfrac{\sqrt[3]{xy^2 3y}}{3y}$.

Answer: $\dfrac{x}{(3x)^{2/3}}$

32. Find the minimum cost C (in dollars), given that $2(C-15) \geq 1.5 + 1.25C$.
Answer: 42

33. Find the maximum profit P (in thousands of dollars), given that $2(P-2) \geq 3.5P - 22$.

Answer: \$12 thousand

Section 1.2

1. Perform the indicated operations and simplify $(2x^2+5x+3)-(4x^2+x-6)$.
   Answer: $-2x^2+4x+9$

2. Perform the indicated operations and simplify $\left(\frac{1}{4}+2+e\right)+\left(-\frac{1}{4}+1-e^{-1}\right)$.
   Answer: $3+e-\frac{1}{e}$

3. Perform the indicated operations and simplify $x-\{3x-[-2x-(2-x)]\}$.
   Answer: $-3x-2$

4. Perform the indicated operations and simplify $(a-4)^2$.
   Answer: $a^2-8a+16$

5. Perform the indicated operations and simplify $(2x-5)(5+2x)$.
   Answer: $4x^2-25$

6. Perform the indicated operations and simplify $3(t-\sqrt{t})^2-3t^2$.
   Answer: $-6t\sqrt{t}+3t$

7. Factor out the greatest common factor from $3ab^2+6ab+3a^2b$.
   Answer: $3ab(b+2+a)$

8. Factor out the greatest common factor from $7xye^{xy}+21x^2ye^{xy}$.
   Answer: $7xye^{xy}(1+3x)$

9. Factor out the greatest common factor from $3x^{-3/2}+6x^{-1/2}$.

   Answer: $3x^{-3/2}(1+2x)$

10. Factor the expression x^2+3x-4.
    Answer: $(x+4)(x-1)$

11. Factor the expression $x^2+13x+12$.

    Answer: $(x+12)(x+1)$

12. Factor the expression $(x-y)^2 - 1$.
Answer: $(x-y+1)(x-y-1)$

13. Perform the indicated operations and simplify the algebraic expression $(x^2 - y^2)x + 2x(2y)$.
Answer: $x^3 - xy^2 + 4xy$

14. Perform the indicated operations and simplify the algebraic expression $4(x^2+2)^2(3x)$.
Answer: $12x^5 + 48x^3 + 48x$

15. Find the real roots of $2x^2 + x - 1 = 0$ by factoring.
Answer: $x = \frac{1}{2}, -1$

16. Use the quadratic formula to solve $3x^2 - 4x - 5 = 0$.
Answer: $x = \frac{2 \pm \sqrt{19}}{3}$

17. Simplify the expression $\frac{2x - 3x^2 + 6x^4}{4 + 12x^3 - 6x}$.
Answer: $\frac{1}{2}x$

18. Simplify the expression $\frac{x^2 - 5x + 6}{x^2 - 9}$.
Answer: $\frac{x-2}{x+3}$

19. Simplify the expression $\frac{x^3 - y^3}{x^2 - y^2}$.
Answer: $\frac{x^2 + xy + y^2}{x + y}$

20. Simplify the expression $\frac{\frac{2}{x} - 1}{1 - \frac{3}{x}}$.
Answer: $\frac{2-x}{x-3}$

21. Simplify the expression $\dfrac{\dfrac{1}{x}-\dfrac{1}{y}}{\dfrac{1}{y^2}-\dfrac{1}{x^2}}$

Answer: $\dfrac{xy}{x+y}$

22. Simplify the expression $\dfrac{4}{x+3}-\dfrac{5}{2x+1}$.

Answer: $\dfrac{3x-11}{(x+3)(2x+1)}$

23. Simplify the expression $\dfrac{x^2+6x+5}{x^2-25}$.

Answer: $\dfrac{x+1}{x-5}$

24. Simplify the expression $\dfrac{5x+1}{x^2-9}-\dfrac{4x-2}{x^2-9}$.

Answer: $\dfrac{1}{x-3}$

25. Rationalize the denominator of the expression $\dfrac{\sqrt{x}+\sqrt{y}}{\sqrt{x}-\sqrt{y}}$.

Answer: $\dfrac{x+2\sqrt{xy}+y}{x-y}$

26. Rationalize the denominator of the expression $\dfrac{2}{\sqrt{x}+1}$.

Answer: $\dfrac{2\sqrt{x}-2}{x-1}$

Section 1.3

1. In which quadrant is the point $(-3,2)$?
   Answer: II

2. In which quadrant is the point $(1,-7)$?
   Answer: IV

3. Find the distance between the points $(3,6)$ and $(6,10)$.
   Answer: 5

4. Find the distance between the points $(-4,5)$ and $(8,10)$.
   Answer: 13

5. Find the distance between the points $(-2,1)$ and $(-2,7)$.
   Answer: 6

6. Find the distance between the points $(-2,5)$ and $(-1,8)$.
   Answer: $\sqrt{10}$

7. Find the distance between the points $(-5,-8)$ and $(-3,5)$.
   Answer: $\sqrt{173}$

8. Find the distance between the points $(-1,-2)$ and $(1,2)$.
   Answer: $2\sqrt{5}$

9. Find the distance between the points $(-2,5)$ and $(-1,8)$.
   Answer: $\sqrt{10}$

10. Find the distance between the points $(-9,9)$ and $(6,-7)$.
    Answer: $\sqrt{481}$

11. Find the distance between the points $(-1,2)$ and $(6,7)$.
    Answer: $\sqrt{74}$

12. Find the coordinates of any points 10 units away from the origin with an x-Coordinate of 8.
    Answer: $(8,6)$ and $(8,-6)$

13. Find the coordinates of any points 5 units away from the origin with an x-coordinate of 4.

Answer: $(4,3)$ and $(4,-3)$

14. Find the coordinates of any points 13 units away from the origin with a y-coordinate of 5.
Answer: $(12,5)$ and $(-12,5)$

15. Find the coordinates of any points 8 units away from the origin with a y-coordinate of 5.
Answer: $(\sqrt{39},5)$ and $(-\sqrt{39},5)$

16. Darryl's range with a water balloon is 15 meters. If John is standing 12 meters south and 10 meters west of Darryl, is Darryl able to hit him?
Answer: No

17. The captain of a sinking ocean liner sends out a distress signal. If the ship's radio has a range of 14 km and the nearest port is located 12 km south and 5 km east of the sinking ship, will the signal reach the port?
Answer: Yes

18. Find an equation of the circle centered at the origin with radius 8.
Answer: $x^2 + y^2 = 64$

19. Find an equation of the circle centered at the origin with radius $\sqrt{3}$.
Answer: $x^2 + y^2 = 3$

20. Find an equation of the circle centered at $(3,5)$ with radius 2.
Answer: $(x-3)^2 + (y-5)^2 = 4$

21. Find an equation of the circle centered at $(-2,0)$ with radius $\frac{1}{3}$.
Answer: $(x+2)^2 + y^2 = \frac{1}{9}$

22. Find an equation of the circle centered at $(1,-3)$ that passes through the point $(3,3)$.
Answer: $(x-1)^2 + (y+3)^2 = 40$

23. Find an equation of the circle centered at $(-1,-3)$ that passes through the point $(0,3)$.
Answer: $(x+1)^2 + (y+3)^2 = 37$

Section 1. 4

1. Find the slope of the line graphed below.

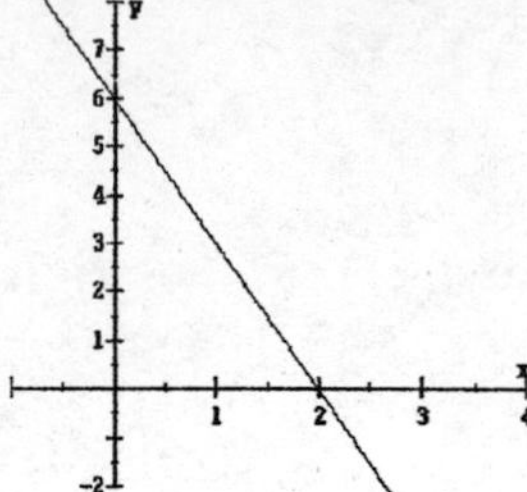

Answer: -3

2. Find the slope of the line graphed below.

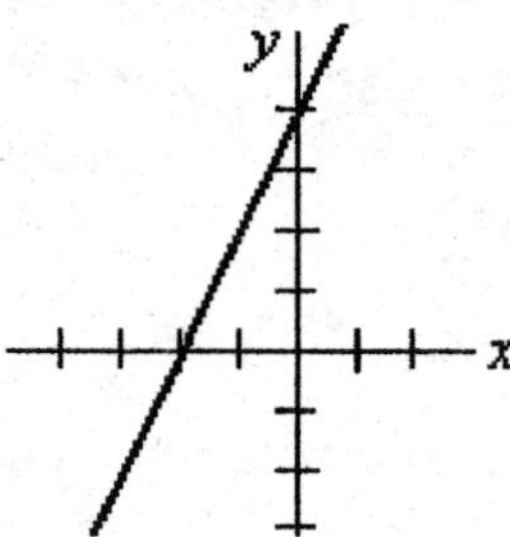

Answer: 2

3. Find the slope of the line graphed below.

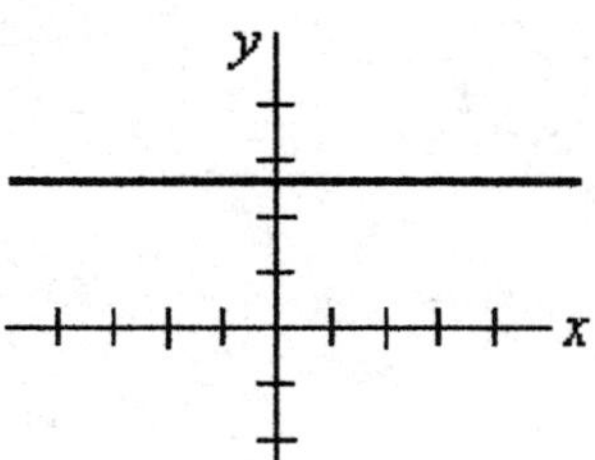

Answer: 0

4. Find the slope of the line graphed below.

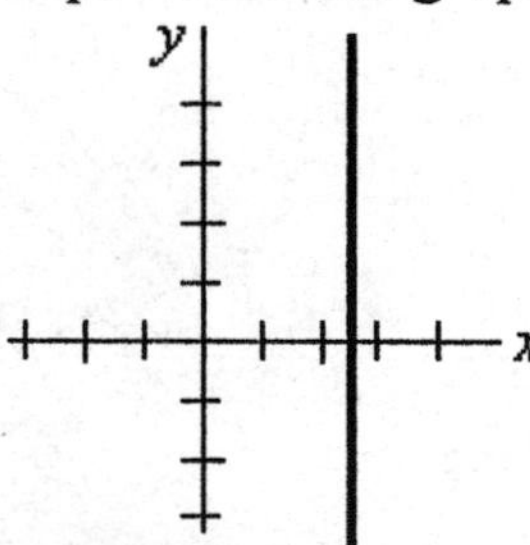

Answer: undefined

5. Find the slope of the line that passes through the points $(2,3)$ and $(4,9)$.
Answer: 3

6. Find the slope of the line that passes through the points $(-2,5)$ and $(2,3)$.
Answer: $-\frac{1}{2}$

7. Find the slope of the line that passes through the points $(3,8)$ and $(12,-2)$.
Answer: $-\frac{10}{9}$

8. Find the slope of the line that passes through the points $(4,2)$ and $(-3,1)$.
Answer: $\frac{1}{7}$

9. Find the slope of the line that passes through the points $(-2,0)$ and $(-5,-3)$.
Answer: 1

10. Find the slope of the line that passes through the points $(5,2)$ and $(9,2)$.
Answer: 0

11. Find the slope of the line that passes through the points $(5,2)$ and $(5,-3)$.
Answer: Undefined

12. Find the slope of the line that passes through the points $(0,-3)$ and $(4,0)$.
Answer: $\frac{3}{4}$

13. Find the slope of the line that passes through the points (a,b) and (c,d).
Answer: $\frac{d-b}{c-a}, c \neq a$

14. If a point moves along the line $y = 6x+1$, what would be the change in y if x were increased by 3 units?
Answer: The y-value would increase by 18 units.

15. If a point moves along the line $4x+2y=8$, what would be the change in y if x were decreased by 1 unit?
Answer: The y-value would increase by 2 units.

16. Determine if the lines through the given pairs of point are parallel, perpendicular, or neither: $A(2,3)$, $B(-1,2)$ and $C(4,-2)$, $D(-2,-4)$.
Answer: parallel

17. Determine if the lines through the given pairs of point are parallel, perpendicular, or neither: $A(1,4)$, $B(-2,3)$ and $C(6,-2)$, $D(5,-5)$.
Answer: neither

18. Determine if the lines through the given pairs of point are parallel, perpendicular, or neither: $A(1,4)$, $B(3,-4)$ and $C(2,1)$, $D(6,2)$.
Answer: perpendicular

19. Express the equation $3x-y=2$ in the slope – intercept form.
Answer: $y=3x-2$

20. Find an equation of the horizontal line that passes through $(2,4)$.
Answer: $y=4$

21. Find an equation of the vertical line that passes through $(-2,3)$.
Answer: $x=-2$

22. Find an equation of the line that passes through the point $(2,-3)$ and has a slope of -2.
Answer: $2x+y-1=0$

23. Find an equation of the line that passes through the point $(-4,-6)$ and has a slope of $\frac{3}{4}$.
Answer: $3x-4y-12=0$

24. Find an equation of the line that passes through the points $(2,3)$ and $(-1,4)$.
Answer: $x+3y-11=0$

25. Find an equation of the line that passes through the points $(1,5)$ and $(9,-9)$.
Answer: $7x+4y-27=0$

26. Find an equation of the line that has a slope of 4 and a y-intercept of -7.
Answer: $y=4x-7$

27. Find an equation of the line that has a slope of $-\frac{5}{4}$ and a y-intercept of 2.
Answer: $y=-\frac{5}{4}x+2$

28. Find the slope and y-intercept of the line $3x+2y-4=0$.
Answer: $m=-\frac{3}{2};b=2$

29. Find the slope and y-intercept of the line $9x-3y+12=0$.
Answer: $m=3; b=4$

30. Find an equation of the line that passes through the point $(2,4)$ and is perpendicular to the line $3x-y-4=0$.
Answer: $x+3y-14=0$

31. Find an equation of the line that passes through the point $(-2,3)$ and is parallel to the line $x+2y-12=0$.
Answer: $x+2y-4=0$

32. Find an equation of the line parallel to the y-axis with an x-intercept of 7.
Answer: $x=7$

33. Find an equation of the line passing through $(6,1)$ and perpendicular to the line joining $(-2,-2)$ and $(3,8)$.
Answer: $x+2y-8=0$

34. Sketch the line given by $2x+2y-4=0$.
Answer:

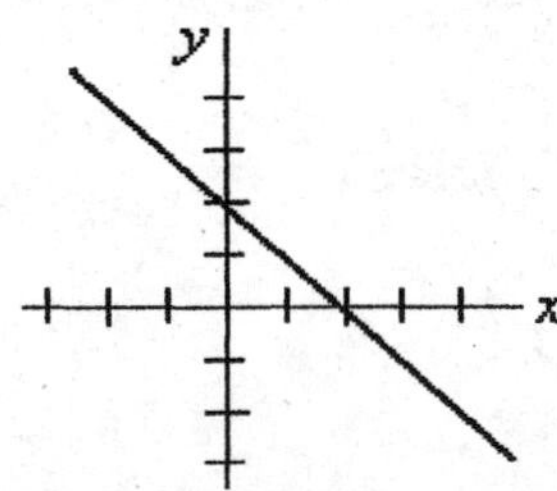

35. Sketch the line given by $3x-5y+15=0$.
Answer:

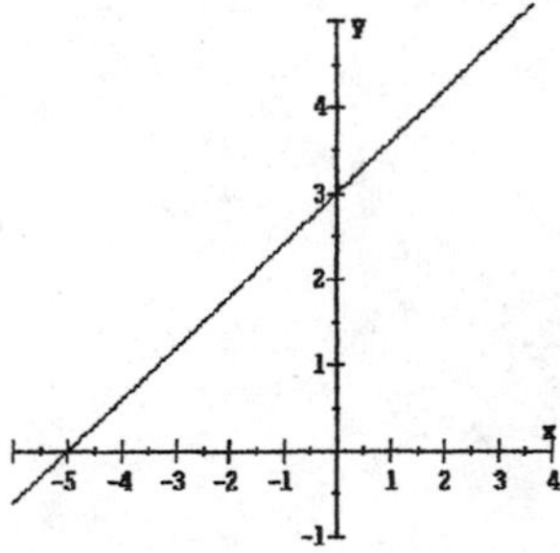

36. Sketch the line given by $x - y - 4 = 0$.
Answer:

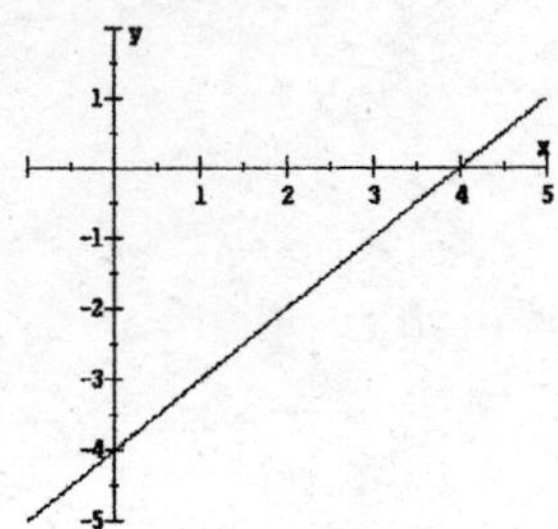

37. Sketch the line given by $3y - 6 = 0$.
Answer:

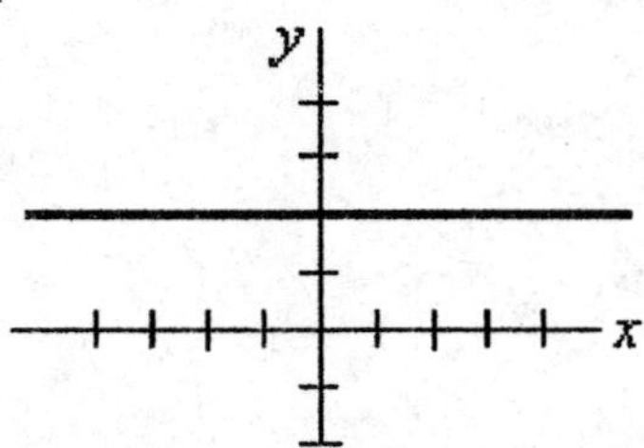

38. Sketch the line given by $\frac{1}{2}x + 2 = 0$.

Answer:

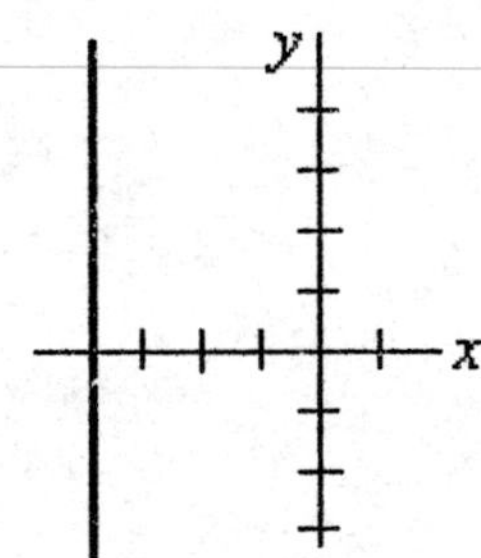

39. Sketch the line given by $2x - 3y + 6 = 0$.
Answer:

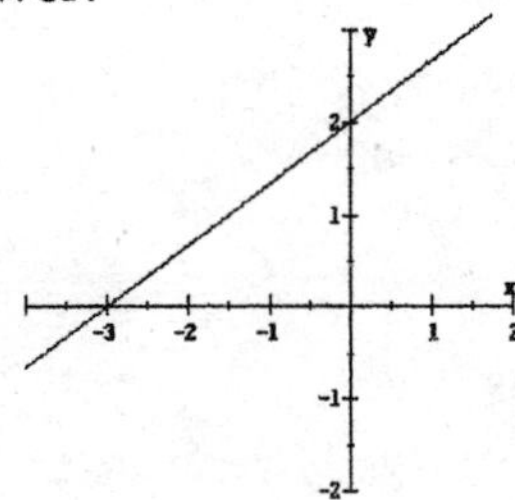

40. Find an equation of a line with an x-intercept of 6 and a y-intercept of 2.
Answer: $x+3y-6=0$

41. Find an equation of a line with an x-intercept of -4 and a y-intercept of 7.
Answer: $7x-4y+28=0$

42. The profit, P (in dollars), from sales of n souvenirs is given by $P=5.5n-220$. Find the profit from the sale of 90 souvenirs.
Answer: \$275

43. 68 percent of the people who apply for admission to a certain university are admitted.
(a) Find an equation that expresses the relationship between the number of applicants (x) and the number of admissions (y).
Answer: $y=0.68x$

(b) If 374 people are accepted this year, how many people applied?
Answer: 550

44. Scientists from the Canadian Wrestling Conglomerate developed the following equation in order to estimate the weight of unfamiliar wrestlers.
$W=7.15H-154$ where W is weight in pounds and H is height in inches.
(a) Invincible Robert is 78 inches tall. What is his expected weight?
Answer: 403.7 pounds
(b) The Muncher weighs 386 pounds. What is his expected height?
Answer: 75.5 inches

45. The price of a car is given by $y=-4000t+32{,}000$, where t is time in years after the car was purchased.
a. Find the original price of the car.
Answer: \$32,000

b. Find the price of the car three years after it was purchased.
Answer: \$20,000

c. Find the price of the car 8 years after it was purchased.
Answer: \$0.

d. Find the slope of the line and interpret your answer in the context of the problem.
Answer: -4000. The price of the car depreciates \$4000 per year.

46. The price for an antique clock was given by $y = 60t + 300$.
(a) Find the original price of the antique clock.

Answer: \$300

(b) Find what the clock will be worth after 7 years.

Answer: \$720

(c) Find the slope of the line and interpret the slope in the context of the problem.

Answer: 60. The price of the antique clock goes up \$60 per year.

47. There is a relationship between the vocabulary a child uses and the child's age. The equation $60A - V = 900$ describes this relationship, where A is the age of the child, in months, and V is the number of words that the child uses. Suppose that a child uses 1500 words. Determine the child's age, in months.

Answer: 40 months.

48. The percentage, P, of adults in the United State who read the daily newspaper can be modeled by the formula $P = -0.7x + 80$, where x is the number of years after 1965. In what year will 52% of U.S. adults read the daily newspaper?

Answer: 2005, 40 years from 1965.

Exam 1A

Name:
Instructor:
Section:

Write your work as neatly as possible.

1. Find the values of x that satisfy the inequality $5x+1>16$.

2. Evaluate the expression $4-|5-11|$.

3. Find the distance between the points $(6,3)$ and $(1,-1)$.

4. Suppose that a and b are real numbers other than zero and that $a>b$. State whether the given inequalities are true or false.
   (a) $b-a<0$
   (b) $\frac{a}{b}<1$
   (c) $-a>-b$

5. Evaluate $25^{-3/2}$.

6. Simplify the expression $\sqrt[4]{x^{-3}}\sqrt{16x^5}$.

7. Rationalize the denominator of the expression $\sqrt{\frac{5}{7x}}$.

8. Perform the indicated operations and simplify $\frac{4}{x+1}-\frac{3}{x-5}$.

9. Factor out the greatest common factor from $2ab^2+4ab+6a^2b$.

10. Factor the expression $x^2+4x-12$.

11. Perform the indicated operation and simplify the algebraic expression $(x^2-2y^2)x+3x(2y)$.

12. Find the real roots of $3x^2-27x=0$.

13. Find the coordinates of any points 1 unit away from the origin with an x-coordinate of 1.

14. Find the equation of the circle centered at $(2,-5)$ with a radius of 6.

15. Find the slope of the line that passes through the points $(0,0)$ and $(-2,4)$.

16. Determine if the lines through the given pairs of points are parallel, perpendicular, or neither: $A(1,1)$, $B(-3,1)$ and $C(2,-2)$, $D(2,5)$.

17. Find the slope of the line graphed below

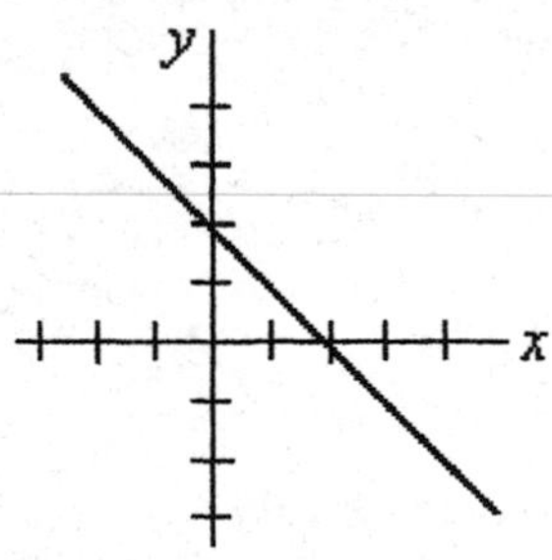

18. Find an equation of the line that passes through the points $(1,5)$ and $(2,8)$.

19. Find an equation of the line parallel to the x-axis with a y-intercept of 3.

20. Find the slope and y-intercept of the line $x-5y=3$.

21. Sketch the line given by $3x-4y=6$.

Exam 1B

Name:
Instructor:
Section:

Write your work as neatly as possible.

1. Find the values of x that satisfy the inequality $2 \le x+1 \le 9$.

2. Simplify the expression $|\pi - 3| - 2$.

3. Evaluate $81^{3/4}$.

4. Rewrite the expression $\left(x^3 y^{-1}\right)^{-2}$ using positive exponents.

5. Rationalize the denominator of the expression $\dfrac{2\sqrt{xy}}{3\sqrt{2x}}$.

6. Perform the indicated operations and simplify $\left(\frac{1}{5}+1+2e\right)+\left(-\frac{1}{5}+2-e^{-1}\right)$.

7. Factor out the greatest common factor from $3x^2y+9xy^4$.

8. Factor the expression $3x^2+10x+8$.

9. Perform the indicated operation and simplify the algebraic expression $(2x^2-y^2)y+2x(2y)$.

10. Simplify the expression $\dfrac{3x^2+10x+8}{6x^2+11x+4}$.

11. Find the distance between the points $(2,8)$ and $(-1,5)$.

12. Find the coordinates of any points 5 units away from the origin with an x-coordinate of -3.

13. Find the equation of the circle centered at $(0,8)$ that passes through the point $(5, 0)$.

14. Find the slope of the line that passes through the points $(2,5)$ and $(-1,6)$.

15. Determine if the lines through the given pairs of points are parallel, perpendicular, or neither: $A(2,2)$, $B(-2,3)$ and $C(6,-1)$, $D(2,0)$.

16. Find an equation of the line that passes through the points $(0,5)$ and $(2,-3)$.

17. Find an equation of the line with x-intercept 2 and y-intercept 1.

18. Find an equation of the line perpendicular to the x-axis passing through the point $(2,3)$.

19. Find the slope and y-intercept of the line $x-3y+2=0$.

20. Find the slope of the line graphed below.

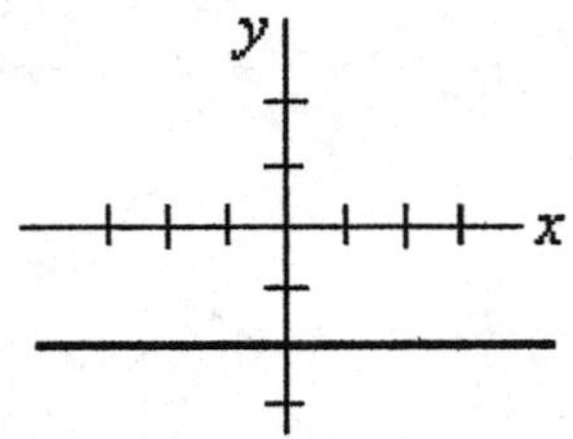

21. Sketch the line $y=-x+1$.

Exam 1C

Name:
Instructor:
Section:

Write your work as neatly as possible.

1. Find the values of x that satisfy the inequality $x-7<3$ and $x+6\geq 5$.

2. Evaluate the expression $|5-2\sqrt{2}|-|3-3\sqrt{2}|$.

3. Evaluate $(2^{1.1}\cdot 2^{2.9})^{\frac{2}{3}}$.

4. Rewrite the expression $\left(3x^2y^{-1}\right)^{-3}$ using positive exponents.

5. Rationalize the denominator of the expression $\dfrac{2}{3\sqrt{3x}}$.

6. Perform the indicated operations and simplify $\left(9x^2+5x+3\right)-\left(x^2+2x-3\right)$.

7. Factor out the greatest common factor from $2xy^3-8x^3y$.

8. Perform the indicated operation and simplify the algebraic expression $\left[\left(x^2-1\right)^2-1\right]\left(2x\right)$.

9. Use the quadratic formula to solve $x^2+7x+1=0$.

10. Simplify the expression $\dfrac{4x^2+8x+3}{8x^2+12x}$.

11. Find the distance between the points $(2,3)$ and $(2,-3)$.

12. Find the coordinates of any points 7 units away from the origin with a y-coordinate of 1.

13. Find the equation of the circle centered at $(3,2)$ that has radius 6.

14. Find the slope of the line that passes through the points $(5,4)$ and $(-1,6)$.

15. Determine the slope of the line graphed below.

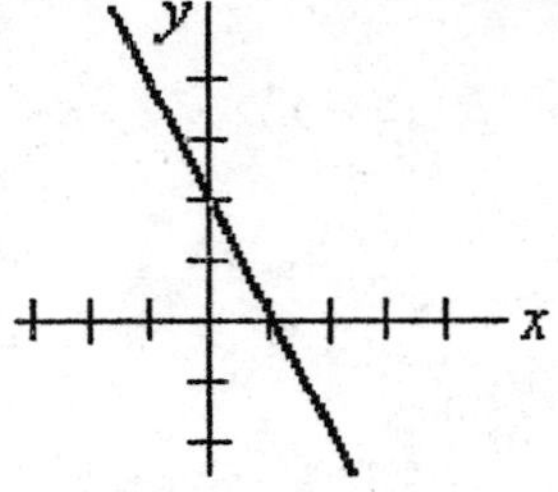

16. Find an equation of the line that passes through the points $(0,1)$ and $(1,3)$.

17. Find an equation of the line with x-intercept 2 that passes through the point $(1,-3)$.

18. Find an equation of the line perpendicular to the x-axis passing through the point $(4,-4)$.

19. Find the slope and y-intercept of the line $2y = \frac{5}{2}x + 1$.

20. If the cost, C (in dollars) to rent a car for m miles is given by $C = 0.25m + 25$, find the cost to rent the car for 130 miles.

21. Sketch the line $3x - 3 = 0$.

Exam 1D

Name:
Instructor:
Section:

Write your work as neatly as possible.

1. Find the values of x that satisfy the inequality $0 \le x + 7 \le 12$.

2. Evaluate the expression $|1-\sqrt{3}| - |3 - 3\sqrt{3}|$.

3. Evaluate $16^{3/2}$.

4. Rewrite the expression $(x^2y^{-1})(x^{-2}y^2)$ using positive exponents.

5. Rationalize the denominator of the expression $\sqrt{\frac{5x}{3y}}$.

6. Find the minimum cost C (in dollars), given that $3(C-10) \ge 1.75 + 2.75C$.

7. Perform the indicated operations and simplify $(x+2)^3$.

8. Factor out the greatest common factor from $2a^2b^2 + 4ab^2 + 8a^3b$.

9. Factor the expression $x^2 - 5x - 6$.

10. Perform the indicated operation and simplify the algebraic expression $(x^2 + y)x + 2x(2y^2)$.

11. Find the real roots of $2x^2 - 3x - 9 = 0$ by factoring.

12. Use the quadratic formula to solve $2x^2 - 5x - 4 = 0$.

13. Simplify the expression $\dfrac{4x^2+16x+15}{6x^2+9x}$.

14. Find the distance between the points $(0,2)$ and $(-3,5)$.

15. Find the coordinates of any points 6 units away from the origin with a y-coordinate of 3.

16. Find the equation of the circle centered at the origin that has radius 5 .

17. Find the slope of the line that passes through the points $(8,1)$ and $(7,-1)$.

18. Determine if the lines through the given pairs of points are parallel, perpendicular, or neither: $A(2,-2)$, $B(-1,3)$ and $C(6,5)$, $D(3,2)$.

19. Find an equation of the line that passes through the points $(4,-1)$ and $(-2,4)$.

20. Find an equation of the line graphed below.

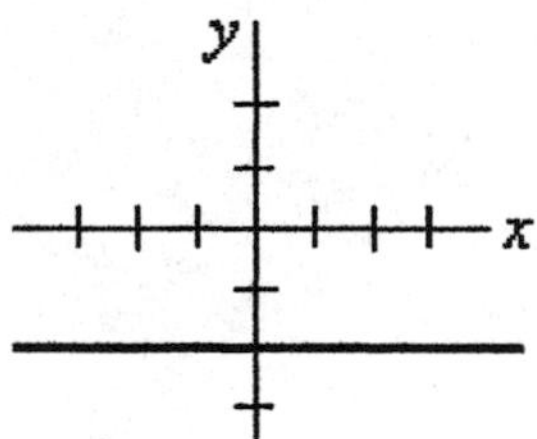

21. Sketch the line $2y=-4x+4$

Answers to Chapter 1 Exams

Exam 1A

1. $(3, \infty)$
2. -2
3. $\sqrt{41}$
4. (a) True

   (b) False

   (c) False
5. 1/125
6. $4x^{7/4}$
7. $\dfrac{\sqrt{35x}}{7x}$
8. $\dfrac{x-23}{(x+1)(x-5)}$
9. $2ab(b+2+3a)$
10. $(x-2)(x+6)$
11. $x^3 - 2xy^2 + 6xy$
12. $x = 0, 9$
13. (1,0)
14. $(x-2)^2 + (y+5)^2 = 36$
15. -2
16. Perpendicular
17. $m = -1$
18. $3x - y + 2 = 0$
19. $y = 3$
20. $m = \dfrac{1}{5}; b = -\dfrac{3}{5}$
21.

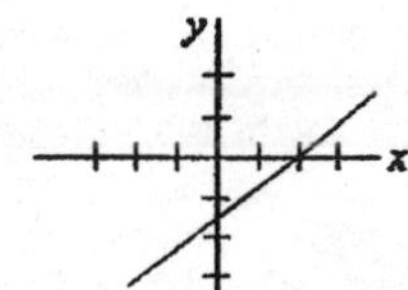

Exam 1B

1. $[1, 8]$
2. $\pi - 5$
3. 27
4. $\dfrac{y^2}{x^6}$
5. $\dfrac{\sqrt{2y}}{3}$
6. $3 + 2e - \dfrac{1}{e}$
7. $3xy(x + 3y^3)$
8. $(3x+4)(x+2)$
9. $2x^2y - y^3 + 4xy$
10. $\dfrac{x+2}{2x+1}$
11. $3\sqrt{2}$
12. $(-3,4), (-3,-4)$
13. $x^2 + (y-8)^2 = 89$
14. $-\dfrac{1}{3}$
15. Parallel
16. $4x + y = 5$
17. $x + 2y = 2$
18. $x = 2$
19. $m = \dfrac{1}{3};\ b = \dfrac{2}{3}$
20. $m = 0$
21.

Exam 1C

1. $[-1,10)$
2. $8-5\sqrt{2}$
3. 4
4. $\dfrac{y^3}{27x^6}$
5. $\dfrac{2\sqrt{3x}}{9x}$
6. $8x^2+3x+6$
7. $2xy(y-2x)(y+2x)$
8. $2x^5-4x^3$
9. $x=\dfrac{-7\pm3\sqrt{5}}{2}$
10. $\dfrac{2x+1}{4x}$
11. 6
12. $(4\sqrt{3},1),(-4\sqrt{3},1)$
13. $(x-3)^2+(y-2)^2=36$
14. $-\dfrac{1}{3}$
15. -2
16. $2x-y+1=0$
17. $3x-y-6=0$
18. $x=4$
19. $m=\dfrac{5}{4};\ b=\dfrac{1}{2}$
20. $57.50
21.

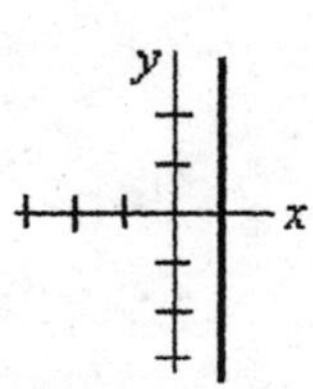

Exam 1D

1. $[-7,5]$
2. $2-2\sqrt{3}$
3. 64
4. y
5. $\dfrac{\sqrt{15xy}}{3y}$
6. 127
7. $x^3+6x^2+12x+8$
8. $2ab\left(ab+2b+4a^2\right)$
9. $(x-6)(x+1)$
10. $x^3+xy+4xy^2$
11. $x=3,-3/2$
12. $x=\dfrac{5\pm\sqrt{57}}{4}$
13. $\dfrac{2x+5}{3x}$
14. $3\sqrt{2}$
15. $(3\sqrt{3},3),\ (-3\sqrt{3},3)$
16. $x^2+y^2=25$
17. $m=2$
18. Neither
19. $5x+6y-14=0$
20. $y=-2$
21.

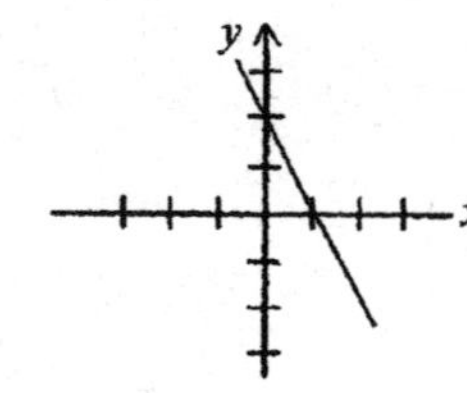

Chapter 2 ■ Functions, Limits, and the Derivative

Section 2.1

1. Let f be the function defined by $f(x) = 2x^2 + 3x - 4$. Find $f(0), f(2), f(a), f(-a)$, and $f(a+1)$.
   Answer: $-4,\ 10,\ 2a^2 + 3a - 4,\ 2a^2 - 3a - 4,\ 2a^2 + 7a + 1$

2. Let g be the function defined by $g(x) = x^3 + 2x^2 - 3$. Find $g(0)$, $g(3)$, $g(a)$, $g(-x)$, and $g(h+1)$.
   Answer: $-3,\ 42,\ a^3 + 2a^2 - 3,\ -x^3 + 2x^2 - 3,\ h^3 + 5h^2 + 7h$

3. Let h be the function defined by $h(x) = \begin{cases} x^2 + 3 \text{ if } x \le 2 \\ \sqrt{2x} \ \text{ if x} > 2 \end{cases}$. Find $h(0)$, $h(2)$, and $h(3)$.
   Answer: $3, 7, \sqrt{6}$

4. Let f be the function defined by $f(x) = \dfrac{3}{4t+2}$ Find $f(1), f(-2)$, and $f(a+1)$.
   Answer: $\dfrac{1}{2},\ -\dfrac{1}{2},\ \dfrac{3}{4a+6}$

5. Find the domain of the function $g(x) = 3x^2 + 2x + 1$.
   Answer: $(-\infty, \infty)$

6. Find the domain of the function $F(x) = 1 - \sqrt{x}$.
   Answer: $[0, \infty)$

7. Find the domain of the function $f(x) = \dfrac{x+2}{x^2 - 1}$.
   Answer: $\{x \mid x \ne \pm 1\}$

8. Find the domain of the function $f(x) = \dfrac{x^4}{x^2 + x - 6}$.
   Answer: $\{x \mid x \ne -3, 2\}$

9. Find the domain of the function $g(x) = \sqrt[4]{x^2 - 6x}$.
   Answer: $(-\infty, 0] \cup [6, \infty)$

10. Sketch a graph of $f(x) = x^2 + 2$
Answer:

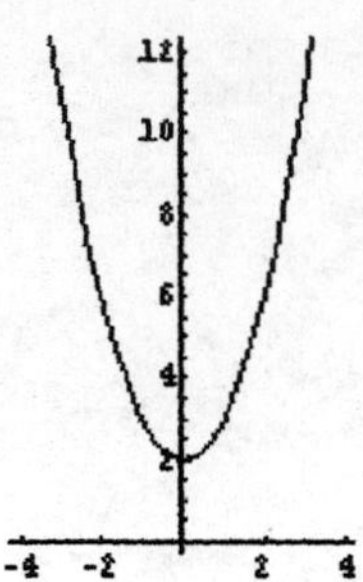

11. Sketch a graph of $h(x) = \sqrt{x} + 3$.
Answer:

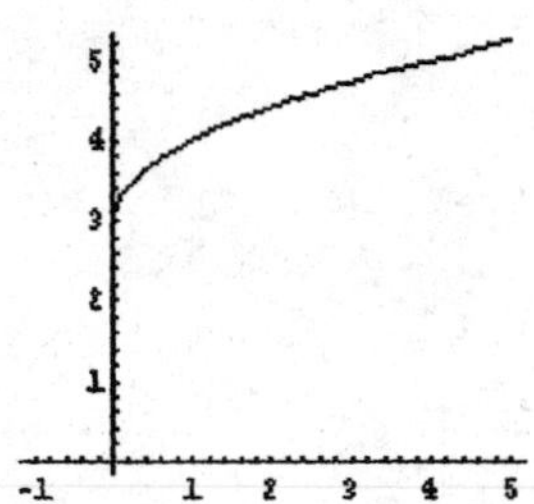

12. Sketch a graph of $g(x) = |x| - 2$.
Answer:

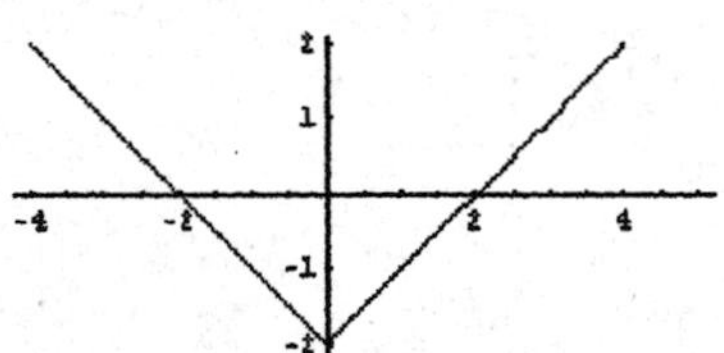

13. Sketch a graph of $h(x) = \begin{cases} 2 - x & \text{if } x \le 0 \\ x^2 + 2 & \text{if } x > 0 \end{cases}$

Answer:

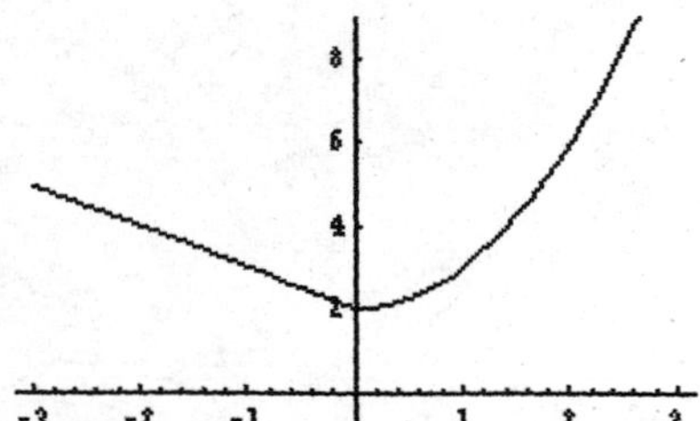

14. Refer the graph of $y = f(x)$ in the following figure.

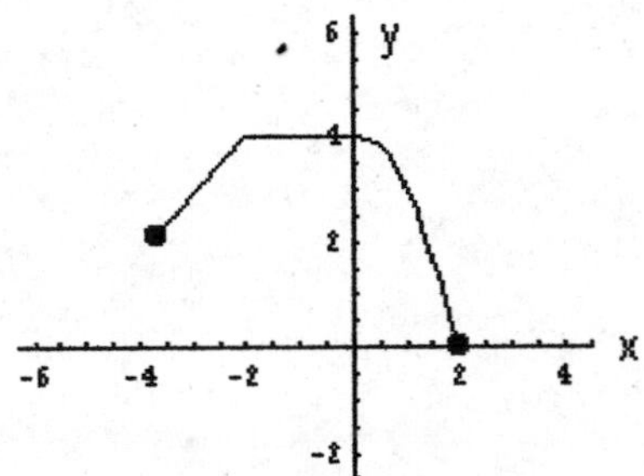

(a) Find the value of $f(-4)$.
Answer: 2
(b) Find the value of x for which $f(x) = 0$
Answer: 2
(b) Find the domain of f.
Answer: $[-4, 2]$
(d) Find the range of f.
Answer: $[0, 4]$

15. Refer the graph of $y = f(x)$ in the following figure.

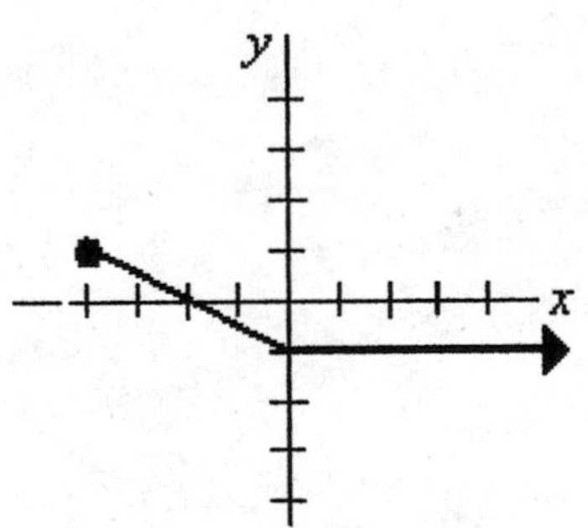

(a) Find the value of $f(-4)$.
Answer: 1

(b) Find the value of x for which $f(x) = 0$
Answer: −2

(c) Find the domain of f.
Answer: $[-4, \infty)$

(d) Find the range of f.
Answer: $[-1, 1]$

16. Determine whether the graph represents y as a function of x.

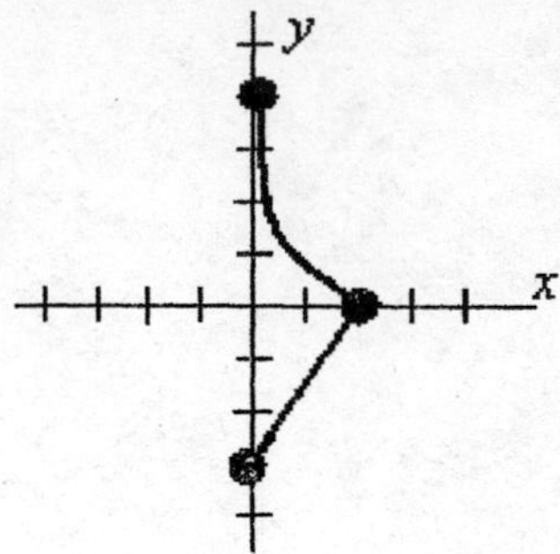

Answer: No

17. Determine whether the graph represents y as a function of x.

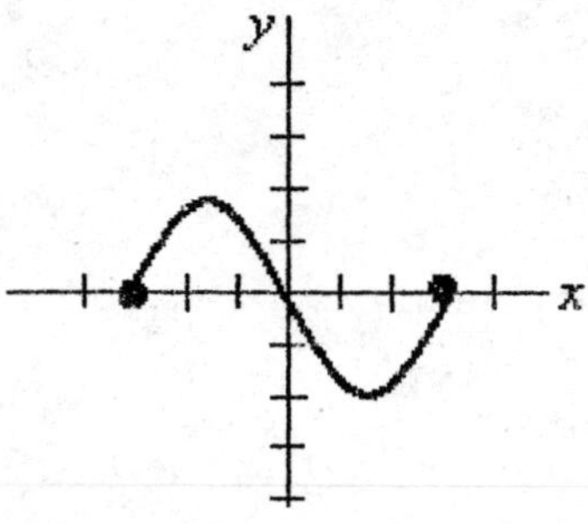

Answer: Yes

18. A company purchases a copier for \$8000. The copier is depreciated linearly over 5 years and has a scrap value of \$1200.
(a) Express the book value of the copier (V) as a function of the age, in years, of the copier (n).
Answer: $V = -1360n + 8000$

(b) Find the copier's value at the end of three years.
Answer: \$3920

Section 2.2

1. Let $f(x) = x^2 - 4$ and $g(x) = 2x - 3$. Find the rule for the function $f + g$.
   Answer: $x^2 + 2x - 7$

2. Let $f(x) = x^2 - 4$ and $g(x) = 2x - 3$. Find the rule for the function fg.
   Answer: $2x^3 - 3x^2 - 8x + 12$

3. Let $f(x) = 2x^2 - 1$ and $g(x) = 3x + 2$. Find the rule for the function $f - g$.
   Answer: $2x^2 - 3x - 3$

4. Let $f(x) = 2x^2 - 1$ and $g(x) = 3x + 2$. Find the rule for the function f / g.
   Answer: $\dfrac{2x^2 - 1}{3x + 2}$

5. Let $f(x) = x + 2$ and $g(x) = \sqrt{x - 1}$. Find the rule for the function fg.
   Answer: $(x + 2)\sqrt{x - 1}$

6. Let $f(x) = x + 2$ and $g(x) = \sqrt{x - 1}$. Find the rule for the function $\dfrac{f}{g}$.
   Answer: $\dfrac{x + 2}{\sqrt{x - 1}}$

7. Let $f(x) = x + 2$, $g(x) = \sqrt{x + 2}$ and $h(x) = 3x^3 - 2$. Find the rule for the function $\dfrac{fg}{h}$.
   Answer: $\dfrac{(x + 2)^{3/2}}{3x^3 - 2}$

8. Let $f(x) = x + 2$, $g(x) = \sqrt{x + 2}$ and $h(x) = 3x^3 - 2$. Find the rule for the function $\dfrac{gh}{g - f}$.
   Answer: $\dfrac{\sqrt{x + 2}\left(3x^3 - 2\right)}{\sqrt{x + 2} - x - 2}$

9. Let $f(x) = x^2 - x - 1$ and $g(x) = 4x$. Find the rule for the composite function $f \circ g$.
   Answer: $16x^2 - 4x - 1$

10. Let $f(x)=x^2-x-1$ and $g(x)=4x$. Find the rule for the composite function $g\circ f$.
Answer: $4x^2-4x-4$

11. Let $f(x)=4x+5$. Find the rule for the composite function $f\circ f$.
Answer: $16x+25$

12. Let $f(x)=\frac{2}{x}$. Find the rule for the composite function $f\circ f\circ f$.
Answer: $\frac{2}{x}$

13. Let $f(x)=3\sqrt{x}+4$ and $g(x)=x^2-1$. Find the rule for the composite function $f\circ g$.
Answer: $3\sqrt{x^2-1}+4$

14. Let $f(x)=3\sqrt{x}+4$ and $g(x)=x^2-1$. Find the rule for the composite function $g\circ f$.
Answer: $9x+24\sqrt{x}+15$

15. Evaluate $h(3)$ where $h=g\circ f$, $f(x)=3x+2$ and $g(x)=x^2+5$.
Answer: 126

16. Evaluate $h(4)$ where $h=g\circ f$, $f(x)=3\sqrt{x}+4$ and $g(x)=x^2-1$
Answer: 99

17. If $h(x)=\sqrt{x^2-4}$, find functions f and g such that $h=g\circ f$ (the answer is not unique).
Answer: $g(x)=\sqrt{x}, f(x)=x^2-4$

18. If $h(x)=\frac{1}{\sqrt{2x-1}}-3\sqrt{2x-1}$, find functions f and g such that $h=g\circ f$ (the answer is not unique).
Answer: $g(x)=\frac{1}{x}-3x, f(x)=\sqrt{2x-1}$

19. If $h(x)=(2x-5)^{5/2}$, find functions f and g such that $h=g\circ f$ (the answer is not unique).
Answer: $g(x)=x^{5/2}, f(x)=2x-5$

20. If $f(x) = 5x + 7$, find and simplify $f(a+h) - f(a)$.
Answer: $5h$

21. If $f(x) = x^2 - 1$, find and simplify $f(a+h) - f(a)$.
Answer: $2ah + h^2$

22. If $f(x) = x^2 - 2$, find and simplify $\dfrac{f(a+h) - f(a)}{h}$, $(h \neq 0)$.
Answer: $2a + h$

23. If $f(x) = {}^2\!/_x$, find and simplify $\dfrac{f(a+h) - f(a)}{h}$, $(h \neq 0)$.
Answer: $-\dfrac{2}{a(a+h)}$

24. Determine whether the equation $15x - 5 = 5y$ defines y as a linear function of x. If so, write it in the form $y = mx + b$.
Answer: $y = 3x - 1$

25. Determine whether the equation $x + y = 3$ defines y as a linear function of x. If so, write it in the form $y = mx + b$.
Answer: $y = -x + 3$

26. Determine whether the equation $\sqrt[3]{x} + 4y = 1$ defines y as a linear function of x. If so, write it in the form $y = mx + b$.
Answer: No

27. Determine whether the equation $x^2 + y^2 = 3$ defines y as a linear function of x. If so, write it in the form $y = mx + b$.
Answer: No

28. Determine whether the equation $x^2 = y^2$ defines y as a linear function of x. If so, write it in the form $y = mx + b$.
Answer: No

29. Find m and b in $f(x) = mx + b$ such that $f(0) = 4$ and $f(4) = 0$.
Answer: $m = -1, b = 4$

30. Find m and b in $f(x) = mx + b$ such that $f(1) = -3$ and $f(2) = 2$.
Answer: $m = 5, b = -8$

31. Determine whether the given function is a polynomial function, a rational function, or some other function. State the degree of each polynomial function.

(a) $f(x) = \sqrt[5]{x}$

Answer: Other

(b) $g(x) = \sqrt{1 - x^2}$

Answer: Other

(c) $h(x) = x^9 + x^4$

Answer: Polynomial, degree 9

(d) $w(x) = \dfrac{x+5}{x-1}$

Answer: Rational function

(e) $w(x) = x^{-5} + x - 10$

Answer: Rational function

32. Determine whether the given function is a polynomial function, a rational function, or some other function. State the degree of each polynomial function.

(a) $r(x) = \dfrac{x^2 + 1}{x^3 + x}$

Answer: Rational Function

(b) $f(t) = 2t^6 + t^4 - \pi$

Answer: Polynomial degree 6

(c) $h(\theta) = \cos\theta + \sin\theta$

Answer: Other

Section 2.3

1. A manufacturer has a monthly fixed cost of \$65,000 and a production cost of \$23 for each unit produced. The product sells for \$30 per unit.
(a) What is the cost function?
Answer: $C(x) = 65{,}000 + 23x$

(b) What is the revenue function?
Answer: $R(x) = 30x$

(c) What is the profit function?
Answer: $P(x) = 7x - 65{,}000$

(d) Compute the profit or loss corresponding to a production level of 12,000 units.
Answer: \$19,000 profit

2. A manufacturer has a monthly fixed cost of \$3500 and a production cost of \$7.50 for each unit produced. The product sells for \$16.75 per unit.
(a) What is the cost function?
Answer: $C(x) = 3500 + 7.5x$

(b) What is the revenue function?
Answer: $R(x) = 16.75x$

(c) What is the profit function?
Answer: $P(x) = 9.25x - 3500$

3. For the following pair of supply and demand equations, where x represents the quantity demanded in units of a thousand and p the unit price in dollars, find the equilibrium price and quantity: $5x + 2p - 33 = 0,\ 7x - 4p + 32 = 0$.
Answer: $x = 2,\ p = \dfrac{23}{2}$

4. For the following pair of supply and demand equations, where x represents the quantity demanded in units of a thousand and p the unit price in dollars, find the equilibrium price and quantity: $3x + 12p - 69 = 0,\ 3x - 4p + 15 = 0$.
Answer: $x = 2,\ p = \dfrac{21}{4}$

5. The cost and revenue functions for a certain firm are given by $C(x) = 12x + 20{,}000$ and $R(x) = 20x$, respectively. Find the company's break-even point.
Answer: 2500

Section 2.4

1. Use the graph of the function f below to determine $\lim_{x\to -1} f(x)$ if it exists.

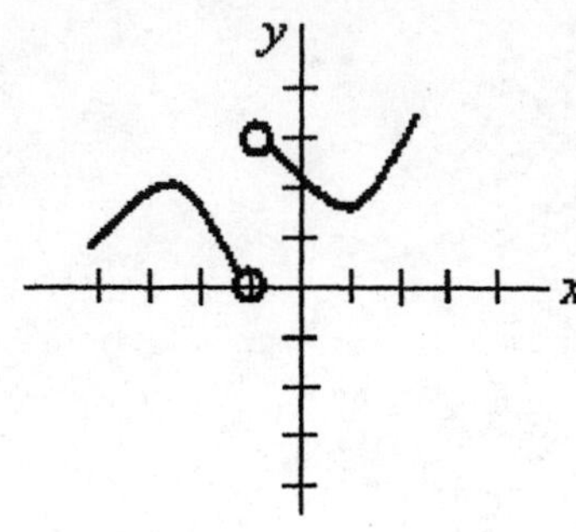

Answer: does not exist

2. Use the graph of the function f below to determine $\lim_{x\to 1} f(x)$ if it exists.

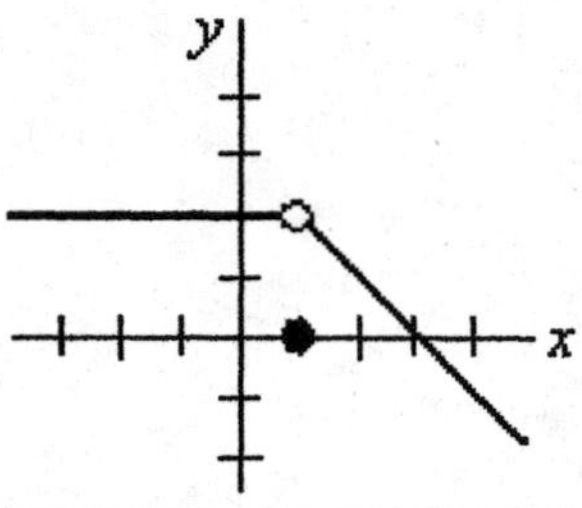

Answer: 2

3. Use the graph of the function f below to determine $\lim_{x\to 1} f(x)$ if it exists.

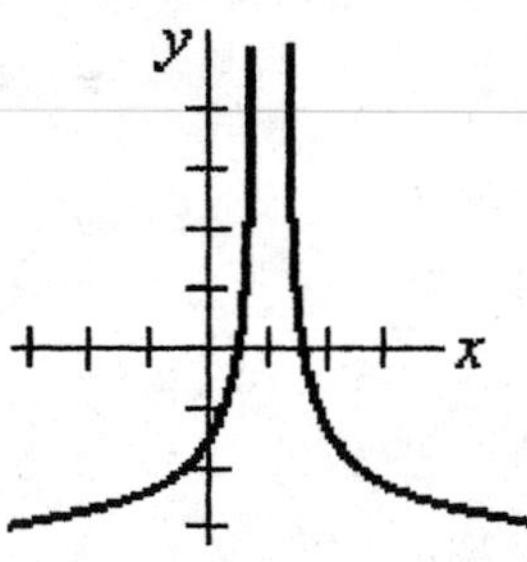

Answer: does not exist $(-\infty)$

4. Use the graph of the function f below to determine $\lim_{x\to 2} f(x)$.

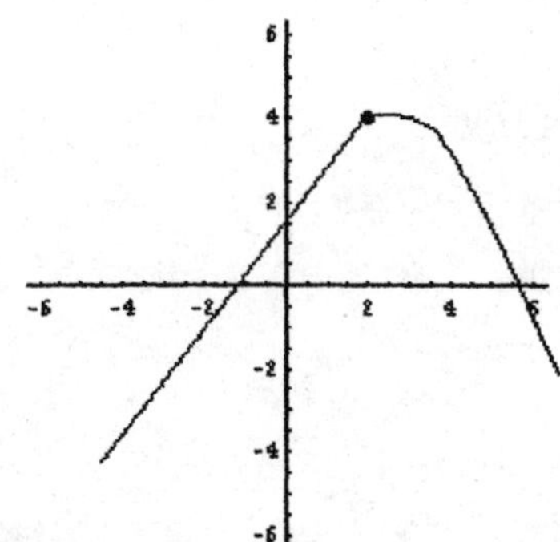

Answer: 4

5. Use the graph of the function f below to determine $\lim_{x \to 4} f(x)$.

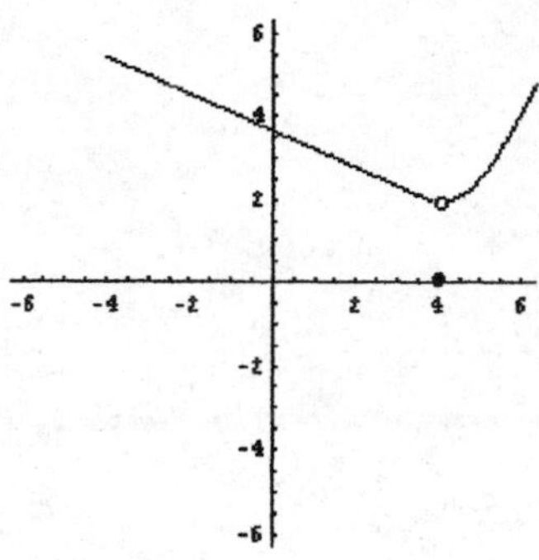

Answer: 2

6. Use the graph of the function f below to determine $\lim_{x \to 1} f(x)$.

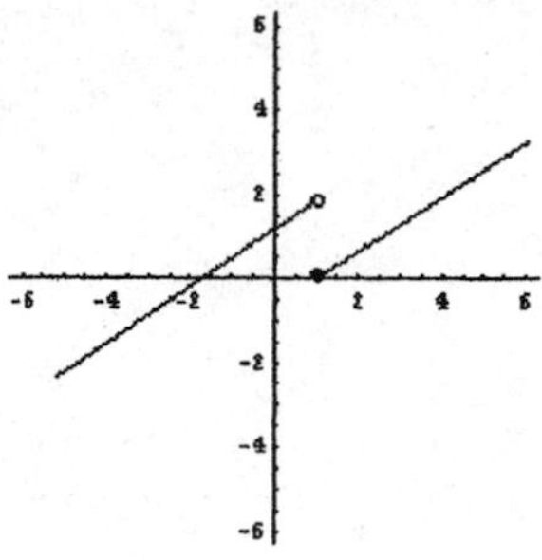

Answer: Does not exist.

7. Consider the function $f(x) = \dfrac{x^2 - 1}{x - 1}$.

(a) Construct a table listing the x-values of 0.9, 0.99, 0.999, 1.001, 1.01, and 1.1 along with the computed values of $f(x)$ (to the nearest thousandth) associated with these x-values.

Answer:

x	0.9	0.99	0.999	1.001	1.01	1.1
$f(x)$	1.9	1.99	1.999	2.001	2.01	2.1

(b) Use the table found in part (a) to determine $\lim_{x \to 1} f(x)$.

Answer: 2

8. Consider the function $f(x) = \dfrac{x-1}{x^2+2x-3}$.

(a) Construct a table listing the x-values of 0.9, 0.99, 0.999, 1.001, 1.01, and 1.1 along with the computed values of $f(x)$ (to the nearest thousandth) associated with these x-values.

Answer:

x	0.9	0.99	0.999	1.001	1.01	1.1
$f(x)$	0.256	0.251	0.250	0.250	0.249	0.244

(b) Use the table found in part (a) to determine $\lim_{x\to 1} f(x)$.

Answer: 0.250

9. Find the value of $\lim_{x\to 2} -4$.

Answer: -4

10. Find the value of $\lim_{x\to 1} \pi$.

Answer: π

11. Find the value of $\lim_{x\to -1} -5x$.

Answer: 5

12. Find the value of $\lim_{t\to 3}\left(t^2+3t-1\right)$.

Answer: 17

13. Find the value of $\lim_{w\to -2} \dfrac{3-w}{3+w}$.

Answer: 5

14. Find the value of $\lim_{x\to 4} \dfrac{x^2-16}{x-4}$, if it exists.

Answer: 8

15. Find the value of $\lim_{x\to 16} \dfrac{\sqrt{x}-4}{x-16}$, if it exists.

Answer: $\dfrac{1}{8}$

16. Find the value of $\lim_{x\to 0} \dfrac{x^2+2x}{x}$.

Answer: 2

17. Find the value of $\lim_{x \to -2} \frac{x}{x+2}$, if it exists.
Answer: Does not exist

18. Find the value of $\lim_{x \to \infty} \frac{2}{x+1}$, if it exists.
Answer: 0

19. Find the value of $\lim_{x \to \infty} \frac{3x^4 + 5x + 2}{x^7 - 2x + 12}$, if it exists.
Answer: 0

20. Find the value of $\lim_{x \to \infty} \frac{3x - 1}{x + 2}$, if it exists.
Answer: 3

21. Find the value of $\lim_{x \to -\infty} \frac{x^2}{3x - 1}$, if it exists.
Answer: $-\infty$

22. Find the value of $\lim_{x \to -\infty} \frac{4x^3 + 2x^2 - 3x + 3}{2x^3 - 3x^2 - 7x - 6}$, if it exists.
Answer: 2

23. The number of fish in a certain lake is given by the function $N(t) = \frac{2000t^2 + 100}{t^2 + 1}$, where t is measured in months. Determine the limit of this function as $t \to \infty$, which represents the upper limit of the fish population.
Answer: 2000

Section 2.5

1. Consider the function f whose graph is shown below. Find the value of each limit if it exists.

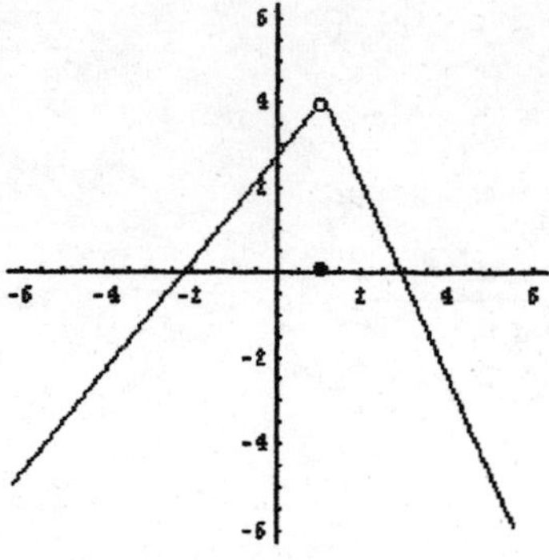

(a) $\lim_{x\to 1^+} f(x)$

Answer: 4

(b) $\lim_{x\to 1^-} f(x)$

Answer: 4

(c) $\lim_{x\to 1} f(x)$

Answer: 4

2. Consider the function f whose graph is shown below. Find the value of each limit if it exists.

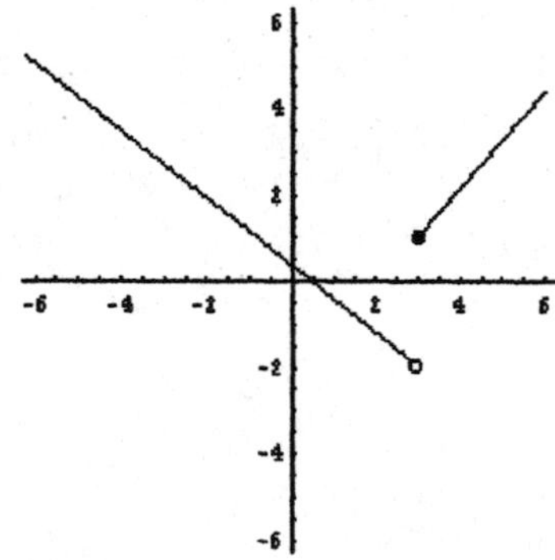

(a) $\lim_{x\to 3^+} f(x)$

Answer: 1

(b) $\lim_{x\to 3^-} f(x)$

Answer: -2

(c) $\lim_{x\to 3} f(x)$

Answer: Does not exist

3. Find the value of the one-sided limit $\lim_{x \to 1^-} \frac{x+2}{x-1}$.

   Answer: $-\infty$

4. Find the value of the one-sided limit $\lim_{x \to 3^-} \sqrt{3-x}$.

   Answer: 0

5. Find the value of the one-sided limit $\lim_{x \to 6^-} \sqrt{6-x} + 3$.

   Answer: 3

6. Find the value of the one-sided limit $\lim_{x \to 1^+} f(x)$ where $f(x) = \begin{cases} 3x & \text{if } x > 1 \\ 4x+2 & \text{if } x \le 1 \end{cases}$.

   Answer: 3

7. Find the value of the one-sided limit $\lim_{x \to 1^-} f(x)$ where $f(x) = \begin{cases} 3x & \text{if } x > 1 \\ 4x+2 & \text{if } x \le 1 \end{cases}$.

   Answer: 6

8. Find the value of the one-sided limit $\lim_{x \to 4^+} \frac{x-1}{x-4}$.

   Answer: ∞

9. Determine the values of x, if any, at which the function $f(x) = \begin{cases} x+3 & \text{if } x < 2 \\ -x+7 & \text{if } x \ge 2 \end{cases}$ is discontinuous.

   Answer: There is no such value of x.

10. Determine the values of x, if any, at which the function $f(x) = \begin{cases} -x & \text{if } x \le 0 \\ x+2 & \text{if } x > 0 \end{cases}$ is discontinuous.

    Answer: $x = 0$.

11. Find the values of x, if any, at which the function $f(x) = x^2 + 2$ is discontinuous.

    Answer: There is no such value of x.

12. Determine the values of x, if any, at which the function $f(x) = \frac{2}{x^2 - 1}$ is discontinuous.

    Answer: $x = 1, -1$

13. Find the values of x, if any, at which the function $f(x) = \begin{cases} x^2 & \text{if } x \leq 0 \\ x & \text{if } x > 0 \end{cases}$ is discontinuous.
Answer: There is no such value of x.

14. Find the values of x, if any, at which the function $f(x) = \dfrac{3}{x^2 + 4}$ is discontinuous.
Answer: There is no such value of x.

15. Find the values of x, if any, at which the function $f(x) = \dfrac{x+3}{|x+3|}$ is discontinuous.
Answer: $x = -3$

16. Find the values of x, if any, at which the function graphed below is discontinuous.

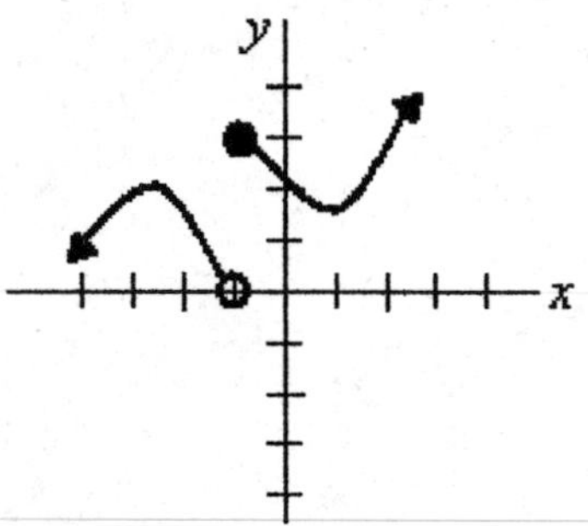

Answer: $x = -1$

17. Use the Intermediate Value Theorem to find c such that $f(c) = 3$ where $f(x) = x^2 + 2x$ on [0, 2].
Answer: $c = 1$.

18. Use the Intermediate Value Theorem to find c such that $f(c) = 3$ where $f(x) = \dfrac{4}{x+1}$ on [0, 1].
Answer: $c = \dfrac{1}{3}$.

Section 2.6

1. Find the slope of the tangent line to the graph of $f(x) = 7x + 8$ at any point x.
   Answer: 7

2. Find the slope of the tangent line to the graph of $f(x) = 3$ at any point x.
   Answer: 0

3. Find the slope of the tangent line to the graph of $f(x) = 3x^2 + 6$ at any point x.
   Answer: $6x$

4. Let $f(x) = 4x + 5$.
   (a) Find the slope of the tangent line to f at the point $(-1,1)$.
   Answer: 4

   (b) Find the equation of the tangent line to f at the point $(-1,1)$.
   Answer: $y = 4x + 5$

5. Let $f(x) = 2x^2$.
   (a) Find the slope of the tangent line to f at the point $(1,2)$.
   Answer: 4

   (b) Find the equation of the tangent line to f at the point $(1,2)$.
   Answer: $y = 4x - 2$

6. Let $f(x) = x^2 + 3x$.
   (a) Find the slope of the tangent line to f at the point $(1,4)$.
   Answer: 5

   (b) Find the equation of the tangent line to f at the point $(1,4)$.
   Answer: $y = 5x - 1$

7. Let $f(x) = \frac{2}{x}$.
   (a) Find the slope of the tangent line to f at the point $(1,2)$.
   Answer: -2

   (b) Find the equation of the tangent line to f at the point $(1,2)$.
   Answer: $y = -2x + 4$

8. A ball is thrown straight up into the air with an initial velocity of 64 feet per second, so that its height (in feet) after t seconds is given by $s(t) = -16t^2 + 64t$.
(a) Calculate the average velocity of the ball over the intervals [1, 1.5], [1, 1.1], and [1, 1.05].

Answer: 24 ft/sec, 30.4 ft/sec, 31.2 ft/sec

(b) Calculate the instantaneous velocity of the ball at time $t = 1$.

Answer: 32 ft/sec

(c) Calculate the time when the ball will hit the ground.

Answer: 4 seconds

Exam 2A

Name:
Instructor:
Section:

Write your work as neatly as possible.

1. Let f be the function defined by $f(x) = 2x^2 - 3x + 4$. Find $f(0), f(2), f(a), f(-a)$, and $f(a+1)$.

2. Find the domain of the function $f(x) = \sqrt{3x+9}$.

3. Refer to the graph of the function f

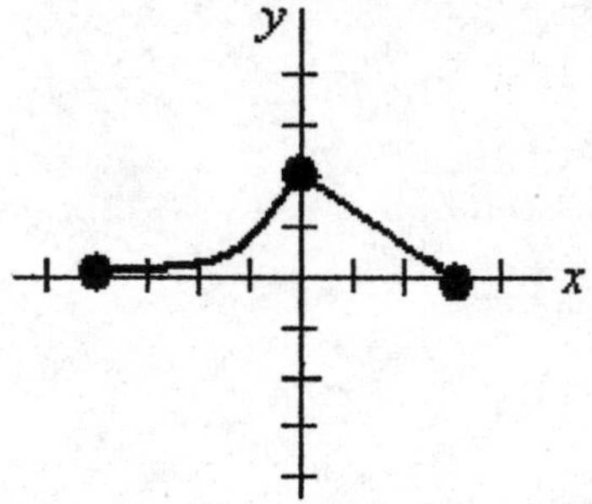

(a) Find the value of $f(0)$.

(b) Find the value(s) of x for which $f(x) = 0$.

(c) Find the domain of f.

(d) Find the range of f.

4. Let $f(x) = x^2 - 3x + 1$ and $g(x) = 4x + 3$. Find the rule for the function $f + g$.

5. Let $f(x) = x^2 - 2x - 1$ and $g(x) = 3x$. Find the rule for the composite function $f \circ g$.

6. If $h(x) = \left(7x^2 - 2x\right)^3$, find functions f and g such that $h = g \circ f$ (the answer is not unique).

7. If $f(x) = x^2 + 2x$, find and simplify $\dfrac{f(a+h) - f(a)}{h}$ $(h \neq 0)$.

8. Determine m and b so that $f(x) = mx + b$ defines a linear function of x with $f(1) = 2$ and $f(0) = -3$.

9. Determine whether the given function is a polynomial function, a rational function, or some other function. State the degree of each polynomial function.

(a) $f(x) = \sqrt[6]{x - x^3}$

(b) $g(x) = \dfrac{\sqrt{5}}{x}$

10. For the following pair of supply and demand equations, where x represents the quantity demanded in units of a thousand and p the unit price in dollars, find the equilibrium quantity and price: $3x + 3p - 17 = 0,\ 5x - 3p + 9 = 0$.

11. Consider the function $f(x) = \begin{cases} x + 2 & \text{if } x \le 2 \\ 6 - x & \text{if } x > 2 \end{cases}$ whose graph is shown below.

Find the value of each limit, if it exists.

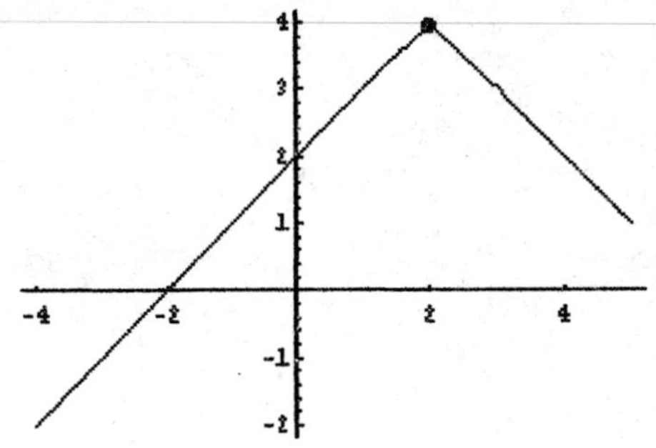

(a) $\lim_{x \to 2^+} f(x)$

(b) $\lim_{x \to 2^-} f(x)$

(c) $\lim_{x \to 2} f(x)$

12. Find the value of $\lim_{x\to 1}\frac{3x-2}{x-2}$, if it exists.

13. Find the value of $\lim_{x\to 3}\frac{x^2-9}{x-3}$, if it exists.

14. The population of a certain town is given by the function $N(t)=\frac{6000t^2+231}{2t^2+75}$, where t is measured in years. Determine the limit of this function as $t\to\infty$, which represents the upper limit of the town's population.

15. Find the value of $\lim_{x\to 2^+}\frac{\sqrt{x-2}}{x+2}$, if it exists.

16. Determine the values of x, if any at which the function $f(x)=\begin{cases} x+2 & \text{if } x\le 2 \\ 6-x & \text{if } x>2 \end{cases}$ is discontinuous.

17. Let $f(x)=2x^2-1$.
(a) Find the slope of the tangent line to the graph of $y=f(x)$ at $x=2$.

(b) Find the equation of the tangent line to the graph of $y=f(x)$ at $x=2$.

18. A ball is thrown straight up into the air so that its height in feet after t seconds is given by $s(t)=128t-16t^2$.
(a) Find the average velocity of the ball during the time interval $[2,2.1]$.

(b) Find the instantaneous velocity of the ball at $t=2$ seconds.

Exam 2B

Name:
Instructor:
Section:

Write your work as neatly as possible.

1. Let *f* be the function defined by $g(x) = x^2 + 2x$.
   (a) Find $g(3)$.

   (b) Find $g(t+1)$.

2. Find the domain of the function $f(x) = \dfrac{x-1}{(x-2)^2}$.

3. Refer to the graph of the function *f*

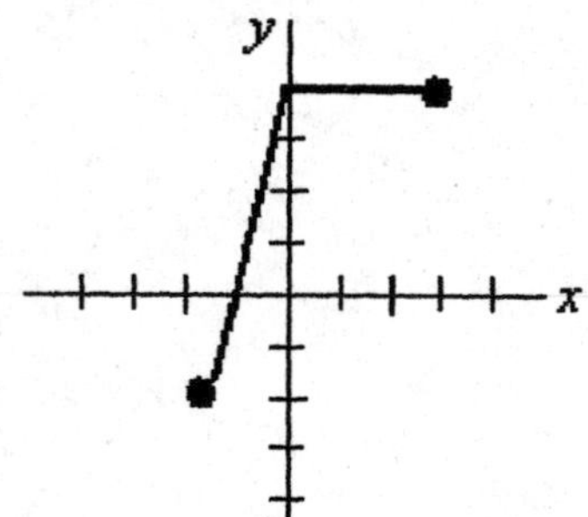

   (a) Find the value of $f(0)$.

   (b) Find the value(s) of *x* for which $f(x) = 0$.

   (c) Find the domain of *f*.

   (d) Find the range of *f*.

4. Let $f(x) = x^2 - 2x$ and $g(x) = 2x - 1$. Find the rule for the function $f \cdot g$.

5. Let $f(x) = x^2 - 2x - 1$ and $g(x) = 3x$. Find the rule for the composite function $g \circ f$.

6. If $h(x) = \dfrac{1}{\sqrt{2x+1}} - 3(2x+1)^3$, find functions f and g such that $h = g \circ f$ (the answer is not unique).

7. If $f(x) = x^2 - 2$, find and simplify $\dfrac{f(a+h) - f(a)}{h}$ $(h \neq 0)$.

8. Determine whether the equation $x^3 - \sqrt{y} = 1$ defines y as a linear function of x. If so, write in the form $y = mx + b$.

9. Determine whether the given function is a polynomial function, a rational function, or some other function. State the degree of each polynomial function.
(a) $f(x) = 4x^3 - 2x^2 + 7x$
(b) $g(x) = \dfrac{6 - x^2}{8x - 1}$

10. For the following pair of supply and demand equations, where x represents the quantity demanded in units of a thousand and p the unit price in dollars, find the equilibrium quantity and price: $5x + 2p - 47 = 0,\ 7x - 4p + 43 = 0$.

11. Consider the function $f(x) = \begin{cases} x & \text{if } x < 3 \\ 1 & \text{if } x = 3 \\ 3 & \text{if } x > 3 \end{cases}$ whose graph is shown below. Find the value of each limit, if it exists.

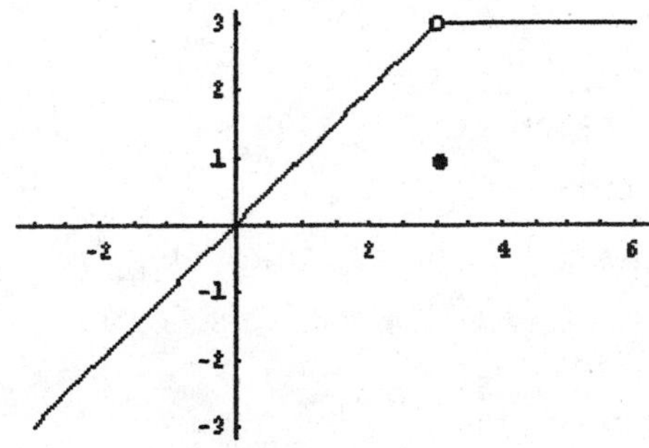

(a) $\lim\limits_{x \to 3^+} f(x)$
(b) $\lim\limits_{x \to 3^-} f(x)$
(c) $\lim\limits_{x \to 3} f(x)$

12. Find the value of $\lim_{x \to 4} \dfrac{3x + x^2}{2x - 4}$, if it exists.

13. Find the value of $\lim_{x \to -1} \dfrac{x^2 + 4x + 3}{x + 1}$, if it exists.

14. The population of a certain town is given by the function $N(t) = \dfrac{12000t^2 + 40}{5t^2 - t}$, where t is measured in years. Determine the limit of this function as $t \to \infty$, which represents the upper limit of the town's population.

15. Find the value of $\lim_{x \to 2^+} \sqrt{2 - x}$, if it exists.

16. Determine the values of x, if any at which the function $f(x) = \begin{cases} x & \text{if } x < 3 \\ 1 & \text{if } x = 3 \\ 3 & \text{if } x > 3 \end{cases}$ is discontinuous.

17. Let $f(x) = 1 - 3x^2$.
    (a) Find the slope of the tangent line to the graph of $y = f(x)$ at $x = 1$.

    (b) Find the equation of the tangent line to the graph of $y = f(x)$ at $x = 1$.

18. A ball is thrown straight up into the air so that its height in feet after t seconds is given by $s(t) = 128t - 16t^2$.
    (a) Find the average velocity of the ball during the time interval $[2.5, 2.6]$.
    (b) Find the instantaneous velocity of the ball at $t = 2.5$ seconds.

Exam 2C

Name:
Instructor:
Section:

Write your work as neatly as possible.

1. Let *f* be the function defined by $g(x) = 2x^2 + x + 1$.
   (a) Find $g(-3)$

   (b) Find $g(t-1)$.

2. Find the domain of the function $f(x) = \sqrt[4]{x^2 + 2x}$.

3. Refer to the graph of the function *f*

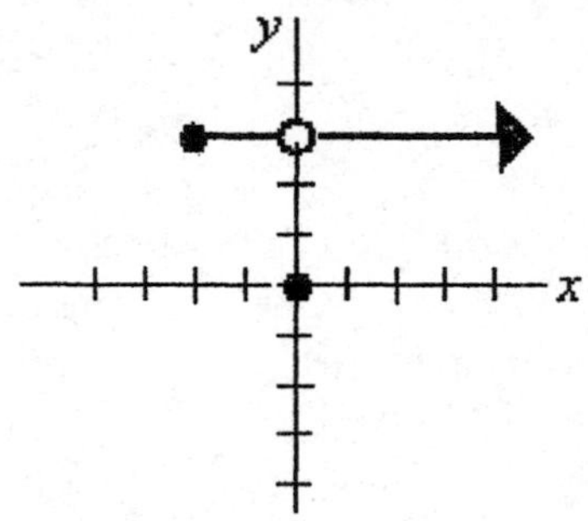

   (a) Find the value of $f(0)$.

   (b) Find the value(s) of *x* for which $f(x) = 0$.

   (c) Find the domain of *f*.

   (d) Find the range of *f*. Let $f(x) = 2x^2 + 3$ and $g(x) = -3x + 1$. Find the rule for the function $f - g$.

4. If $h(x) = \sqrt{3x} + 3x$, find functions *f* and *g* such that $h = g \circ f$. (The answer is not unique.)

5. Let $f(x) = 3\sqrt{2x} + 1$ and $g(x) = x^2 - 2$. Find the rule for the composite function $f \circ g$.

6. If $f(x) = \dfrac{1}{x+2}$, find and simplify $\dfrac{f(a+h) - f(a)}{h}$ $(h \neq 0)$.

7. Determine m and b so that $f(x) = mx + b$ defines a linear function of x with $f(-2) = 4$ and $f(1) = 3$.

8. Determine whether the given function is a polynomial function, a rational function, or some other function. State the degree of each polynomial function.
(a) $r(t) = 7t^3 - \pi$

(b) $f(x) = \dfrac{\sqrt{x+4}}{x-1}$

9. The demand and supply functions associated with a certain commodity are $13x - 9p + 27 = 0$ and $9x + p - 139 = 0$, respectively, where x denotes the quantity demanded in units of a thousand and p is the unit price in dollars. Find the equilibrium quantity and the equilibrium price.

10. Consider the function $f(x) = \begin{cases} x & \text{if } x < 3 \\ 1 & \text{if } x = 3 \\ 3 & \text{if } x > 3 \end{cases}$ whose graph is shown below. Find the value of each limit, if it exists.

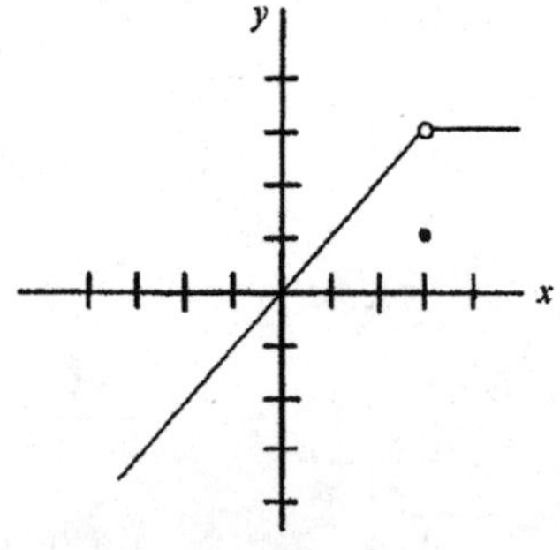

(a) $\lim_{x \to 3^+} f(x)$
(b) $\lim_{x \to 3^-} f(x)$
(c) $\lim_{x \to 3} f(x)$

11. Find the value of $\lim_{x \to 4} \frac{8+2x}{x}$, if it exists.

12. Find the value of $\lim_{x \to -1} \frac{x^2+4x+3}{x+1}$, if it exists.

13. The population of a certain town is given by the function $N(t) = \frac{9000t^2+100}{3t^2+10t+5}$, where t is measured in years. Determine the limit of this function as $t \to \infty$, which represents the upper limit of the town's population.

14. Find the value of $\lim_{x \to -5^+} \sqrt{5+x}$, if it exists.

15. Determine the values of x, if any at which the function $f(x) = \begin{cases} x & \text{if } x < 3 \\ 1 & \text{if } x = 3 \\ 3 & \text{if } x > 3 \end{cases}$ is discontinuous.

16. Let $f(x) = 6 + 2x^2$.
(a) Find the slope of the tangent line to the graph of $y = f(x)$ at $x = 2$.

(b) Find the equation of the tangent line to the graph of $y = f(x)$ at $x = 2$.

17. A ball is thrown straight up into the air so that its height in feet after t seconds is given by $s(t) = 128t - 16t^2$.
(a) Find the average velocity of the ball during the time interval $[2.5, 2.6]$.

(b) Find the instantaneous velocity of the ball at $t = 2.5$ seconds.

Exam 2D

Name:
Instructor:
Section:

Write your work as neatly as possible.

1. Let g be the function defined by $g(x) = x^2 + x + 5$.
   (a) Find $g(5)$.

   (b) Find $g(t - 3)$.

2. Determine the domain of the function $f(x) = \dfrac{x}{3x - 5}$.

3. Refer to the graph of the function f

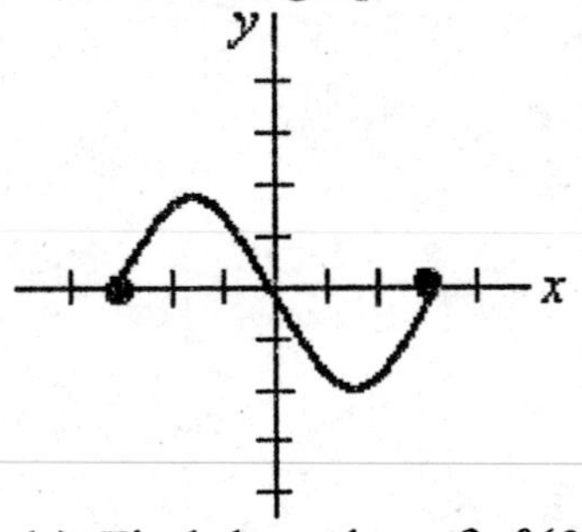

(a) Find the value of $f(0)$.

(b) Approximate the value(s) of x for which $f(x) = -2$.

(c) Find the domain of f.

(d) Find the range of f.

4. Let $f(x) = 5x^2 - 1$ and $g(x) = -5x + 2$. Find the rule for the function $\dfrac{f}{g}$.

5. Let $f(x) = 3\sqrt{2x} + 1$ and $g(x) = x^2 - 2$. Find the rule for the composite function $f \circ g$.

6. If $h(x) = \left(8x^2 - 2x\right)^{1/3}$, find functions f and g such that $h = g \circ f$ (the answer is not unique).

7. If $f(x) = \dfrac{1}{x+3}$, find and simplify $\dfrac{f(a+h) - f(a)}{h}$ $(h \neq 0)$.

8. Determine whether the equation $x + 5 = 2y^{5/2}$ defines y as a linear function of x. If so, write in the form $y = mx + b$.

9. Determine whether the given function is a polynomial function, a rational function, or some other function. State the degree of each polynomial function.
(a) $r(x) = x^{18} - 2x^{13} + 5x$

(b) $g(x) = \dfrac{\sqrt{x}}{3x^2 + 2x + 5}$

10. For the following pair of supply and demand equations, where x represents the quantity demanded in units of a thousand and p the unit price in dollars, find the equilibrium quantity and price: $5x + 3p - 117 = 0$, $7x - 3p + 69 = 0$.

11. Consider the function $f(x) = \begin{cases} -x & \text{if } x \leq 1 \\ -1 & \text{if } x > 1 \end{cases}$ whose graph is shown below. Find the value of each limit, if it exists.

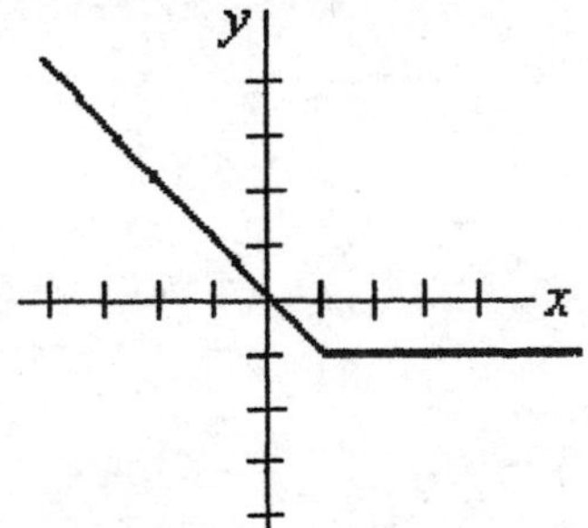

(a) $\lim\limits_{x \to 1^+} f(x)$

(b) $\lim\limits_{x \to 1^-} f(x)$

(c) $\lim\limits_{x \to 1} f(x)$

12. Find the value of $\lim_{x \to -2} \frac{x+8}{x-1}$, if it exists.

13. Find the value of $\lim_{x \to 0} \frac{x^2+6x}{x}$, if it exists.

14. The population of a certain town is given by the function $N(t) = \frac{9000t^2+150}{2t^2+t+4}$, where t is measured in years. Determine the limit of this function as $t \to \infty$, which represents the upper limit of the town's population.

15. Find the value of $\lim_{x \to -3^-} \frac{4-x}{x+3}$, if it exists.

16. Determine the values of x, if any at which the function $f(x) = \begin{cases} -x & \text{if } x \le 1 \\ -1 & \text{if } x > 1 \end{cases}$ is discontinuous.

17. Let $f(x) = \frac{1}{2}x^2 + 3x$.

(a) Find the slope of the tangent line to the graph of $y = f(x)$ at $x = 2$.

(b) Find the equation of the tangent line to the graph of $y = f(x)$ at $x = 2$.

18. A ball is thrown straight up into the air so that its height in feet after t seconds is given by $s(t) = 128t - 16t^2$.

(a) Find the average velocity of the ball during the time interval [3, 3.1].

(b) Find the instantaneous velocity of the ball at $t = 3$ seconds.

Answers to Chapter 2 Exams

Exam 2A

1. $4, 6, 2a^2-3a+4, 2a^2+3a+4,$
   $2a^2+a+3$
2. $[-3,\infty)$
3. (a) 2
   (b) -4,3
   (c) $[-4,3]$
   (d) $[0,2]$
4. x^2+x+4
5. $9x^2-6x-1$
6. $g(x)=x^3, f(x)=7x^2-2x$
7. $2a+h+2$
8. $m=5, b=-3$
9. (a) Other
   (b) Rational
10. $x=1, p=\frac{14}{3}$
11. (a) 4
    (b) 4
    (c) 4
12. -1
13. 6
14. 3000
15. 0
16. There is no such value of x
17. (a) 8
    (b) $y=8x-9$
18. (a) 62.4 ft/s
    (b) 64 ft/s

Exam 2B

1. (a) 15
   (b) t^2+4t+3
2. $\{x \mid x\neq -2\}$
3. (a) 4
   (b) -1
   (c) $[-2,3]$
   (d) $[-2,4]$
4. $2x^3-5x^2+2x$
5. $3x^2-6x-3$
6. $g(x)=\frac{1}{\sqrt{x}}-3x^3, f(x)=2x+1$
7. $2a+h$
8. No
9. (a) Polynomial (degree 3)
   (b) Rational
10. $x=3, p=16$
11. (a) 3
    (b) 3
    (c) 3
12. 7
13. 2
14. 2400
15. DNE
16. At $x=3$
17. (a) -6
    (b) $y=-6x+4$
18. (a) 46.4 ft/s
    (b) 48 ft/s

Exam 2C

1. (a) 16
   (b) $2t^2 - 3t + 2$
2. $(-\infty, -2] \cup [0, \infty)$
3. (a) 0
   (b) 0
   (c) $[-2, \infty)$
   (d) $\{0\} \cup \{3\}$
4. $g(x) = \sqrt{x} + x,\ f(x) = 3x$
5. $3\sqrt{2x^2 - 4} + 1$
6. $-\dfrac{1}{a^2 + ah + 4a + 2h + 4}$
7. $m = -\dfrac{1}{3}, b = \dfrac{10}{3}$
8. (a) Polynomial (degree 3)
   (b) Other
9. 13,021; \$21.81
10. (a) 3
    (b) 3
    (c) 3
11. 4
12. 2
13. 3000
14. 0
15. At $x = 3$
16. (a) 8
    (b) $y = 8x - 2$
17. (a) 46.4 ft/s
    (b) 48 ft/s

Exam 2D

1. (a) 35
   (b) $t^2 - 5t + 11$
2. $\left(-\infty, \dfrac{5}{3}\right) \cup \left(\dfrac{5}{3}, \infty\right)$
3. (a) 0
   (b) 1.5
   (c) $[-3, 3]$
   (d) $[-2, 2]$
4. $\dfrac{5x^2 - 1}{-5x + 2}$
5. $3\sqrt{2x^2 - 4} + 1$
6. $g(x) = x^{1/3},\ f(x) = 8x^2 - 2x$
7. $-\dfrac{1}{(a+3)(a+h+3)}$
8. No
9. (a) Polynomial (degree 18)
   (b) Other
10. $4, \dfrac{97}{3}$
11. (a) −1
    (b) −1
    (c) −1
12. −2
13. 6
14. 4500
15. $-\infty$
16. There is no such value of x
17. (a) 5
    (b) $y = 5x - 2$
18. (a) 30.4 ft/s
    (b) 32 ft/s

Chapter 3 ■ Differentiation

Section 3.1

1. Find the derivative of $f(x) = 22$. Answer: 0

2. Find the derivative of $f(x) = \pi^3$. Answer: 0

3. Find the derivative of $f(x) = \sqrt{5} + 3$ Answer: 0

4. Find the derivative of $f(x) = x^9$. Answer: $9x^8$

5. Find the derivative of $f(x) = -3x^4$. Answer: $-12x^3$

6. Find the derivative of $f(x) = \dfrac{3}{x^2}$. Answer: $-\dfrac{6}{x^3}$

7. Find the derivative of $f(x) = 2x^3 - 4x^2 + 3$. Answer: $6x^2 - 8x$

8. Find the derivative of $f(x) = 3x^4 - 2x^{5/3} + \sqrt{x}$. Answer: $12x^3 - \dfrac{10}{3}x^{2/3} + \dfrac{1}{2}x^{-1/2}$

9. Find the derivative of $f(x) = -0.3x^4 + 2x^2 + 4.5x$. Answer: $-1.2x^3 + 4x + 4.5$

10. Find the derivative of $f(x) = 3x^2 + \dfrac{2}{3x^2}$. Answer: $6x - \dfrac{4}{3x^3}$

11. Find the derivative of $g(t) = 5t^3 - 2t^2 + t - 3$. Answer: $15t^2 - 4t + 1$

12. Find the derivative of $s(m) = \dfrac{m^3 + 3m}{m}$. Answer: $2m$

13. Find the derivative of $f(x) = 4x^{7/3} + \dfrac{4}{\sqrt{x}}$. Answer: $\dfrac{28}{3}x^{4/3} - 2x^{-3/2}$

14. Let $f(x) = 3x^{3/2} - 2x$. Find
    (a) $f'(0)$ Answer: -2

    (b) $f'(4)$ Answer: 7

    (c) $f'(8)$ Answer: $9\sqrt{2} - 2$

15. Find the slope and an equation of the tangent line to the graph of the function $f(x) = 2x^2 + 4x + 1$ at the point $(1,7)$.
Answer: 8; $y = 8x - 1$

16. Find the slope and an equation of the tangent line to the graph of the function $f(x) = \sqrt{x} - \dfrac{2}{\sqrt{x}}$ at the point $(4,1)$.
Answer: $\dfrac{3}{8}$; $y = \dfrac{3}{8}x - \dfrac{1}{2}$

17. Let $f(x) = 2x^3 + 1$.
(a) Find the point(s) on the graph of *f* where the slope of the tangent line is equal to 6.
Answer: $(-1,-1)$, $(1,3)$
(b) Find the equation(s) of the tangent line(s) of part (a).
Answer: $y = 6x + 5$, $y = 6x - 3$

18. Let $f(x) = \dfrac{1}{3}x^3 - 4x + 5$. Find the *x*-values of the point(s) on the graph of *f* where the slope of the tangent line is equal to
(a) -2 Answer: $\pm\sqrt{2}$
(b) 0 Answer: ± 2
(c) 5 Answer: ± 3

19. A town's population is growing according to the function $P(t) = 10{,}000 + 30t + t^2$, where $P(t)$ denotes the town's population t months from now.
(a) How fast will the population be increasing four months from now?
Answer: 38 people per month

(b) How fast will the population be increasing twelve months from now?
Answer: 54 people per month

Section 3.2

1. Find the derivative of the function $f(x) = x^2(2x-3)$.
   Answer: $6x^2 - 6x$

2. Find the derivative of the function $f(x) = (x^2+2)(x^2-2x+4)$.
   Answer: $4x^3 - 6x^2 + 12x - 4$

3. Find the derivative of the function $f(x) = \dfrac{x+2}{x-1}$.
   Answer: $\dfrac{-3}{(x-1)^2}$

4. Find the derivative of the function $f(t) = \dfrac{t}{t+3}$.
   Answer: $\dfrac{3}{(t+3)^2}$

5. Find the derivative of the function $f(x) = \dfrac{x}{x^2+x+1}$.
   Answer: $\dfrac{-x^2+1}{(x^2+x+1)^2}$

6. Find the derivative of the function $f(x) = \left(x^2 + \dfrac{1}{x^2}\right)(2x+4)$.
   Answer: $6x^2 + 8x - \dfrac{2}{x^2} - \dfrac{8}{x^3}$

7. Find the derivative of the function $f(x) = (x^2+1)\left(2x^2 - \dfrac{1}{x}\right)$.
   Answer: $8x^3 + 4x + \dfrac{1}{x^2} - 1$

8. Find the derivative of the function $f(x) = \dfrac{x+3}{x+2}$.
   Answer: $\dfrac{-1}{(x+2)^2}$

9. Find the derivative of the function $f(x) = \dfrac{x+\sqrt{2}x}{4x+1}$.
   Answer: $\dfrac{1+\sqrt{2}}{(4x+1)^2}$

10. Find the derivative of the function $f(x) = \dfrac{x^3+2}{x^2-3}$.

Answer: $\dfrac{x^4 - 9x^2 - 4x}{\left(x^2-3\right)^2}$

11. Find the derivative of the function $f(x) = \dfrac{1}{4}x^4 + \left(x^2-1\right)\left(x^2-2x+4\right)+4$.

Answer: $5x^3 - 6x^2 + 6x + 2$

12. Find the derivative of the function $f(x) = \dfrac{u}{u^2-1}$.

Answer: $-\dfrac{u^2+1}{\left(u^2-1\right)^2}$

13. Find the derivative of the function $s(t) = \dfrac{t-1}{2t^2+5}$.

Answer: $\dfrac{-2t^2-4t+5}{\left(2t^2+5\right)^2}$

14. Find the derivative of the function $f(x) = \left(x^3+x^2-x-1\right)\left(x^2+3\right)$.

Answer: $5x^4 + 4x^3 + 6x^2 + 4x - 3$

15. Let $H(x) = f(x)g(x)$, with f and g differentiable at $x = 2$. Find $H'(2)$ if $f(2) = 4, f'(2) = 3, g(2) = -2,$ and $g'(2) = 5$.

Answer: 14

16. Let $H(x) = \dfrac{f(x)}{g(x)}$, with f and g differentiable at $x = 2$. Find $H'(2)$ if $f(2) = 4, f'(2) = 3, g(2) = -2,$ and $g'(2) = 5$.

Answer: $-\dfrac{13}{4}$

17. Let $f(x) = (2x+1)\left(x^2-2\right)$. Find

(a) $f'(0)$

Answer: -4

(b) $f'(2)$

Answer: 24

(c) $f'(4)$

Answer: 100

18. Find the slope and an equation of the tangent line to the graph of the function $f(x) = (x+2)(2x^2+1)$ at the point $(-1,3)$.
Answer: -1; $y = -x + 2$

19. Find the slope and an equation of the tangent line to the graph of the function $f(x) = \dfrac{2x-1}{2x+1}$ at the point $\left(2, \dfrac{3}{5}\right)$.

Answer: $\dfrac{4}{25}$; $y = \dfrac{4}{25}x + \dfrac{7}{25}$

20. Find the point(s) on the graph of $f(x) = \dfrac{x}{x^2+x+4}$ where the tangent line is horizontal.
Answer: $\left(-2, -\dfrac{1}{3}\right)$, $\left(2, \dfrac{1}{5}\right)$

21. Find the point(s) on the graph of $f(x) = 3x^2 - 4x$ where the tangent line is horizontal.
Answer: $\left(\dfrac{2}{3}, -\dfrac{4}{3}\right)$

22. Let $f(x) = \dfrac{1}{3}(x^2+1)(x+2)$. Find the point(s) on the graph of *f* where the slope of the tangent line is equal to
(a) 0
Answer: $\left(-1, \dfrac{2}{3}\right)$, $\left(-\dfrac{1}{3}, \dfrac{50}{81}\right)$

(b) 7
Answer: $\left(-\dfrac{10}{3}, -\dfrac{436}{81}\right)$, $\left(2, \dfrac{20}{3}\right)$

Section 3.3

1. Find the derivative of the function $f(x)=(3x+1)^4$.
   Answer: $12(3x+1)^3$

2. Find the derivative of the function $f(t)=3(t^2+1)^5$.
   Answer: $30t(t^2+1)^4$

3. Find the derivative of the function $f(m)=(3m^2+2)^3+(4m-6)^5$.
   Answer: $18m(3m^2+2)^2+20(4m-6)^5$

4. Find the derivative of the function $f(x)=(3x+1)^{-3}$.
   Answer: $-9(3x+1)^{-4}$

5. Find the derivative of the function $f(x)=(4x^2+3x-1)^{3/2}$.
   Answer: $\frac{3}{2}(8x+3)\sqrt{4x^2+3x-1}$

6. Find the derivative of the function $f(x)=\sqrt[4]{1+x^2}$.
   Answer: $\frac{1}{2}x(1+x^2)^{-3/4}$

7. Find the derivative of the function $f(x)=\frac{3}{(x^2+1)^3}$.
   Answer: $-18x(1+x^2)^{-4}$

8. Find the derivative of the function $f(x)=\frac{2x}{\sqrt{3x^2+1}}$.
   Answer: $\frac{2}{(3x^2+1)^{3/2}}$

9. Find the derivative of the function $f(t)=\left(5+\dfrac{2}{t}\right)^3$.

Answer: $-\dfrac{6}{t^2}\left(5+\dfrac{2}{t}\right)^2$

10. Find the derivative of the function $f(x)=\dfrac{2}{\left(3x^3+x\right)^{5/2}}$.

Answer: $-5\left(9x^2+1\right)\left(3x^3+x\right)^{-7/2}$

11. Find the point(s) on the graph of $f(x)=\dfrac{\sqrt{x}}{x+2}$ where the tangent line is horizontal.

Answer: $\left(2,\dfrac{\sqrt{2}}{4}\right)$

12. Find the derivative of the function $f(t)=\left(3t^3+2t^2-2t+3\right)^{-2}$.

Answer: $-2\left(9t^2+4t-2\right)\left(3t^3+2t^2-2t+3\right)^{-3}$

13. Let $H(x)=\left(f(x)\right)^2$, with f differentiable at $x=2$. Find $H'(2)$ if $f(2)=4$ and $f'(2)=3$..

Answer: 24

14. Let $H(x)=\sqrt{f(x)}$, with f differentiable at $x=2$. Find $H'(2)$ if $f(2)=4$ and $f'(2)=-8$..

Answer: –2

15. Find the derivative of the function $f(t)=\left(t^{-2}-t^{-3}\right)^4$.

Answer: $4\left(t^{-2}-t^{-3}\right)^3\left(-2t^{-3}+3t^{-4}\right)$

16. Find the derivative of the function $f(x)=(3x-2)^{-3/2}+\left(x^2+1\right)^{3/2}$.

Answer: $-\dfrac{9}{2}(3x-2)^{-5/2}+3x\sqrt{x^2+1}$

17. Find the derivative of the function $f(x)=(x+1)^3(2x-1)^5$.
Answer: $3(x+1)^2(2x-1)^5+10(x+1)^3(2x-1)^4$

18. Find the derivative of the function $f(x)=\left(\dfrac{x-1}{x+2}\right)^4$.

Answer: $12\left(\dfrac{x-1}{x+2}\right)^3\dfrac{1}{(x+2)^2}$

19. Find the derivative of the function $f(x)=\sqrt{\dfrac{x+2}{3x-1}}$.

Answer: $-\dfrac{7}{2}\left(\dfrac{x+2}{3x-1}\right)^{-1/2}(3x-1)^{-2}$

20. Find the derivative of the function $f(x)=\dfrac{x}{\left(x^2+3\right)^4}$.

Answer: $\dfrac{\left(-7x^2+3\right)}{\left(x^2+3\right)^5}$

21. Find $\dfrac{dy}{du}$, $\dfrac{du}{dx}$, and $\dfrac{dy}{dx}$ if $y=u^{-4/3}$ and $u=x^2-2x+2$.

Answer:
$\dfrac{dy}{du}=-\dfrac{4}{3}u^{-7/3}$, $\dfrac{du}{dx}=2x-2$, and $\dfrac{dy}{dx}=-\dfrac{4}{3}\left(x^2-2x+2\right)^{-7/3}(2x-2)$

22. Find $\dfrac{dy}{dx}$ if $y=u^5$ and $u=3x^2+7x$.

Answer: $\dfrac{dy}{dx}=5\left(3x^2+7x\right)^4(6x+7)$

23. Find $\dfrac{dy}{dx}$ if $y=\sqrt{u}$ and $u=13x-3$.

Answer: $\dfrac{dy}{dx}=\dfrac{13}{2\sqrt{13x-3}}$

24. Find $\dfrac{dy}{dx}$ if $y=\sqrt[3]{u+7}$ and $u=8$.
Answer: 0

Section 3.4

1. The cost C, in dollars, for a company to produce a total of x refrigerators is $C(x) = 30{,}000 + 700x - 0.01x^2$.
   (a) Find the actual cost incurred in producing the 150th refrigerator.
   Answer: \$697.01
   (b) Find the marginal cost when $x = 149$
   Answer: \$697.02

2. The cost, in dollars, for a company to produce a total of x souvenirs is $C(x) = 100 + 3.25x - 0.002x^2$.
   (a) Find the actual cost incurred in producing the 50th souvenir.
   Answer: \$3.05
   (b) Find the marginal cost when $x = 49$
   Answer: \$3.05

3. The cost, in dollars, for a company to produce a total of x shirts is $C(x) = 340 + 8.25x - 0.008x^2$.
   (a) Find the actual cost incurred in producing the 100th shirt.
   Answer: \$6.66
   (b) Find the marginal cost when $x = 99$
   Answer: \$6.67

4. The cost for a company to produce a total of x personal stereos is $C(x) = 20{,}000 + 120x$.
   (a) Find the average cost function $\overline{C}$.
   Answer: $\overline{C}(x) = \dfrac{20{,}000}{x} + 120$
   (b) Find the marginal average cost function $\overline{C}'$
   Answer: $-\dfrac{20{,}000}{x^2}$

5. The weekly demand for apartments in a large city is $p = -0.5x + 1200$, where p denotes the monthly rent for the apartment and x denotes the number of apartments rented. The monthly cost associated with renting a total of x apartments is $C = 30{,}000 + 400x$.
   (a) Find the revenue function R.
   Answer: $R(x) = 1200x - 0.5x^2$
   (b) Find the profit function P.
   Answer: $P(x) = -30{,}000 + 800x - 0.5x^2$
   (c) Find the marginal profit function P'.
   Answer: $P'(x) = 800 - x$

6. For the demand equation $x = -\frac{4}{3}p + 15$, compute the elasticity of demand and determine whether the demand is elastic, unitary, or inelastic if $p = 8$.

Answer: $-\frac{4p}{4p-45}$; elastic

7. For the demand equation $x + \frac{1}{4}p - 15 = 0$, compute the elasticity of demand and determine whether the demand is elastic, unitary, or inelastic if $p = 20$.

Answer: $-\frac{p}{p-60}$; inelastic

8. For the demand equation $p = 324 - x^2$, compute the elasticity of demand and determine whether the demand is elastic, unitary, or inelastic if $p = 216$.

Answer: $-\frac{p}{2p-648}$; unitary

9. A certain bug population *P*, after *t* months can be approximated by $P(t) = 3\sqrt{t^2 + 2t}$ $(t \geq 2)$. Find the rate at which the population is changing at the end of 6 months.

Answer: ≈ 3.03 bugs/month

10. A child is flying a kite at a height of 40 ft, which is moving horizontally at a rate of 3 ft/sec. If the string is taut, at what rate is the string being paid out when the length of the string released is 50 ft?

Answer: 1.8 ft/sec

11. A travel company plans to sponsor a special tour to Asia. There will be accommodations for no more than 40 people, and the tour will be canceled if no more than 10 people book reservations. Based on the past experience, the manager determines that if *n* people book the tour, the profit (in dollars) may be modeled by the function:
$P(n) = -n^3 + 27.6n^2 + 970.2n - 4{,}235$.
For what size tour group is profit maximized.

Answer: When 29 people book the tour and the maximum profit is $22,723.40.

Section 3.5

1. Find the first and second derivatives of $f(x) = 2x^3 - 4x^2 + 7$.
   Answer: $6x^2 - 8x,\ 12x - 8$

2. Find the first and second derivatives of $f(x) = 2x^4 - 3x^{5/3} + \sqrt{x}$.
   Answer: $8x^3 - 5x^{2/3} + \frac{1}{2}x^{-1/2},\ 24x^2 - \frac{10}{3}x^{-1/3} - \frac{1}{4}x^{-3/2}$

3. Find the first and second derivatives of $f(x) = -0.2x^4 + 8.1x^2 + 24.5x$.
   Answer: $-0.8x^3 + 16.2x + 24.5,\ -2.4x^2 + 16.2$

4. Find the first and second derivatives of $f(x) = x^2(3x - 1)$.
   Answer: $9x^2 - 2x,\ 18x - 2$

5. Find the first and second derivatives of $f(x) = (x^2 + 1)(x^2 - 2x + 4)$.
   Answer: $4x^3 - 6x^2 + 10x - 2,\ 12x^2 - 12x + 10$

6. Find the first and second derivatives of $f(x) = (x^2 + 2)\left(3x^2 - \frac{1}{x}\right)$.
   Answer: $12x^3 + 12x - 1 + 2x^{-2},\ 36x^2 + 12 - 4x^{-3}$

7. Find the first and second derivatives of $f(x) = \frac{x+4}{x+7}$.
   Answer: $\frac{3}{(x+7)^2},\ -\frac{6}{(x+7)^3}$

8. Find the first and second derivatives of $f(t) = 2(t^2 - 2)^4$.
   Answer: $16t(t^2 - 2)^3,\ 96t^2(t^2 - 2)^2 + 16(t^2 - 2)^3$

9. Find the first and second derivatives of $f(x) = (2x + 3)^{-3}$.
   Answer: $-6(2x + 3)^{-4},\ 48(2x + 3)^{-5}$

10. Find the first and second derivatives of $f(x) = (3x^2 + 4x - 2)^{3/2}$.
    Answer: $3(3x + 2)\sqrt{3x^2 + 4x - 2},\ 6(9x^2 + 12x - 1)(3x^2 + 4x - 2)^{-1/2}$

11. Find the first and second derivatives of $f(x)=\left(\frac{x-2}{x-3}\right)^4$.

Answer: $-4\frac{(x-2)^3}{(x-3)^5}$, $4\frac{(x-2)^2(2x-1)}{(x-3)^6}$

12. Find the second derivative of $f(x)=-\frac{9}{2}(x+7)^{2/3}$.

Answer: $(x+7)^{-4/3}$

13. Find the second derivative of $s(t)=\frac{t+2}{t-3}$.

Answer: $\frac{10}{(t-3)^3}$

14. Find the second derivative of $f(x)=4\sqrt{x+1}$.

Answer: $\frac{3}{2}(x+1)^{-5/2}$

15. Find the third derivative of $f(x)=\frac{3}{x^3}$.

Answer: $-180x^{-6}$

16. Let $f(x)=3x^3-2x^2+6x-1$. Find
(a) the first derivative of f.
Answer: $9x^2-4x+6$

(b) the second derivative of f.
Answer: $18x-4$

(c) the third derivative of f.
Answer: 18

Section 3.6

1. If $x^2 + y^2 = 25$, find $\frac{dy}{dx}$ by implicit differentiation.

   Answer: $-x/y$

2. If $x^3 + y^3 + y - 5 = 0$, find $\frac{dy}{dx}$ by implicit differentiation.

   Answer: $-3x^2/(3y^2 + 1)$

3. If $x^2y^2 - 3xy = 4$, find $\frac{dy}{dx}$ by implicit differentiation.

   Answer: $-\frac{3y - 2xy^2}{3x - 2x^2y}$

4. If $x^{2/3} + y^{2/3} = 4$, find $\frac{dy}{dx}$ by implicit differentiation.

   Answer: $-y^{1/3}/x^{1/3}$

5. If $(4x + y)^{1/2} = 5x$, find $\frac{dy}{dx}$ by implicit differentiation.

   Answer: $10(4x + y)^{1/2} - 4$

6. If $\frac{1}{x^3} + \frac{1}{y^3} = 1$, find $\frac{dy}{dx}$ by implicit differentiation.

   Answer: $-y^4/x^4$

7. If $\sqrt{xy} = 3x + 2y^2$, find $\frac{dy}{dx}$ by implicit differentiation.

   Answer: $(6\sqrt{xy} - y)/(x - 8y\sqrt{xy})$

8. Find the slope of the line tangent to the graph of $y^3 + 2x^2 = 3$ at the point $(1, 1)$.

   Answer: $-\frac{4}{3}$

9. Find the slope of the line tangent to the graph of $2xy + 3\sqrt{y} = 3$ at the point $(0,1)$.

Answer: $-\frac{4}{3}$

10. Find the second derivative $\frac{d^2y}{dx^2}$ of the function defined implicitly by $xy^2 = 1$.

Answer: $3y/(4x^2)$

11. Find the second derivative $\frac{d^2y}{dx^2}$ of the function defined implicitly by $x^2y^2 - 2xy = 0$.

Answer: $2y/x^2$

12. A can in the shape of a right circular cylinder with radius 8 in. is being filled at a constant rate. If the fluid is rising at a rate of 0.1 in/sec, what is the rate at which the fluid is flowing into the can?

Answer: $6.4\pi \text{ in}^3/\text{sec}$

13. A can in the shape of a right circular cone with radius 9 in. is being filled at a constant rate. If the fluid is rising at a rate of 0.5 in/sec, what is the rate at which the fluid is flowing into the can?

Answer: $13.5\pi \text{ in}^3/\text{sec}$

14. An automobile traveling at a rate of 30 ft/sec is approaching an intersection. When the automobile is 120 ft from the intersection, a truck traveling at the rate of 40 ft/sec crosses the intersection. The automobile and the truck are on roads that are at right angles to each other. How fast are the automobile and the truck separating 2 seconds after the truck leaves the intersection?

Answer: 14 ft/sec

15. A man 6 ft tall is walking toward a building at the rate of 5 ft/sec. If there is a light on the ground 50 ft from the building, how fast is the man's shadow on the building growing shorter when he is 30 ft from the building?

Answer: -3.75 ft/sec

16. Oil spilled from a ruptured tank spreads in a circular pattern whose radius increases at a constant rate of 2 ft/sec. How fast the area of the spill increasing when the radius of the spill is 60 ft?

Answer: $240\pi \text{ ft}^2/\text{sec}$

Section 3.7

1. Find the differential of the function $f(x) = 3x^3$.
   Answer: $9x^2dx$

2. Find the differential of the function $f(x) = 3x^2 + 2x$.
   Answer: $(6x+2)dx$

3. Find the differential of the function $f(x) = 3x^{3/2} - x^{1/2}$.
   Answer: $\left(\frac{9}{2}x^{1/2} - \frac{1}{2}x^{-1/2}\right)dx$

4. Find the differential of the function $f(x) = \frac{2}{x-2}$.
   Answer: $-\frac{2dx}{(x-2)^2}$

5. Find the differential of the function $f(x) = \sqrt{2x^2 - 3x}$.
   Answer: $\frac{(4x-3)dx}{2\sqrt{2x^2 - 3x}}$

6. Find the differential of the function $f(t) = \sqrt{5-7t}$.
   Answer: $-\frac{7}{2}(5-7t)^{-1/2}\,dt$

7. Let *f* be the function defined by $y = f(x) = 4x^2 - 3x + 5$.
   (a) Find the differential of *f*.
   Answer: $(8x-3)dx$

   (b) Use your result from (a) to find the approximate change in *y* if *x* changes from 1 to 1.02.
   Answer: 0.1

   (c) Find the actual change in *y* if *x* changes from 1 to 1.02 and compare your result with that obtained in part (b)
   Answer: 0.1016; larger

8. Use differentials to approximate $\sqrt{15}$.
   Answer: 3.875

9. Use differentials to approximate $\sqrt{101}$.
   Answer: 10.05

10. Use differentials to approximate $\sqrt[3]{60}$.

Answer: 3.917

11. Approximate the volume of a spherical shell whose inner radius is 4 inches and whose thickness is one-sixteenth of an inch.

Answer: 4π in^2

12. A closed container in the form of a cube having a volume of 1000 in^3 is to be made by using six equal squares of material costing 20 cents per square inch. How accurately must the side of each square be measured so that the total cost of material will be correct to within \$3.00?

Answer: Within 0.125 inches.

13. Find the differential of the function $f(x) = \sqrt{3x^2 - 5x}$

Answer: $\dfrac{(6x-5)dx}{2\sqrt{3x^2-5x}}$

Exam 3A

Name:
Instructor:
Section:

Write your work as neatly as possible.

1. Find the derivative of the function $f(x) = 3x + 10$.

2. Find the derivative of the function $f(x) = \dfrac{x^2 + 1}{x - 3}$.

3. Find the derivative of the function $f(x) = \sqrt{5x - 2}$.

4. Find the slope and an equation of the tangent line to the graph of the function $f(x) = 3x^2 + 2x - 1$ at the point $(1,4)$.

5. Find the derivative of the function $f(x) = \left(x^2 + \dfrac{2}{x^2}\right)(3x + 2)$.

6. Find the slope and an equation of the tangent line to the graph of the function $f(x) = 3x^2 - 6x + 1$ at the point $(0, 1)$.

7. Find the derivative of the function $f(x) = \left(8x^2 + x\right)^7$.

8. Find the derivative of the function $f(t) = \left(-t^{-2} + t^{-4}\right)^3$.

9. For the demand equation $x = -\dfrac{5}{3}p + 20$, compute the elasticity of demand and determine whether the demand is elastic, unitary, or inelastic if $p = 5$.

10. Find the first and second derivatives of $f(x)=5x^3+2x^2+7x+2$.

11. A company manufactures a product with a cost function $C(x)=600+200x-0.2x^2$, where $C(x)$ is the cost of manufacturing a total of x units of the product.

    (a) Find the average cost function $\overline{C}$.

    (b) Find the marginal cost function C'.

12. If $x^3+3y^2=2$, find $\dfrac{dy}{dx}$ by implicit differentiation.

13. A can in the shape of a right circular cylinder with radius 6 in. is being filled at a constant rate. If the fluid is rising at a rate of 0.2 in/sec, what is the rate at which the fluid is flowing into the can?

14. Find the differential of the function $f(x)=8x^3+1$.

Exam 3B

Name:
Instructor:
Section:

Write your work as neatly as possible.

1. Find the derivative of the function $f(x) = 1 - 5x + x^2$.

2. Find the derivative of the function $f(x) = 12x^{2/3} - 9x^{1/3}$.

3. Find the derivative of the function $f(x) = \dfrac{x^2}{x^2 - 3}$.

4. Find the derivative of the function $f(x) = \sqrt{x^2 + 2}$.

5. Find the slope and an equation of the tangent line to the graph of the function $f(x) = \sqrt{x} + 1$ at the point $(4, 3)$.

6. Find the derivative of the function $f(x) = \left(3x^2 - \dfrac{2}{x}\right)\left(3x^2 + 2\right)$.

7. Find the slope and an equation of the tangent line to the graph of the function $f(x) = x^3 - 9x + 1$ at the point (0, 1).

8. Find the derivative of the function $f(x) = (12x - 2)^{-3}$.

9. Find the derivative of the function $f(x) = (3x + 2)^4 (3x - 1)^3$.

10. For the demand equation $x + \dfrac{1}{5}p - 16 = 0$, compute the elasticity of demand and determine whether the demand is elastic, unitary, or inelastic if $p = 50$.

11. Find the first and second derivatives of $f(x) = 3x^4 - 2x^{5/3} + \sqrt{2x}$.

12. A company manufactures a product with a cost function $C(x) = 3000 + 600x - 0.3x^2$, where $C(x)$ is the cost of manufacturing a total of x units of the product
(a) Find the average cost function $\overline{C}$.

(b) Find the marginal cost function C'.

13. A rock is tossed into a pond creating an expanding circular ripple. If the radius of the ripple is increasing at a rate of 1.5 ft/sec, find out how fast the area is increasing when the radius is 2 feet.

14. If $2xy = 3x + 5y^2$, find $\frac{dy}{dx}$ by implicit differentiation.

15. Find the differential of the function $f(x) = 12x^3 - 2x$.

16. Let f be a function defined by $y = f(x) = 5x^2 - 2x + 1$.
(a) Find the differential of f.

(b) Use your result from (a) to approximate the change in y if x changes from 2 to 2.02.

(c) Find the actual change in y if x changes from 2 to 2.02 and compare your result with that obtained in (b)

Exam 3C

Name:
Instructor:
Section:

Write your work as neatly as possible.

1. Find the derivative of the function $f(x) = 7x^2 + 1$.

2. Find the derivative of the function $f(x) = 4x^{5/3} + 7x^{2/3}$.

3. Find the derivative of the function $f(x) = \dfrac{3x^2}{x^2 + 2}$.

4. Find the derivative of the function $f(x) = \sqrt{5 - 2x^2}$.

5. Let $f(x) = 3x^3 + 2$.
   (a) Find the point(s) on the graph of f where the slope of the tangent line is equal to 4.

   (b) Find the equation(s) of the tangent line(s) of part (a).

6. Find the point(s) on the graph of $f(x) = \dfrac{2x}{x^2 - 2x + 3}$ where the tangent line is horizontal.

7. Find the derivative of the function $f(x) = \sqrt[5]{2 + x^2}$.

8. Find the derivative of the function $f(x) = \sqrt{\dfrac{7x}{2x - 1}}$.

9. For the demand equation $p = 220 - x^2$, compute the elasticity of demand and determine whether the demand is elastic, unitary, or inelastic if $p = 104$.

10. Find the first and second derivatives of $f(x) = -0.8x^3 + 7.1x^2 + 32.5x + 0.6^2$.

11. A company manufactures a product with a cost function $C(x) = 2000 + 800x - 0.4x^2$, where $C(x)$ is the cost of manufacturing a total of x units of the product.
(a) Find the average cost function $\overline{C}$.

(b) Find the marginal cost function C'.

12. If $x^2y^2 - 2xy + x = 2$, find the slope of the tangent line at (2,1) by implicit differentiation.

13. Find the second derivative $\frac{d^2y}{dx^2}$ of the function defined implicitly by $x^2y = 2$.

14. Find the differential of the function $f(x) = 4x^{5/2} - x^{-1/2}$.

15. Use differentials to approximate $\sqrt{82}$.

Exam 3D

Name:
Instructor:
Section:

Write your work as neatly as possible.

1. Find the derivative of the function $f(x) = \frac{1}{8}x + 1$.

2. Find the derivative of the function $f(x) = \sqrt{x} - \frac{1}{x}$.

3. Find the derivative of the function $f(x) = \frac{4x^3}{x^2 + 1}$.

4. Find the derivative of the function $f(x) = \sqrt{x^2 - 4x}$.

5. Let $f(x) = \frac{2}{3}x^3 - 3x + 1$. Find the x-values of the point(s) on the graph of f where the slope of the tangent line is equal to
(a) -3

(b) 0

(c) 5

6. Find the derivative of the function $f(x) = \frac{-x}{x^2 + 2x - 1}$.

7. Let $f(x) = \frac{1}{4}(x^2 + 2)(2x + 3)$. Find the point(s) on the graph of f where the slope of the tangent line is equal to
(a) 1

(b) 10

8. Find the derivative of the function $f(x) = \frac{3}{\left(2x^3 + 3x\right)^{3/2}}$.

9. Find $\frac{dy}{du}$, $\frac{du}{dx}$, and $\frac{dy}{dx}$ if $y = u^{-5/3}$ and $u = x^3 - 2x + 1$.

10. Find $F'(3)$ if $F(x) = f(g(x))$ and
$f(3) = 2$, $f'(3) = 5$, $f'(4) = 6$, $g(3) = 4$, and $g'(3) = -2$.

11. Find the first and second derivatives of $f(x) = x^4\left(3x^2 + 1\right)$.

12. A company manufactures a product with a cost function $C(x) = 1200 + 600x - 0.8x^2$, where $C(x)$ is the cost of manufacturing a total of x units of the product
(a) Find the average cost function $\overline{C}$.

(b) Find the marginal cost function C'.

13. If $x^{5/3} + y^{1/3} = 3x$, find $\frac{dy}{dx}$ by implicit differentiation.

14. Find the differential of the function $f(x) = \frac{3}{x-1}$.

15. Use differentials to approximate $\sqrt[3]{128}$.

Answers to Chapter 3 Exams

Exam 3A

1. 3
2. $\dfrac{x^2-6x-1}{(x-3)^2}$
3. $\dfrac{5}{2\sqrt{5x-2}}$
4. $8;\ y=8x-4$
5. $9x^2+4x-\dfrac{6}{x^2}-\dfrac{8}{x^3}$
6. $-1;\ y=-x+13$
7. $7(16x+1)(8x^2+x)^6$
8. $3(-t^{-2}+t^{-4})^2(2t^{-3}-4t^{-5})$
9. $\dfrac{-p}{p-12}$; inelastic
10. $15x^2+4x+7,\ 30x+4$
11. (a) $\overline{C}(x)=\dfrac{600}{x}+200-0.2x$

    (b) $C'(x)=200-0.4x$
12. $\dfrac{-x^2}{2y}$
13. $7.2\pi\ \text{in}^3/\text{sec}$
14. $24x^2dx$

Exam 3B

1. $-5+2x$
2. $\dfrac{8}{x^{1/3}}-\dfrac{3}{x^{2/3}}$
3. $\dfrac{-6x}{(x^2-3)^2}$
4. $\dfrac{x}{\sqrt{x^2+2}}$
5. $\dfrac{1}{4};\ y=\dfrac{1}{4}x+2$
6. $36x^3+12x+\dfrac{4}{x^2}-6$
7. $-9,\ y=-9x+1$
8. $-36(12x-2)^{-4}$
9. $3(21x+2)(3x+2)^3(3x-1)^2$
10. $\dfrac{-p}{p-80}$; elastic
11. $12x^3-\dfrac{10}{3}x^{2/3}+\dfrac{\sqrt{2}}{2}x^{-1/2}$

    $36x^2-\dfrac{20}{9}x^{-1/3}-\dfrac{\sqrt{2}}{4}x^{-3/2}$
12. (a) $\overline{C}(x)=\dfrac{3000}{x}+600-0.3x$

    (b) $C'(x)=600-0.6x$
13. $6\pi\ \text{ft}^2/\text{sec}$
14. $\dfrac{3-2y}{2x-10y}$
15. $(36x^2-2)dx$
16. (a) $(10x-2)dx$ (b) 0.36

    (c) 0.362; larger

Exam 3C

1. $14x$

2. $\frac{20}{3}x^{2/3}+\frac{14}{3}x^{-1/3}$

3. $\frac{12x}{\left(x^2+2\right)^2}$

4. $\frac{-2x}{\sqrt{5-2x^2}}$

5. (a) $\left(-\frac{2}{3},\frac{10}{9}\right),\left(\frac{2}{3},\frac{26}{9}\right)$

   (b) $y=4x+\frac{34}{9}, y=4x+\frac{2}{9}$

6. $\left(-\sqrt{3},\frac{-\sqrt{3}}{3+\sqrt{3}}\right),\left(\sqrt{3},\frac{\sqrt{3}}{3-\sqrt{3}}\right)$

7. $\frac{2}{5}x\left(2+x^2\right)^{-4/5}$

8. $-\frac{7}{2}\left(\frac{7x}{2x-1}\right)^{-1/2}(2x-1)^{-2}$

9. $-\frac{p}{2p-440}$; inelastic

10. $-2.4x^2+14.2x+32.5, -4.8x+14.2$

11. (a) $\overline{C}(x)=\frac{2000}{x}+800-0.4x$

    (b) $C'(x)=800-0.8x$

12. $-\frac{3}{4}$

13. $\frac{12}{x^4}$

14. $\left(10x^{3/2}+\frac{1}{2}x^{-3/2}\right)dx$

15. $\frac{163}{18}=9.0\overline{5}$

Exam 3D

1. $\frac{1}{8}$

2. $\frac{1}{2\sqrt{x}}+\frac{1}{x^2}$

3. $\frac{4x^4+12x^2}{\left(x^2+1\right)^2}$

4. $\frac{x-2}{\sqrt{x^2-4x}}$

5. (a) 0; (b) $\pm\sqrt{6}/2$; (c) ± 2

6. $\frac{x^2+1}{\left(x^2+2x-1\right)^2}$

7. (a) $\left(0,\frac{3}{2}\right),\left(-1,\frac{3}{4}\right)$;

   (b) $\left(-3,-\frac{33}{4}\right),\left(2,\frac{21}{2}\right)$

8. $-\frac{27\left(2x^2+1\right)}{2\left(2x^3+3x\right)^{5/2}}$

9. $-\frac{5}{3}u^{-8/3}, 3x^2-2,$

   $-\frac{5}{3}\left(x^3-2x+1\right)^{-8/3}\left(3x^2-2\right)$

10. -12

11. $18x^5+4x^3, 90x^4+12x^2$

12. (a) $\overline{C}(x)=\frac{1200}{x}+600-0.8x$

    (b) $C'(x)=600-1.6x$

13. $\left(9-5x^{2/3}\right)y^{2/3}$

14. $-\frac{3dx}{(x-1)^2}$

15. 5.04

Chapter 4 ■ Applications of the Derivative

Section 4.1

1. Find the interval(s) where $f(x) = -3x + 10$ is increasing and the interval(s) where it is decreasing.
Answer: Decreasing: $(-\infty, \infty)$; never increasing

2. Find the interval(s) where $f(x) = \frac{1}{5}x - 1$ is increasing and the interval(s) where it is decreasing.
Answer: Increasing: $(-\infty, \infty)$; never decreasing

3. Find the interval(s) where $f(x) = x^2 + 4x + 8$ is increasing and the interval(s) where it is decreasing.
Answer: Increasing: $(-2, \infty)$; decreasing: $(-\infty, -2)$

4. Find the interval(s) where $f(x) = 5 - 2x^2$ is increasing and the interval(s) where it is decreasing.
Answer: Increasing: $(-\infty, 0)$; decreasing: $(0, \infty)$

5. Find the interval(s) where $f(x) = 2x^2 - 3x + 4$ is increasing and the interval(s) where it is decreasing.
Answer: Increasing: $\left(\frac{3}{4}, \infty\right)$; decreasing: $\left(-\infty, \frac{3}{4}\right)$

6. Find the interval(s) where $f(x) = 2x^3 - 6x^2 - 18x$ is increasing and the interval(s) where it is decreasing.
Answer: Increasing: $(-\infty, -1) \cup (3, \infty)$; decreasing: $(-1, 3)$

7. Find the interval(s) where $f(x) = \frac{1}{3}x^3 - 4x^2 + 4x - 12$ is increasing and the interval(s) where it is decreasing.
Answer: Increasing: $\left(-\infty, 4 - 2\sqrt{3}\right) \cup \left(4 + 2\sqrt{3}, \infty\right)$; decreasing: $\left(4 - 2\sqrt{3}, 4 + 2\sqrt{3}\right)$

8. Find the interval(s) where $s(t) = \frac{t}{t-2}$ is increasing and the interval(s) where it is decreasing.
Answer: Decreasing: $(-\infty, 2) \cup (2, \infty)$; never increasing

9. Find the interval(s) where $s(t) = \frac{3t}{t^2 + 2}$ is increasing and the interval(s) where it is decreasing.
Answer: Increasing: $\left(-\sqrt{2}, \sqrt{2}\right)$; decreasing: $\left(-\infty, -\sqrt{2}\right) \cup \left(\sqrt{2}, \infty\right)$

10. Find the interval(s) where $f(x) = \sqrt{x+4}$ is increasing and the interval(s) where it is decreasing.
Answer: Increasing: $(-4, \infty)$; never decreasing

11. Find the interval(s) where $f(x) = x\sqrt{x+12}$ is increasing and the interval(s) where it is decreasing.
Answer: Increasing: $(-8, \infty)$; decreasing: $(-12, -8)$

12. Find the interval(s) where $f(x) = \sqrt{25 - x^2}$ is increasing and the interval(s) where it is decreasing.
Answer: Increasing: $(-5, 0)$; decreasing: $(0, 5)$

13. Find the interval(s) where $f(x) = \frac{x^2}{x+1}$ is increasing and the interval(s) where it is decreasing.
Answer: Increasing: $(-\infty, -2) \cup (0, \infty)$; decreasing: $(-2, -1) \cup (-1, 0)$

14. Find the interval(s) where $f(x) = \frac{2x}{(x+2)^2}$ is increasing and the interval(s) where it is decreasing.
Answer: Increasing: $(-2, 2)$; decreasing: $(-\infty, -2) \cup (2, \infty)$

15. Given the graph of f determine the interval(s) where f is increasing, decreasing, or constant.

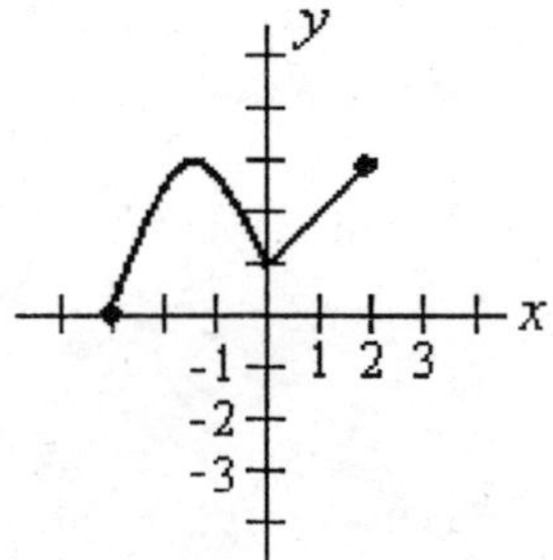

Answer: Increasing: $(-3, -1.5) \cup (0, 2)$; decreasing: $(-1.5, 0)$

16. Given the graph of *f*, determine the interval(s) where *f* is increasing, decreasing, or constant.

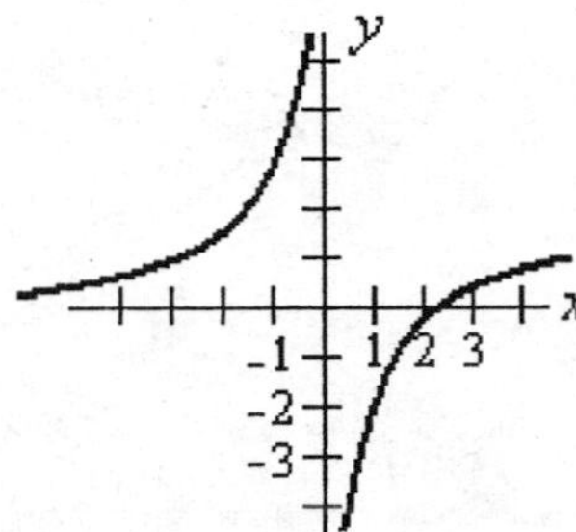

Answer: Increasing: $(-\infty, 0) \cup (0, \infty)$; decreasing: nowhere

17. Given the graph of *f*, determine the interval(s) where *f* is increasing, decreasing, or constant.

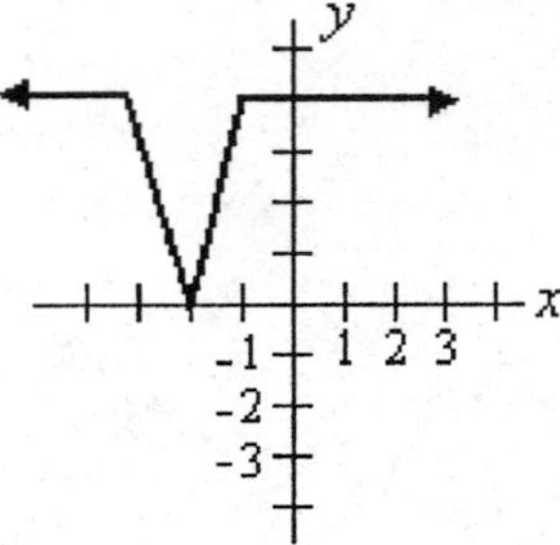

Answer: Constant $(-\infty, -3) \cup (-1, \infty)$; Increasing: $(-2, -1)$; Decreasing: $(-3, -2)$

18. A stone is thrown straight up from the roof of a 192-foot building. The distance of the stone from the ground (in feet) at any time t (in seconds) is given by $h(t) = -16t^2 + 64t + 192$. When is the stone rising and when is it falling? If the stone were to miss the building, when would it hit the ground?
Answer: Rising when $0 < t < 2$, falling when $2 < t < 4$; after 6 seconds

19. The concentration (in milligrams per cubic centimeter) of a certain drug in a patient's body t hours after injection is given by $C(t) = \dfrac{t^2}{3t^3 + 1}$, $0 \le t \le 5$. When is the concentration of the drug increasing and when is it decreasing?
Answer: Increasing when $0 < t < \frac{1}{3}\sqrt[3]{18}$, decreasing when $\frac{1}{3}\sqrt[3]{18} < t < 5$.

20. Find the relative maxima and relative minima, if any, of $f(x) = x^2 - 8x$.
Answer: Relative minimum $f(4) = -16$; no relative maximum

21. Find the relative maxima and relative minima, if any, of $f(x) = x^{4/3}$.
Answer: Relative minimum $f(0) = 0$; no relative maximum

22. Find the relative maxima and relative minima, if any, of $f(x) = 3 - x^{2/3}$.
Answer: Relative maximum $f(0) = 3$; no relative minimum

23. Find the relative maxima and relative minima, if any, of $g(t) = -t^2 + 4t + 4$.
Answer: Relative maximum $g(2) = 8$; no relative minimum

24. Find the relative maxima and relative minima, if any, of $g(x) = x^3 - x^2 - 5x + 6$.
Answer: Relative minimum $g\left(\frac{5}{3}\right) = -\frac{13}{27}$; relative maximum $g(-1) = 9$

25. Find the relative maxima and relative minima, if any, of $g(x) = -\frac{1}{4}x^4 + 2x^2$.
Answer: Relative minimum $g(0) = 0$; relative maxima $g(\pm 2) = 4$

26. Find the relative maxima and relative minima, if any, of $g(x) = 3x^4 - 4x^3 + 5$.
Answer: Relative minimum $g(1) = 4$; no relative maximum

27. Find the relative maxima and relative minima, if any, of $f(x) = \frac{x}{2x+3}$.
Answer: No relative extremum

28. Find the relative maxima and relative minima, if any, of $f(x) = \frac{2x+3}{x}$.
Answer: No relative extremum

29. Find the relative maxima and relative minima, if any, of $g(x) = x + 3x^{-1}$.
Answer: Relative minimum $g(\sqrt{3}) = 2\sqrt{3}$; relative maximum $g(-\sqrt{3}) = -2\sqrt{3}$

30. Find the relative maxima and relative minima, if any, of $f(x) = x\sqrt{x-9}$.
Answer: No relative extremum

31. Given the graph of *f*, determine the relative maxima and relative minima.

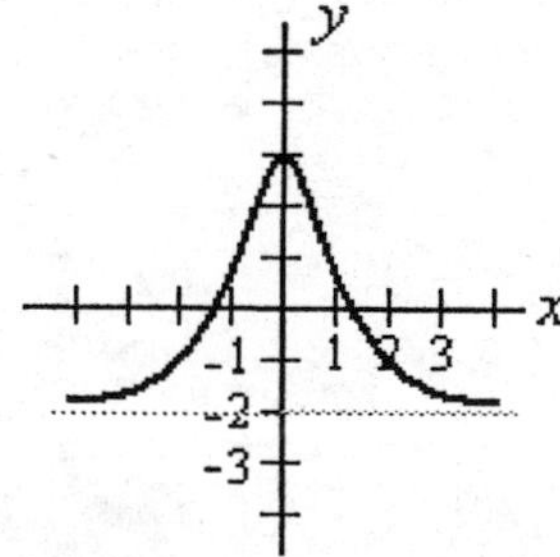

Answer: relative max: $(0, 3)$; relative min: none

32. Given the graph of f, determine the relative maxima and relative minima.

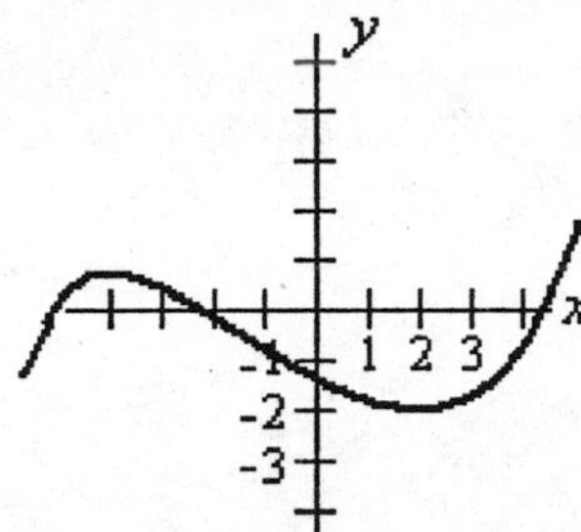

Answer: relative max: $(-4,1)$; relative min: $(2,-2)$

33. Given the graph of f, determine the relative maxima and relative minima.

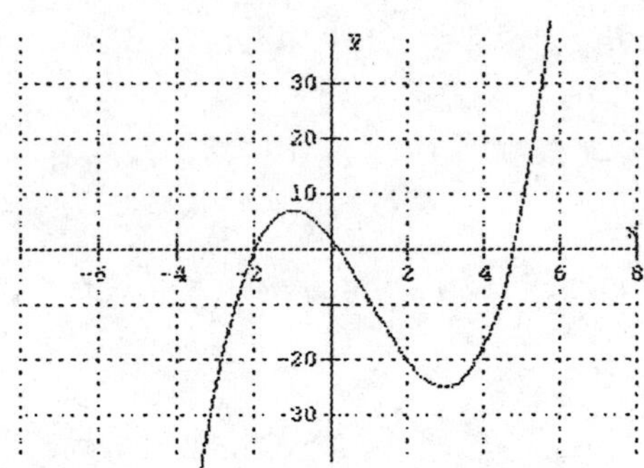

Answer: relative max (-1, 7); relative min: (3, -25).

34. Given the graph of f, determine the relative maxima and relative minima.

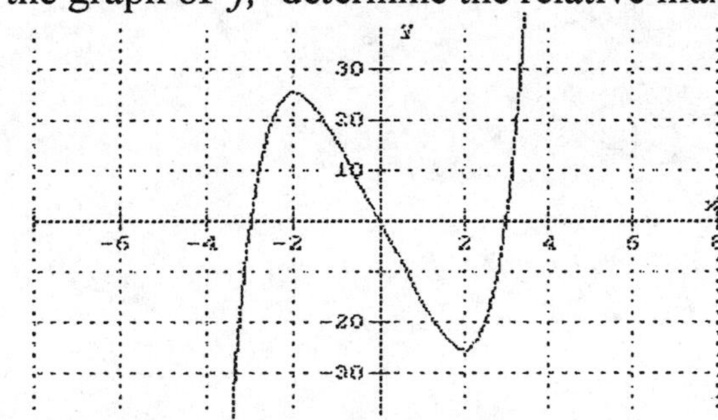

Answer: relative max (-2, 25.6); relative min: (2, 25.6).

Section 4.2

1. Determine where $f(x) = x^2 + 4x + 8$ is concave upward and where it is concave downward.
   Answer: Concave upward: $(-\infty, \infty)$; never concave downward

2. Determine where $f(x) = x^3 - 3x$ is concave upward and where it is concave downward.
   Answer: Concave downward: $(-\infty, 0)$; concave upward $(0, \infty)$

3. Determine where $f(x) = -2x^2 - 3x + 4$ is concave upward and where it is concave downward.
   Answer: Concave downward: $(-\infty, \infty)$; never concave upward

4. Determine where $g(x) = 2x^3 - 6x^2 - 18x$ is concave upward and where it is concave downward.
   Answer: Concave upward: $(1, \infty)$; concave downward: $(-\infty, 1)$.

5. Determine where $g(x) = \frac{1}{3}x^3 - 4x^2 + 4x - 12$ is concave upward and where it is concave downward.
   Answer: Concave upward: $(4, \infty)$; concave downward: $(-\infty, 4)$.

6. Determine where $s(t) = \frac{t}{t-2}$ is concave upward and where it is concave downward.
   Answer: Concave upward: $(2, \infty)$; concave downward: $(-\infty, 2)$.

7. Determine where $s(t) = \frac{3t}{t^2 + 2}$ is concave upward and where it is concave downward.

   Answer: Concave upward: $(-\sqrt{6}, 0) \cup (\sqrt{6}, \infty)$; concave downward: $(-\infty, -\sqrt{6}) \cup (0, \sqrt{6})$

8. Determine where $f(x) = \sqrt{x+4}$ is concave upward and where it is concave downward.

   Answer: Concave downward: $(-4, \infty)$; never concave upward

9. Determine where $f(x) = x\sqrt{x+12}$ is concave upward and where it is concave downward.
Answer: Concave upward: $(-12, \infty)$; never concave downward

10. Determine where $f(x) = \sqrt{25 - x^2}$ is concave upward and where it is concave downward.
Answer: Concave downward: $(-5,5)$; never concave upward

11. Determine where $f(x) = \dfrac{x^2}{x+1}$ is concave upward and where it is concave downward.
Answer: Concave upward: $(-1, \infty)$; concave downward: $(-\infty, -1)$

12. Determine where $f(x) = \dfrac{2x}{(x+2)^2}$ is concave upward and where it is concave downward.
Answer: Concave upward: $(4, \infty)$; concave downward: $(-\infty, -2) \cup (-2, 4)$

13. Given the graph of *f*, determine the interval(s) where *f* is concave upward and concave downward.

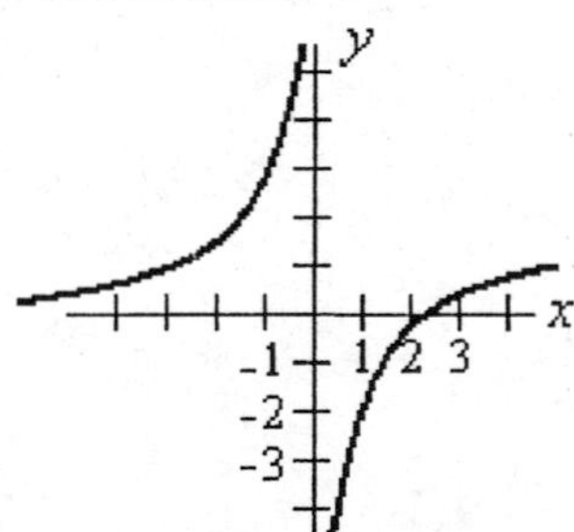

Answer: Concave upward: $(-\infty, 0)$; Concave downward: $(0, \infty)$

14. Given the graph of *f*, determine the interval(s) where *f* is concave upward and concave downward.

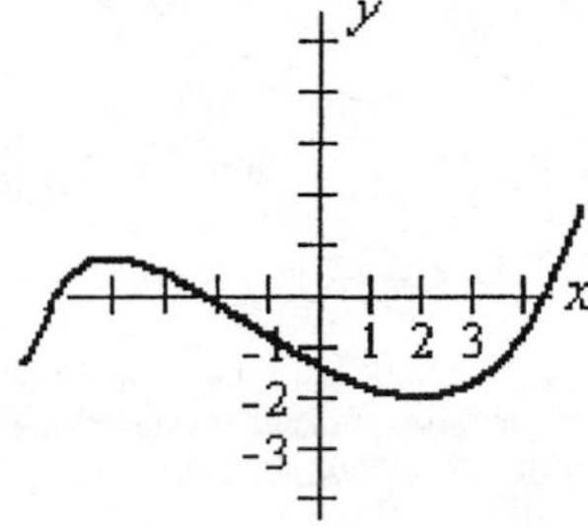

Answer: Concave upward: $(-1, \infty)$; Concave downward: $(-\infty, -1)$

15. Find the inflection points, if any, of $g(t) = -t^2 + 4t + 4$.
Answer: None

16. Find the inflection points, if any, of $g(x) = x^3 - x^2 - 5x + 6$.
Answer: $\left(\frac{1}{3}, \frac{115}{27}\right)$

17. Find the inflection points, if any, of $g(x) = -\frac{1}{4}x^4 + 2x^2$.
Answer: $\left(\pm\frac{2\sqrt{3}}{3}, \frac{20}{9}\right)$

18. Find the inflection points, if any, of $g(x) = 3x^4 - 4x^3 + 5$.
Answer: $(0,5)$, $\left(\frac{2}{3}, \frac{119}{27}\right)$

19. Find the inflection points, if any, of $f(x) = x^3 - 17x$.
Answer: $(0,0)$

20. Find the inflection points, if any, of $h(t) = \sqrt[5]{t}$.
Answer: $(0,0)$

21. Find the inflection points, if any, of $f(x) = \frac{x}{2x+3}$.
Answer: None

22. Find the inflection points, if any, of $g(x) = x + 3x^{-1}$.
Answer: None

23. Find the inflection points, if any, of $s(t) = \frac{3t}{t^2 + 2}$
Answer: $\left(-\sqrt{6}, \frac{-3\sqrt{6}}{8}\right)$, $(0,0)$, $\left(\sqrt{6}, \frac{3\sqrt{6}}{8}\right)$

24. Find the inflection points, if any, of $f(x) = \frac{2x}{(x+2)^2}$.
Answer: $\left(4, \frac{2}{9}\right)$

25. An efficiency study conducted for the Cassiopeia Cabbage Company showed that the number of cases of cabbage packed by the average worker t hours after starting work at 8 a.m. is given by $-t^3+4t^2+12t,\ 0 \le t \le 4$. At what time during the morning shift is the average worker at peak efficiency?
Answer: At 9:20 a.m.

26. Let $f(x)=x^3+x$.
(a) Find the interval(s) on which $f(x)$ is concave upward.
Answer: $(0,\infty)$
(b) Find the interval(s) on which $f(x)$ is concave downward.
Answer: $(-\infty,0)$
(c) Find the x-coordinate(s) of any point(s) of inflection of f.
Answer: $x=0$

27. Let $f(x)=x^4-4x^3-48x^2-64x-32$.
(a) Find the interval(s) on which $f(x)$ is concave upward.
Answer: $(-\infty,-2)\cup(4,\infty)$
(b) Find the interval(s) on which $f(x)$ is concave downward.
Answer: $(-2,4)$
(c) Find the x-coordinate(s) of any point(s) of inflection of f.
Answer: $x=-2$ and $x=4$

28. Let $f(x)=2x\sqrt{x-4}$.
(a) Find the interval(s) on which $f(x)$ is concave upward.
Answer: $\left(\frac{16}{3},\infty\right)$
(b) Find the interval(s) on which $f(x)$ is concave downward.
Answer: $\left(4,\frac{16}{3}\right)$
(c) Find the x-coordinate(s) of any point(s) of inflection of f.
Answer: $x=\frac{16}{3}$

Section 4.3

1. Find the horizontal and vertical asymptotes of the following graph.

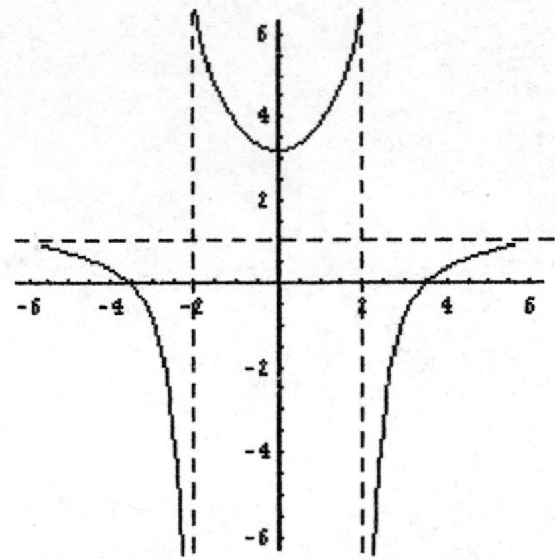

Answer: Horizontal: $y = 1$; vertical: $x = \pm 2$

2. Find the horizontal and vertical asymptotes of the following graph.

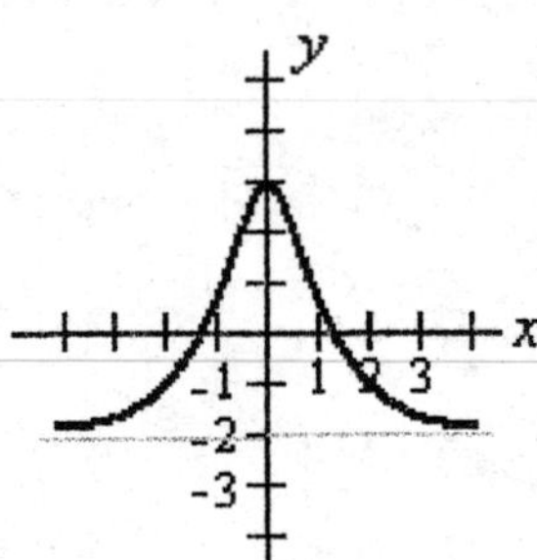

Answer: Horizontal: $y = -2$; vertical: none

3. Find the horizontal and vertical asymptotes of the following graph.

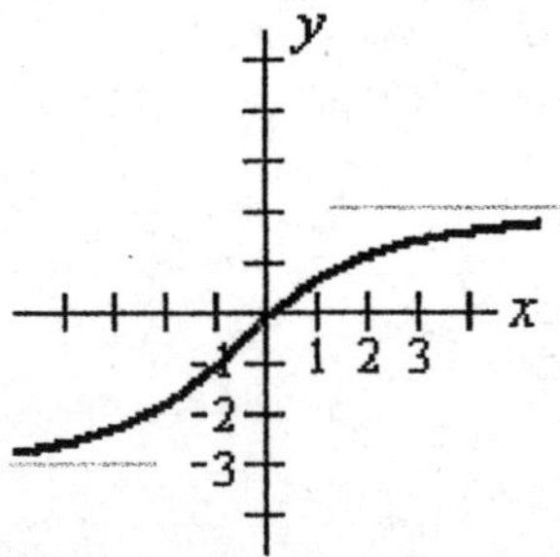

Answer: Horizontal: $y = -3, y = 2$; vertical: none

4. Find the horizontal and vertical asymptotes of the graph of $f(x) = \dfrac{2}{2x+1}$.

   Answer: Horizontal: $y = 0$; vertical: $x = -\dfrac{1}{2}$

5. Find the horizontal and vertical asymptotes of the graph of $h(x) = \dfrac{4}{x^2}$.

   Answer: Horizontal: $y = 0$; vertical: $x = 0$

6. Find the horizontal and vertical asymptotes of the graph of $f(x) = \dfrac{1}{1+3x^2}$.

   Answer: Horizontal: $y = 0$; vertical: none

7. Find the horizontal and vertical asymptotes of the graph of $h(x) = 3x^3 - 4x + 2$.

   Answer: Horizontal: none; vertical: none

8. Find the horizontal and vertical asymptotes of the graph of
   $f(x) = \dfrac{-3x^2 + 2x - 1}{x^2 + 2x - 15}$.

   Answer: Horizontal: $y = -3$; vertical: $x = -5$, $x = 3$

9. Find the horizontal and vertical asymptotes of the graph of $h(x) = 2 + \dfrac{1}{1-x}$.

   Answer: Horizontal: $y = 2$; vertical: $x = 1$

10. Sketch the graph of $f(x) = x^3 + 6x^2 + 9x$.

    Answer:

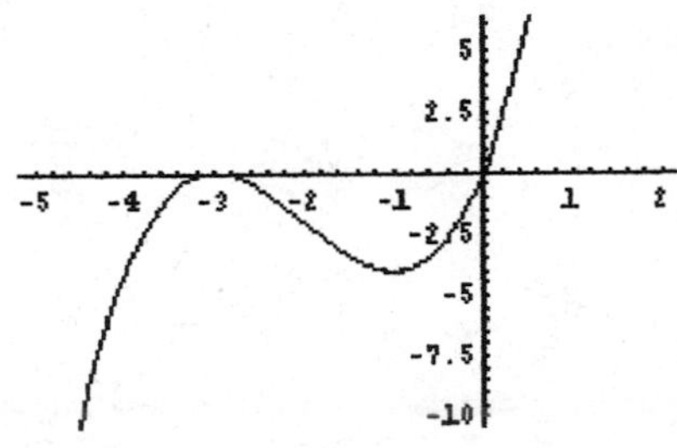

11. Sketch the graph of $h(x) = 2x^3 - 4x + 1$.

Answer:

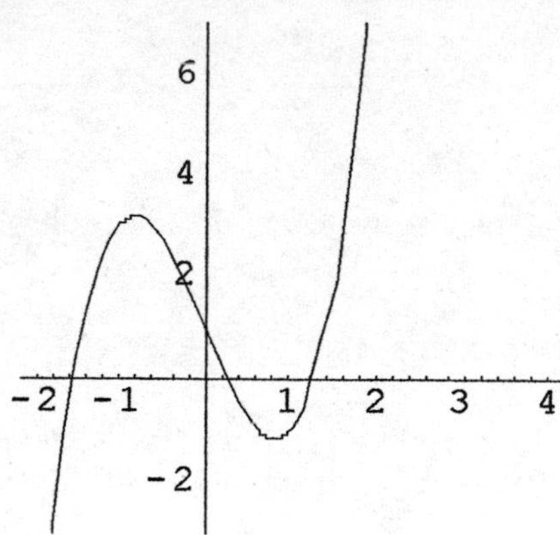

12. Sketch the graph of $f(x) = -x^3 + 2x^2 + 2$.

Answer:

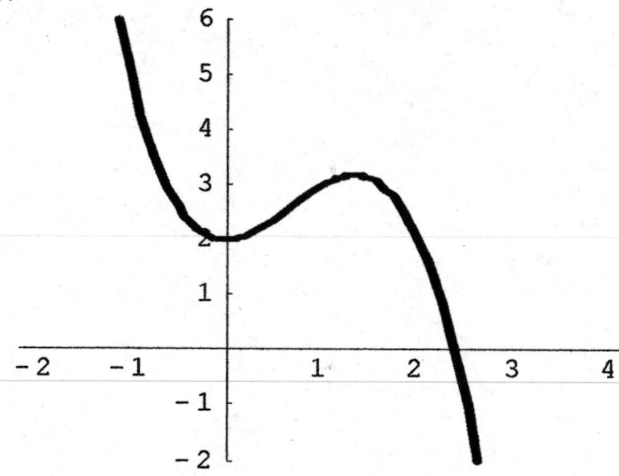

13. Sketch the graph of $f(x) = \dfrac{x^2 - 8}{x^2 - 4}$.

Answer:

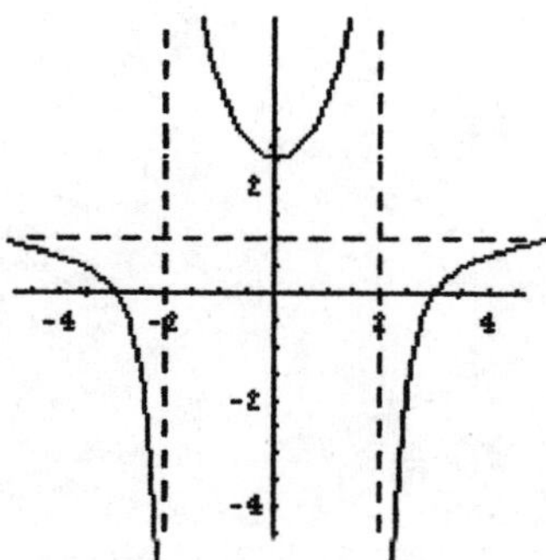

14. Sketch the graph of $h(x) = x^2 - 4\sqrt{x}$.
Answer:

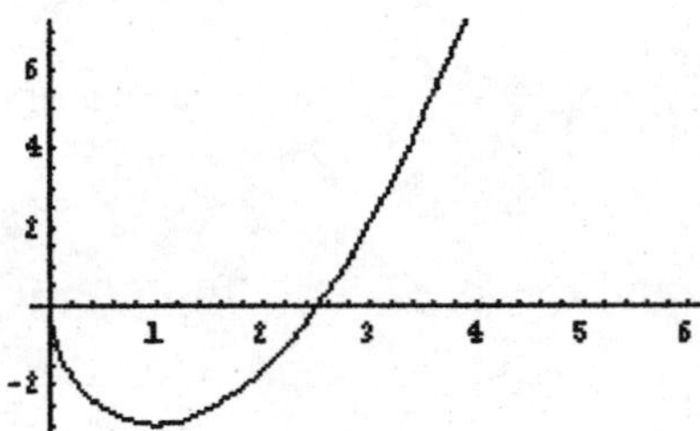

15. Sketch the graph of $h(x) = \dfrac{x}{2x-5}$.

Answer:

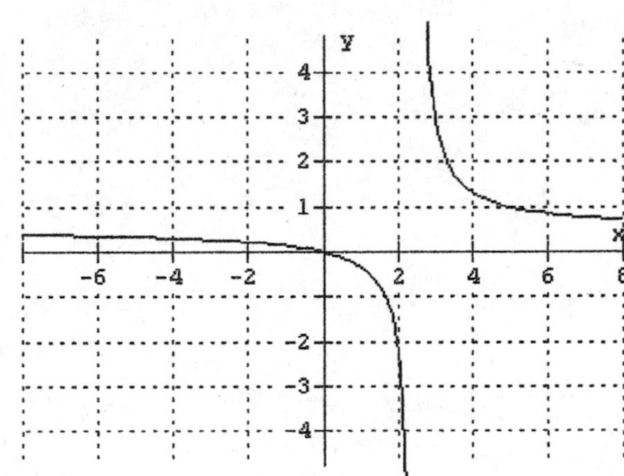

16. Sketch the graph of $f(x) = \dfrac{3x^2}{x^2-16}$.

Answer:

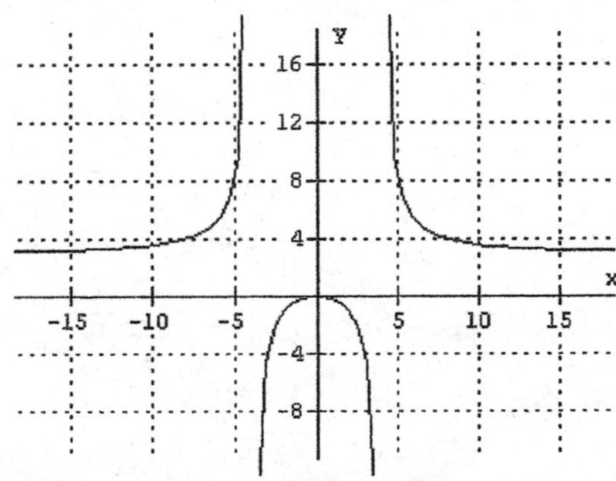

Section 4.4

1. Find the absolute maximum and the absolute minimum of $f(x) = 2x^2 - 6x + 6$.
   Answer: Absolute minimum: $f\left(\frac{3}{2}\right) = \frac{3}{2}$; no absolute maximum

2. Find the absolute maximum and the absolute minimum of $f(x) = 4 - x^{2/3}$.
   Answer: Absolute maximum: $f(0) = 4$; no absolute minimum

3. Find the absolute maximum and the absolute minimum of $f(x) = 3x + 4$.
   Answer: No absolute maximum: no absolute minimum

4. Find the absolute maximum and the absolute minimum of $f(x) = x^2 - 6x + 6$ on $[-2, 4]$.
   Answer: Absolute maximum: $f(-2) = 22$; absolute minimum: $f(3) = -3$

5. Find the absolute maximum and the absolute minimum of $f(x) = -x^2 + 2x$ on $[-2, 2]$.
   Answer: Absolute maximum: $f(1) = 1$; absolute minimum: $f(-2) = -8$

6. Find the absolute maximum and the absolute minimum of $f(x) = -2x + 6$ on [0,5].
   Answer: Absolute maximum (0,6): Absolute minimum (5, -4)

7. Find the absolute maximum and the absolute minimum of $f(x) = x^3 + 3x^2$ on $[-2, 3]$.
   Answer: Absolute maximum: $f(3) = 54$; absolute minimum: $f(0) = 0$

8. Find the absolute maximum and the absolute minimum of $g(x) = \frac{x+2}{x-2}$ on $[-4, 4]$.
   Answer: Absolute maximum: none; absolute minimum: none

9. Find the absolute maximum and the absolute minimum of $g(x) = \frac{x+2}{x-2}$ on $[-4, 1]$.
   Answer: Absolute maximum: $g(-4) = \frac{1}{3}$; absolute minimum: $g(1) = -3$

10. Find the absolute maximum and the absolute minimum of $f(x)=3x^{2/3}-6x+6$ on $[1,8]$.

Answer: Absolute maximum: $f(1)=3$; absolute minimum: $f(8)=-30$

11. Find the absolute maximum and the absolute minimum of $f(x)=\dfrac{x}{x^2+4}$ on $[-4,8]$.

Answer: Absolute maximum: $f(2)=\dfrac{1}{4}$; absolute minimum: $f(-2)=-\dfrac{1}{4}$

12. Find the absolute maximum and the absolute minimum of $f(x)=\dfrac{1}{x^2+3x+4}$ on $[-2,2]$.

Answer: Absolute maximum: $f\left(-\dfrac{3}{2}\right)=\dfrac{4}{7}$; absolute minimum: $f(2)=\dfrac{1}{14}$

13. Find the absolute maximum and the absolute minimum of $f(x)=\dfrac{x}{x^2+3x+4}$ on $[-3,3]$.

Answer: Absolute maximum: $f(2)=\dfrac{1}{7}$; absolute minimum: $f(-2)=-1$

14. Given the graph of *f*, determine the absolute maximum and absolute minimum.

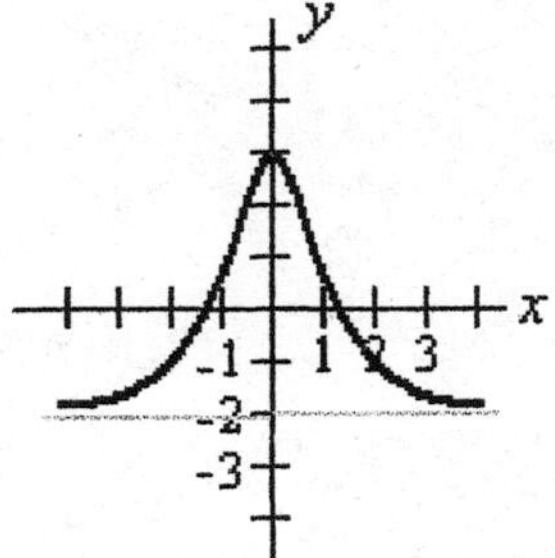

Answer: Absolute max: $(0,3)$; Absolute min: none

15. Given the graph of *f*, determine the absolute maximum and absolute minimum.

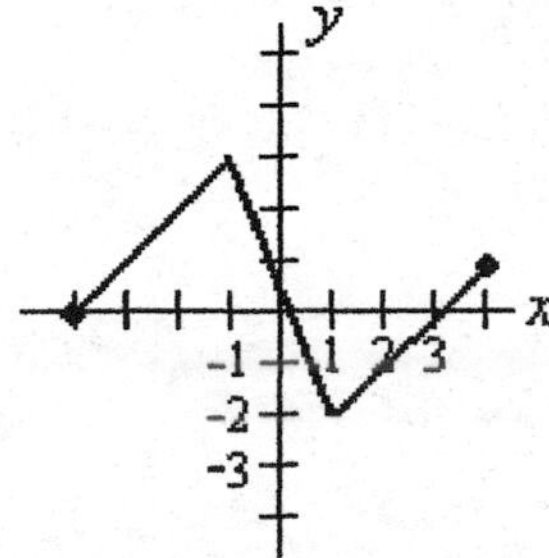

Answer: Absolute max: $(-1,3)$; Absolute min: $(1,-2)$

16. Given the graph of *f*, determine the absolute maximum and absolute minimum.

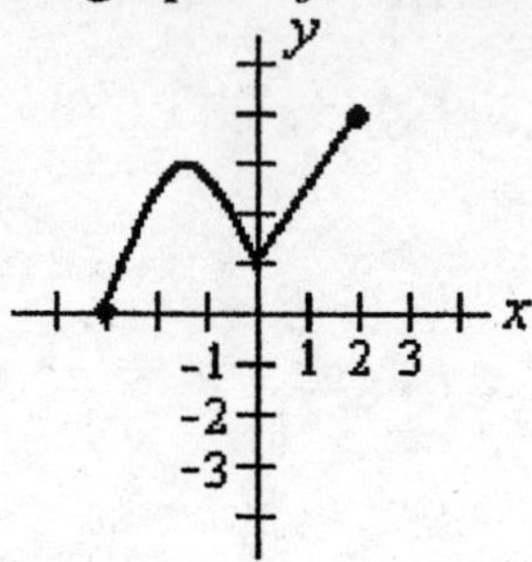

Answer: Absolute max: $(2, 4)$; Absolute min: $(-3, 0)$

Section 4.5

1. An arrow is shot from a cliff 100 feet above the ground. The height of the arrow above the ground at any time t (measured in seconds) is given by $h(t) = -16t^2 + 320t + 100$ (with h measured in feet). Find the maximum height of the arrow above the ground.
Answer: 1700 feet

2. A company has determined that its profit (P) depends on the amount of money spent on advertising (x). The relationship is given by the equation
$P(x) = \dfrac{2x}{x^2 + 4} + 70$, where P and x are measured in thousands of dollars.
(a) What amount should the company spend on advertising to assure maximum profit?
Answer: $2000
(b) What is the maximum profit?
Answer: $70,500

3. The price of a certain stock at time t ($0 \le t \le 5$) is estimated by $P(t) = 0.1t^3 + 0.05t^2 - 3t + 10$. When will the stock price be at a maximum, and when will it reach a maximum?
Answer: Maximum price at $t = 0$; Minimum price at $t = 3$

4. A farmer has 300 feet of fencing with which to enclose a rectangular grazing pen next to a barn. The farmer will use the barn as one side of the pen, and will use the fencing for the other three sides. Find the dimensions of the pen with the maximum area.
Answer: 75 feet by 150 feet

5. A farmer has 460 feet of fencing with which to enclose a rectangular grazing pen next to a barn. The farmer will use the barn as one side of the pen, and will use the fencing for the other three sides. Find the dimensions of the pen with the maximum area.
Answer: 115 feet by 230 feet

6. By cutting away identical squares from each corner of a rectangular piece of cardboard and folding up the resulting flaps, an open box may be made. If the cardboard is 10 inches long and 10 inches wide, find the dimensions of the box that will yield the maximum volume.
Answer: $\dfrac{20}{3}$ inches by $\dfrac{20}{3}$ inches by $\dfrac{5}{3}$ inches

7. By cutting away identical squares from each corner of a rectangular piece of cardboard and folding up the resulting flaps, an open box may be made. If the

cardboard is 30 inches long and 14 inches wide, find the dimensions of the box that will yield the maximum volume.
Answer: 24 inches by 8 inches by 3 inches

8. A property management company manages 200 apartments renting for \$800 each with all the apartments rented. For each \$10 per month increase in rent there will be two vacancies with no possibility of filling them. What rent per apartment will maximize the total monthly revenue?
Answer: \$900

9. The window below is to have a perimeter of 20 feet. Find the dimensions that will maximize the area (to let the most light in).

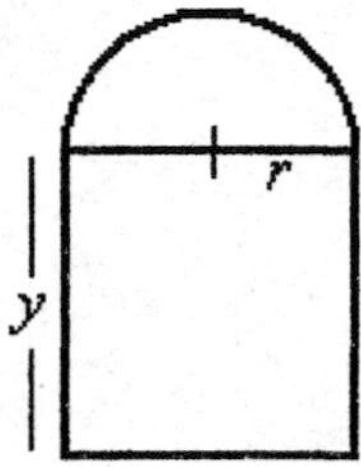

Answer: $r = \dfrac{20}{4+\pi} \approx 2.8$ feet, $y \approx 2.8$ feet

10. An editorial assistant at Bloke/Coors Publishing Company arbitrarily decided that the pages of a book should have three-quarter-inch margins at the top and bottom and half-inch margins on the sides. She further stipulated that each page should have an area of 40 square inches. Determine the page dimensions that will result in the maximum printed area on the page.
Answer: Height: $2\sqrt{15}$; width: $\dfrac{4}{3}\sqrt{15}$

11. You wish to construct an open rectangular box with a volume of 18 cubic feet. The length of the base of the box is to be twice as long as the width. The material for the bottom of the box costs 10 cents per square foot, while the material for the sides of the box costs 20 cents per square foot. Find the dimensions of the least expensive box which can be constructed.
Answer: width = 3 feet, length = 6 feet, height = 1 foot

Exam 4A

Name:
Instructor:
Section:

Write your work as neatly as possible.

1. Find the interval(s) where $f(x) = x^3 + 12x^2 + 21x + 1$ is increasing and the interval(s) where it is decreasing.

2. Given the graph of f below, find the interval(s) where f is increasing and the interval(s) where it is decreasing.

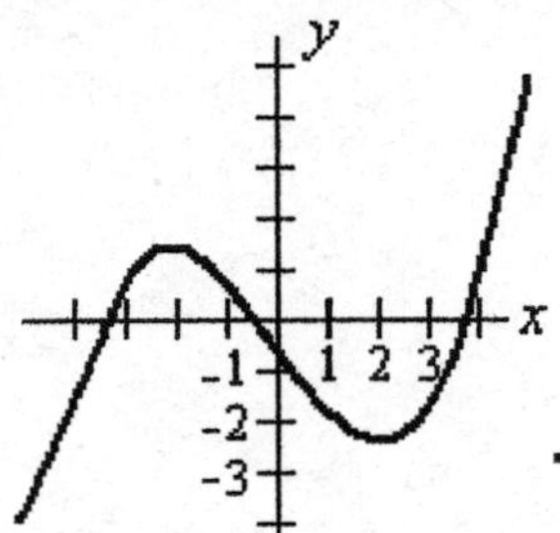

3. Find the relative maxima and minima, if any, of $g(x) = \frac{1}{3}x^3 - \frac{3}{2}x^2 + 2$.

4. Find the relative maxima and minima, if any, of $h(t) = 3 - t^{2/3}$.

5. Let $f(x) = x^3 + 12x^2 + 21x + 1$.
   (a) Find the interval(s) where $f(x)$ is concave upward.

   (b) Find the interval(s) where $f(x)$ is concave downward.

   (c) Find the x-coordinate(s) of any point(s) of inflection.

6. Let $f(x) = \dfrac{x+3}{x+2}$.
   (a) Find the interval(s) where $f(x)$ is concave upward.

   (b) Find the interval(s) where $f(x)$ is concave downward.

   (c) Find the x-coordinate(s) of any point(s) of inflection.

7. Find the horizontal and vertical asymptotes of the graph of the function shown below.

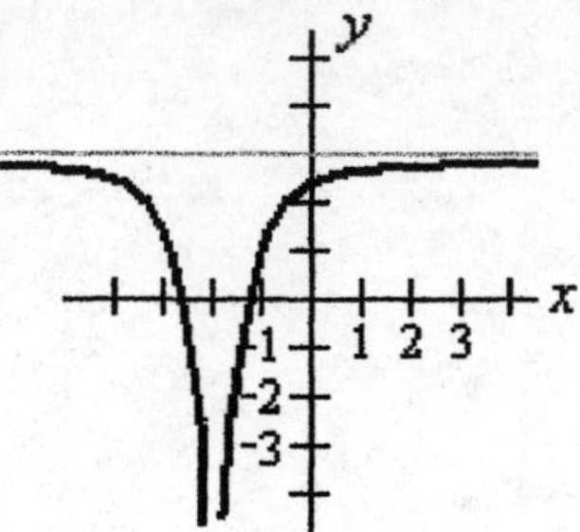

8. Sketch the graph of $y = \dfrac{1}{x+3}$.

9. Sketch the graph of $y = x^3 - 6x$.

10. Find the absolute maximum and the absolute minimum of $f(x) = 36x - 3x^2$ on $[0,7]$.

11. Find the absolute maximum and the absolute minimum of $f(x) = x^2 + 3x^3$ on $[-2,3]$.

12. The mosquito population is a function of rainfall, and can be approximated by the formula $N(x) = 1000 + 30x + 44.5x^2 - x^3$, where x is the number of inches of rainfall $(0 \le x \le 43)$. What amount of rainfall will result in a maximum number of mosquitoes?

13. A farmer wants to create a divided grazing area like the one shown below. The barn will be one side of the grazing area. The farmer has a total of 1200 feet of fencing material to enclose the grazing area and provide the dividing fence down the middle. What is the maximum area that can be enclosed?

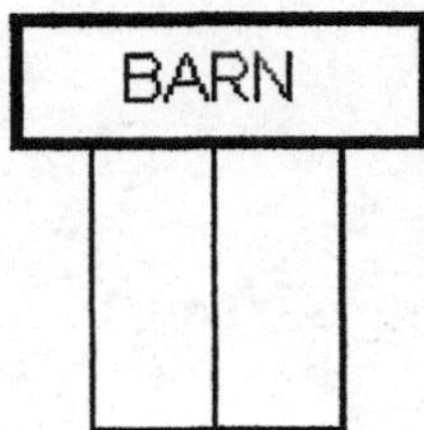

14. The window below is to have a perimeter of 32 feet. Find the dimensions that will maximize the area (to let the most light in).

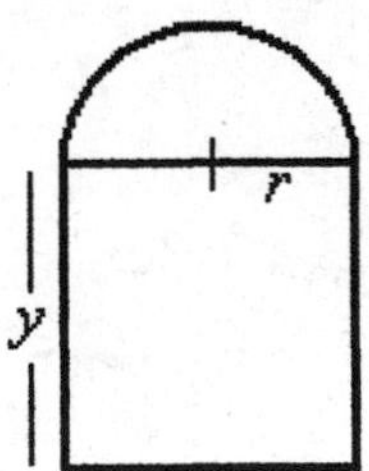

15. An apple orchard has an average yield of 40 bushels of apples per tree if the tree density is 10 trees per acre. For each unit increase in tree density, the average yield decreases by 2 bushels per acre. Find how many trees should be planted per acre to maximize the number of apples produced per acre.

Exam 4B

Name:
Instructor:
Section:

Write your work as neatly as possible.

1. Find the interval(s) where $f(x)=x^3+x^2-5x+2$ is increasing and the interval(s) where it is decreasing.

2. Find the interval(s) where $f(x)=\sqrt{2-4x}$ is increasing and the interval(s) where it is decreasing.

3. Find the relative maxima and minima, if any, of $g(x)=x^3-12x^2$.

4. Find the relative maxima and minima, if any, of $h(t)=3+\sqrt{t-2}$.

5. Let $f(x)=x^3+5x^2-1$.
   (a) Find the interval(s) where $f(x)$ is concave upward.

   (b) Find the interval(s) where $f(x)$ is concave downward.

   (c) Find the x-coordinate(s) of any point(s) of inflection.

6. Let $f(x)=\dfrac{x-2}{x+1}$.
   (a) Find the interval(s) where $f(x)$ is concave upward.

   (b) Find the interval(s) where $f(x)$ is concave downward.

   (c) Find the x-coordinate(s) of any point(s) of inflection.

7. Find the horizontal and vertical asymptotes of the graph of $y=\dfrac{3x^2}{x^2-5x-6}$.

8. Sketch the graph of $y = \frac{2-x}{x+3}$.

9. Sketch the graph of $y = x^4 - 4x^2$.

10. Find the absolute maximum and the absolute minimum of $f(x) = 2x^2 + 1$ on $[-2, 3]$.

11. Find the absolute maximum and the absolute minimum of $f(x) = \frac{x}{x^2+4}$ on $[0,3]$.

12. The quantity demanded per month, x, of a certain brand of electric shavers is related to the price, p, per shaver by the equation $p = -0.1x + 10{,}000$ $(0 \le x \le 20{,}000)$, where p is measured in dollars. The total monthly cost for manufacturing the shavers is given

$$C(x) = 0.00002x^3 - 0.4x^2 + 10{,}000x + 20{,}000.$$

How many shavers should be produced per month in order to maximize the company's profit? What is the maximum profit?

13. A farmer wants to create a pen inside a barn like the one shown below. The sides of the barn will form two sides of the pen, while fencing material will be used for the other two sides. The farmer has a total of 80 feet of fencing material to enclose the pen. What is the maximum area that can be enclosed?

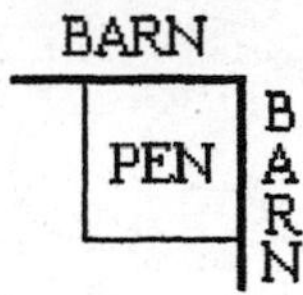

14. To make a rectangular trough, you bend the sides of a 32-inch wide sheet of metal to obtain the cross section pictured below. Find the dimensions of the cross section with the maximum area (this will result in the trough with the largest possible volume).

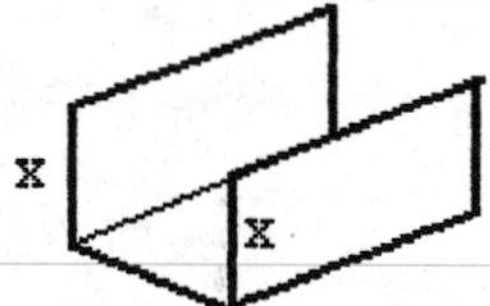

15. An apple orchard has an average yield of 64 bushels of apples per tree if the tree density is 24 trees per acre. For each unit increase in tree density, the average yield decreases by 2 bushels per acre. Find how many trees should be planted per acre to maximize the number of apples produced per acre.

Exam 4C

Name:
Instructor:
Section:

Write your work as neatly as possible.

1. Find the interval(s) where $f(x) = x^2 + 4x - 3$ is increasing and the interval(s) where it is decreasing.

2. Find the interval(s) where $f(x) = \sqrt{6 - 2x}$ is increasing and the interval(s) where it is decreasing.

3. Given the graph of *f* below, find the relative maxima and minima, if any.

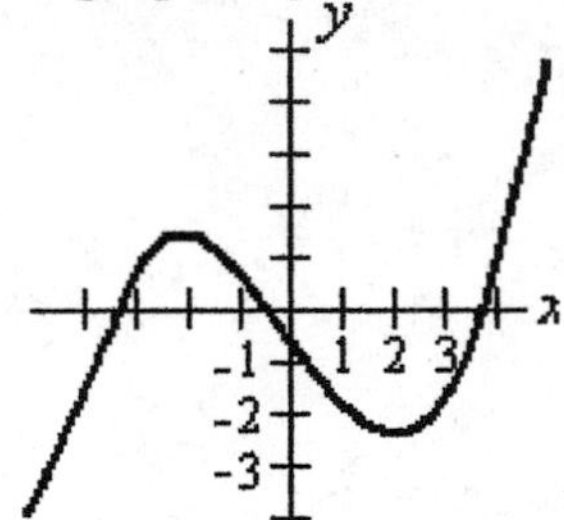

4. Find the relative maxima and minima, if any, of $h(t) = 4 - \sqrt{t}$.

5. Let $f(x) = 3x^3 + x + 1$.
   (a) Find the interval(s) where $f(x)$ is concave upward.

   (b) Find the interval(s) where $f(x)$ is concave downward.

   (c) Find the *x*-coordinate(s) of any point(s) of inflection.

6. Let $f(x) = x^4 - 4x^3 - 48x^2 - 64x - 32$.
   (a) Find the interval(s) where $f(x)$ is concave upward.

   (b) Find the interval(s) where $f(x)$ is concave downward.

   (c) Find the *x*-coordinate(s) of any point(s) of inflection.

7. Find the horizontal and vertical asymptotes of the graph below.

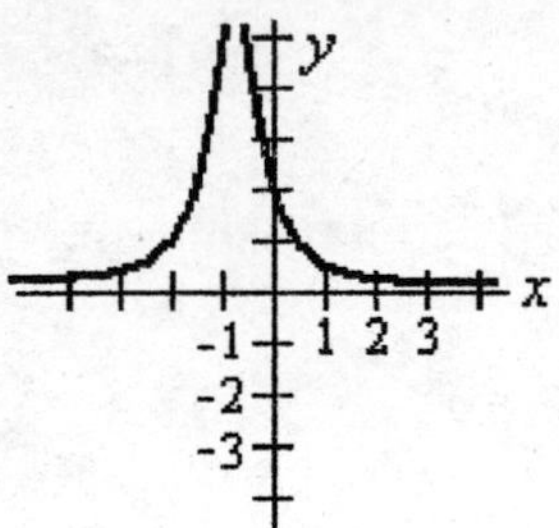

8. Sketch the graph of $y = \dfrac{-2}{x^2 - 9}$.

9. Sketch the graph of $y = 3\sqrt{x} - x$.

10. Find the absolute maximum and the absolute minimum of $f(x) = 3x^3 - 4x$ on $[-1, 0]$.

11. Find the absolute maximum and the absolute minimum of $f(x) = \dfrac{x+2}{x-2}$ on $[-4, 4]$.

12. A farmer wants to create a grazing area beside a river like the one shown below. The river will form one side of the area, while fencing will be used for the other sides. The farmer has a total of 680 feet of fencing to enclose the area. What is the maximum area that can be enclosed?

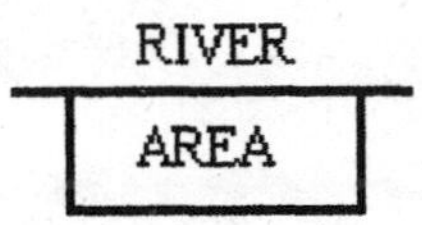

RIVER

AREA

13. By cutting away identical squares from each corner of a rectangular piece of cardboard and folding up the resulting flaps, an open box may be made. If the cardboard is 16 inches long and 16 inches wide, find the dimensions of the box that will yield the maximum volume.

14. A landlord owns an apartment building. When the rent for each apartment is \$400 per month, all 50 apartments are rented. The landlord estimates that each \$50 increase in the monthly rent will result in 5 apartments becoming vacant with no chance of being rented. What monthly rent amount will maximize the total monthly revenue?

Exam 4D

Name:
Instructor:
Section:

Write your work as neatly as possible.

1. Find the interval(s) where $f(x) = x^3 + \frac{9}{2}x^2 + 6x - 3$ is increasing and the interval(s) where it is decreasing.

2. Find the interval(s) where $f(x) = \sqrt{1 + \frac{1}{5}x}$ is increasing and the interval(s) where it is decreasing.

3. Find the relative maxima and minima, if any, of $g(x) = 4x - x^4$.

4. Find the relative maxima and minima, if any, of $h(t) = t^{1/3} - 3t$.

5. The graph of f follows. Given that the point of inflection is (0,-1), find the interval(s) where f is concave upward and where f is concave downward.

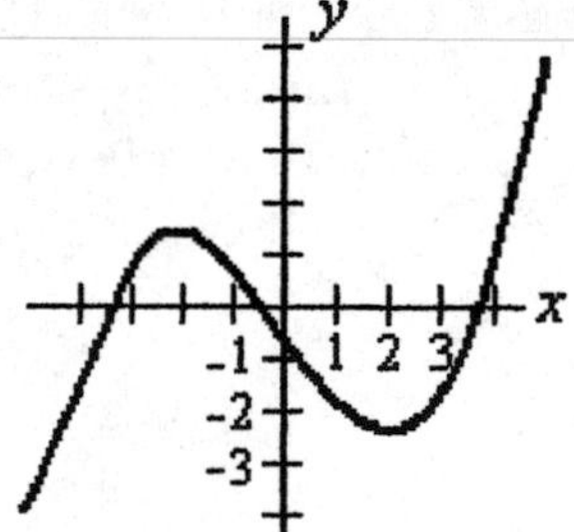

6. Let $f(x) = \sqrt[3]{x+1}$.
(a) Find the interval(s) where $f(x)$ is concave upward.

(b) Find the interval(s) where $f(x)$ is concave downward.

(c) Find the x-coordinate(s) of any point(s) of inflection.

7. Find the horizontal and vertical asymptotes of the graph of $y = \dfrac{x^2 + 2x + 1}{x^2 - 6x + 8}$.

8. Sketch the graph of $y = 3x - 2x^3$. Label at least three points in the graph.

9. Sketch the graph of $y = \dfrac{4x^2}{x^2 - 4}$. Label at least three points in the graph.

10. Find the absolute maximum and the absolute minimum of $f(x) = x^3 - 3x + 2$ on $[-2, 4]$.

11. Find the absolute maximum and the absolute minimum of

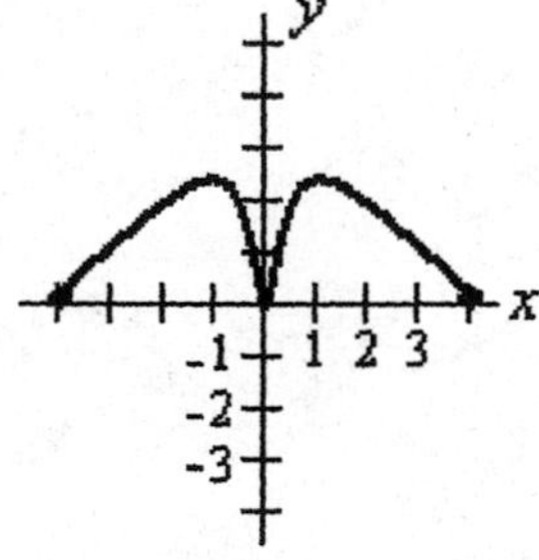

12. A farmer wants to create a pen inside a barn like the one shown below. The barn will form two sides of the pen, while fencing material will be used for the other side. The farmer wants the walls of the pen to take up a total of only 80 feet of the barn walls. What is the maximum area that can be enclosed?

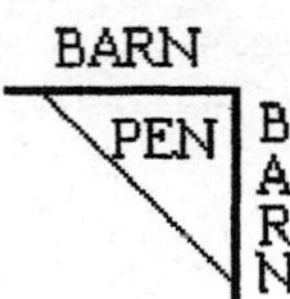

13. The window below is to have a perimeter of 36 feet. Find the dimensions that will maximize the area (to let the most light in).

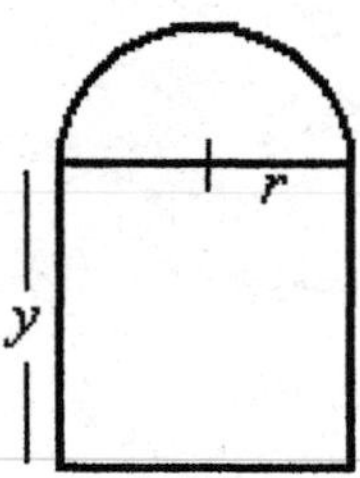

14. A landlord owns an apartment building. When the rent for each apartment is \$700 per month, all 100 apartments are rented. The landlord estimates that each \$100 increase in the monthly rent will result in 10 apartments becoming vacant with no chance of being rented. What monthly rent amount will maximize the total monthly revenue?

Answers to Chapter 4 Exams

Exam 4A

1. Increasing: $(-\infty, -7) \cup (-1, \infty)$;

   Decreasing: $(-7, -1)$

2. Inc: $(-\infty, -2) \cup (2, \infty)$;dec (-2,2)

3. Relative maximum $g(0) = 2$;

   relative minimum $g(3) = -\frac{5}{2}$

4. Relative maximum $h(0) = 3$;
   No relative minimum

5. (a) $(-4, \infty)$

   (b) $(-\infty, -4)$

   (c) $x = -4$

6. (a) $(-2, \infty)$

   (b) $(-\infty, -2)$

   (c) None

7. Horizontal: $y = 3$;
   vertical: $x = -2$

8.

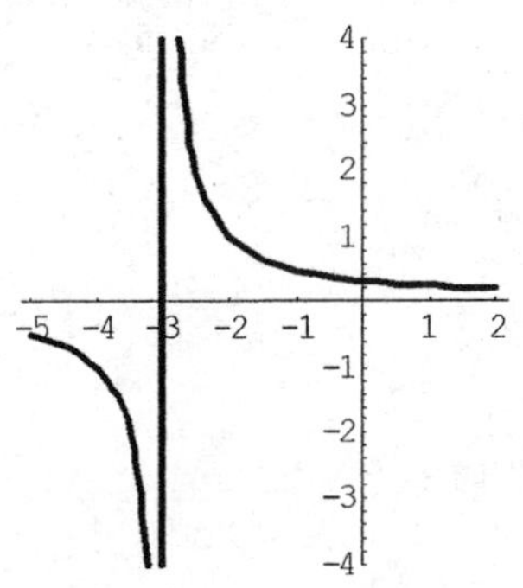

Exam 4B

1. Increasing: $\left(-\infty, -\frac{5}{3}\right) \cup (1, \infty)$;

   Decreasing: $\left(-\frac{5}{3}, 1\right)$

2. Inc: never ; dec $(-\infty, 1/2]$

3. Relative maximum $g(0) = 0$;

   relative minimum $g(8) = -256$

4. No relative maximum;
   relative minimum $h(2) = 3$

5. (a) $\left(-\frac{5}{3}, \infty\right)$

   (b) $\left(-\infty, -\frac{5}{3}\right)$

   (c) $x = -\frac{5}{3}$

6. (a) $(-\infty, -1)$

   (b) $(-1, \infty)$

   (c) None

7. Horizontal: $y = 3$;
   vertical: $x = 6$, $x = -1$

8.

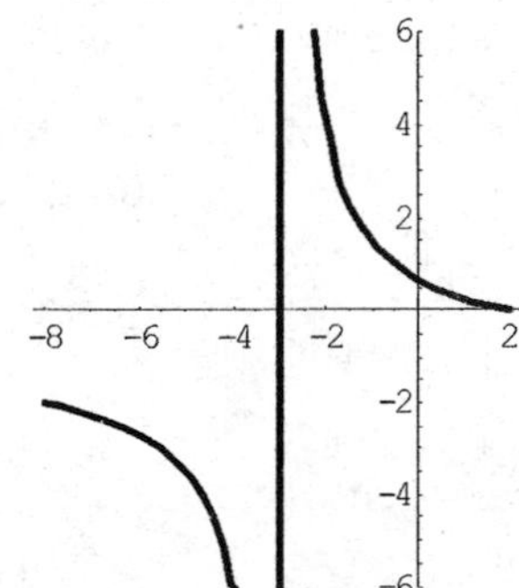

9.

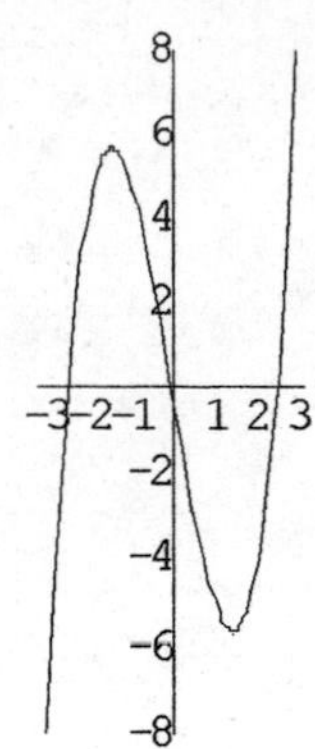

10. Absolute maximum $f(6)=108$; absolute minimum $f(0)=0$

11. Absolute maximum $f(3)=90$;

absolute minimum $f(-2)=-20$

12. 30 inches

13. 120,000 square feet

14. $r=\dfrac{32}{4+\pi}\approx 4.48$ ft, $y\approx 4.48$ ft

15. 15 trees per acre

9.

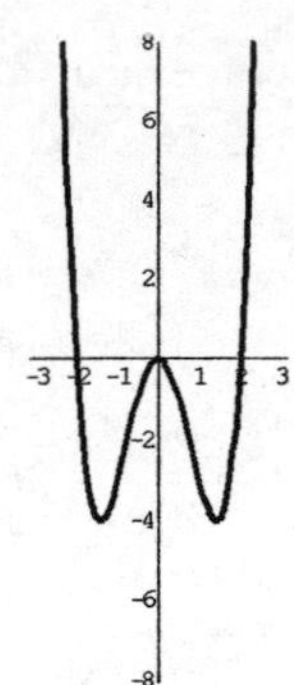

10. Absolute maximum $f(3)=19$; absolute minimum $f(0)=1$

11. Absolute maximum $f(2)=\dfrac{1}{4}$;

absolute minimum $f(0)=0$

12. 10,000; \$9,980,000

13. 1600 square feet

14. 8 inches by 16 inches

15. 28 trees per acre

Exam 4C

1. Increasing: $(-2,\infty)$;

   Decreasing: $(-\infty,-2)$

2. Inc: nowhere; dec$(-\infty,3]$

3. Relative maximum $f(-2)=1.5$;

   relative minimum $f(2)=-2.5$

4. Relative maximum $h(0)=4$;

   No relative minimum

5. (a) $(0,\infty)$; (b) $(-\infty,0)$;

   (c) $x=0$

6. (a) $(-\infty,-2)\cup(4,\infty)$

   (b) $(-2,4)$

   (c) $x=-2$ and $x=4$

Exam 4D

1. Increasing: $(-\infty,-2)\cup(-1,\infty)$;

   Decreasing: $(-2,-1)$

2. Increasing: $[-5,\infty)$; never decreasing

3. Rel maximum (1, 3)

   rel minimum none

4. relative maximum; $g(\frac{1}{27})=\frac{2}{9}$

   rel minimum $g(-\frac{1}{27})=-\frac{2}{9}$

5. concave down $(-\infty,0)$

   concave upward $(0,\infty)$

6. (a) $(-\infty,-1)$

   (b) $(-1,\infty)$

   (c) $x=-1$

7. Horizontal: $y = 0$; vertical: $x = -1$

8.

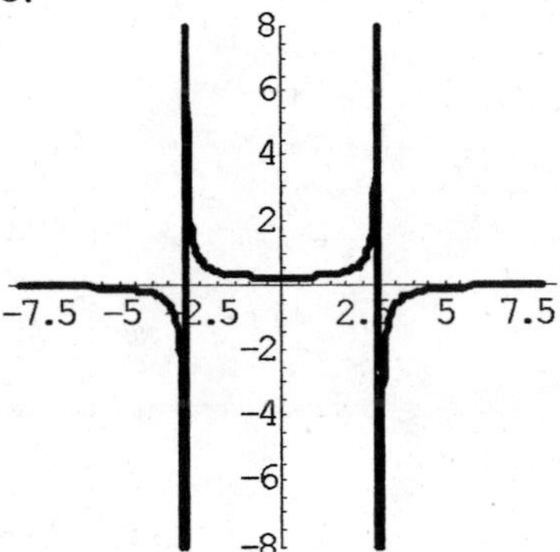

9.

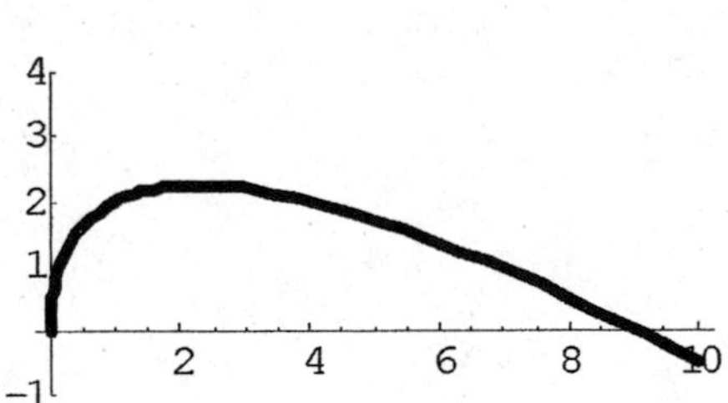

10. Absolute maximum $f(-\frac{2}{3}) = \frac{16}{9}$; Abs min $f(0) = 0$

11. No absolute maximum, nor minimum

12. 57,800 square feet

13. $\frac{32}{3}$ in. by $\frac{16}{3}$ in. by $\frac{8}{3}$ in.

14. \$450

7. Horizontal: $y = 1$; vertical: $x = 2$, $x = 4$

8.

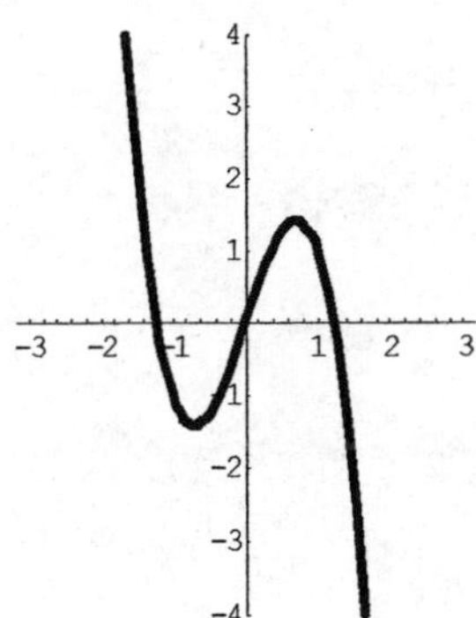

9.

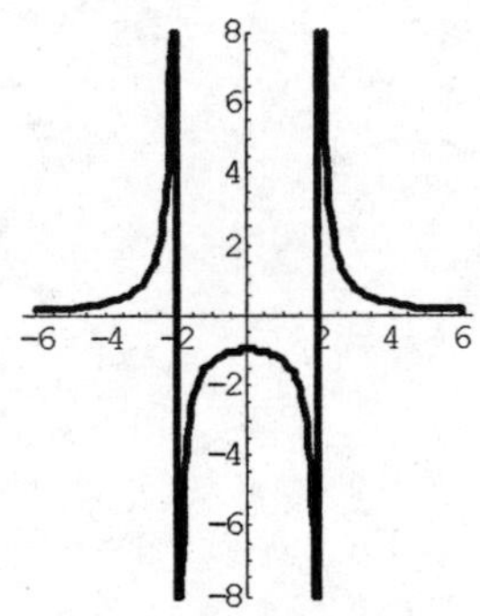

10. Absolute maximum $f(4) = 54$; abs minimum $f(1) = f(-2) = 0$

11. Abs max $(1, 2.5), (-1, 2.5)$; Abs min $(-4, 0), (0, 0), (4, 0)$

12. 800 square feet

13. $r = \dfrac{36}{4+\pi} \approx 3.88$ ft, $y \approx 8.03$ ft

14. \$850

Chapter 5 ■ Exponential and Logarithmic Functions

Section 5.1

1. Evaluate

(a) $3^{-2} \cdot 3^5$ — Answer: 27

(b) $\left(\frac{1}{4}\right)^{-1/2}\left(\frac{1}{3}\right)^{-2}$ — Answer: 18

2. Evaluate $9^{3/2}27^{-1/3}$. — Answer: 9

3. Evaluate $\left(\frac{125}{8}\right)^{-1/3} 81^{-1/4}$. — Answer: $\frac{2}{15}$

4. Evaluate

(a) $\left(9^{-1/2}\right)^3$ — Answer: $\frac{1}{27}$

(b) $3^{1/3}\left(9^{1/6}\right)^2$ — Answer: 3

5. Evaluate

(a) $\frac{5^{2.2} \cdot 5^{-1.3}}{5^{-0.1}}$ — Answer: 5

(b) $\left[\left(-\frac{2}{3}\right)^2\right]^{-2}$ — Answer: $\frac{81}{16}$

6. Simplify

(a) $\left(16x^4\right)^{1/2}$ — Answer: $4x^2$

(b) $\left(2x^2y^3\right)^2$ — Answer: $4x^4y^6$

7. Simplify

(a) $\left(2x^4\right)\left(-3x^{-1}\right)$ — Answer: $-6x^3$

(b) $\frac{8a^{-4}}{2a^{-2}}$ — Answer: $\frac{4}{a^2}$

8. Simplify

(a) $\frac{7^0}{\left(3^{-2}x^{-1}y\right)^2}$ — Answer: $\frac{81x^2}{y^2}$

(b) $\dfrac{\left(a^{-m}\cdot a^{n}\right)^{2}}{\left(a^{m-n}\right)^{-2}}$ Answer: 1

9. Simplify $\left(5x^3y^2z^4\right)^3$. Answer: $125x^9y^6z^{12}$

10. Simplify $x^{-5/2}x^{10/3}$. Answer: $x^{5/6}$

11. Solve the equation $5^{2x}=5^4$ for x. Answer: $x=2$

12. Solve the equation $2.4^{-2x+1}=2.4^{-3}$ for x. Answer: $x=2$

13. Solve the equation $7^{3x-2}=7^{5x+1}$ for x. Answer: $x=-\dfrac{3}{2}$

14. Solve the equation $8.6^{x^2-5x}=8.6^6$ for x. Answer: $x=-1,6$

15. Solve the equation $5^{3x+1}=5^{-5}$ for x. Answer: $x=-2$

16. Sketch the graph of $f(x)=3^x$.
Answer:

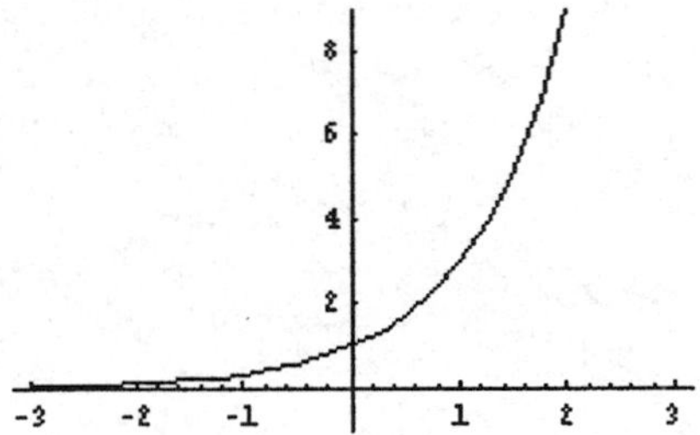

17. Sketch the graph of $f(x)=\left(\dfrac{1}{3}\right)^x$.

Answer:

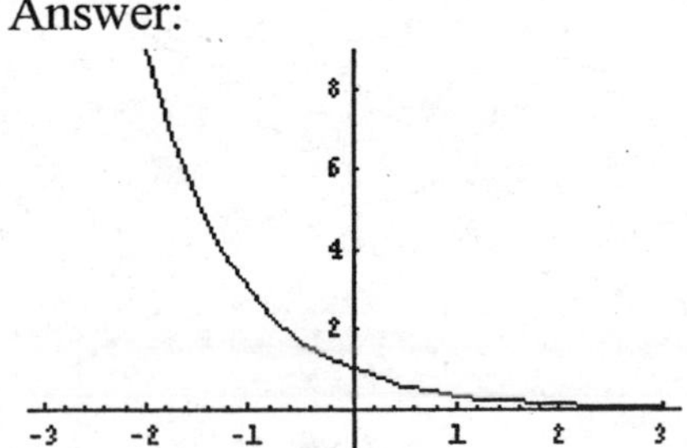

18. Sketch the graph of $f(x) = 2e^{-x}$.

Answer:

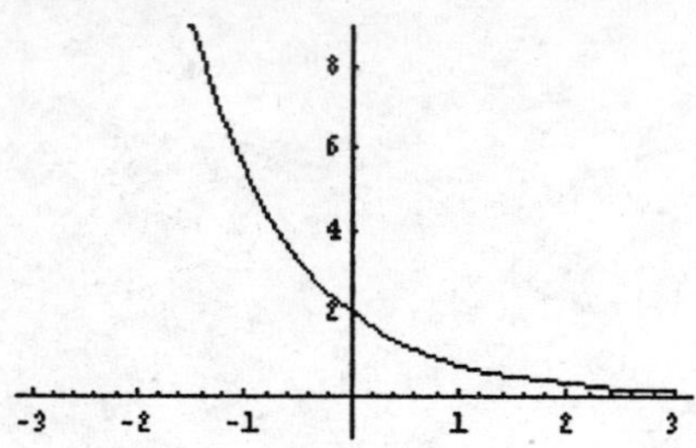

19. Sketch the graph of $f(x) = 5^{0.75x}$.

Answer:

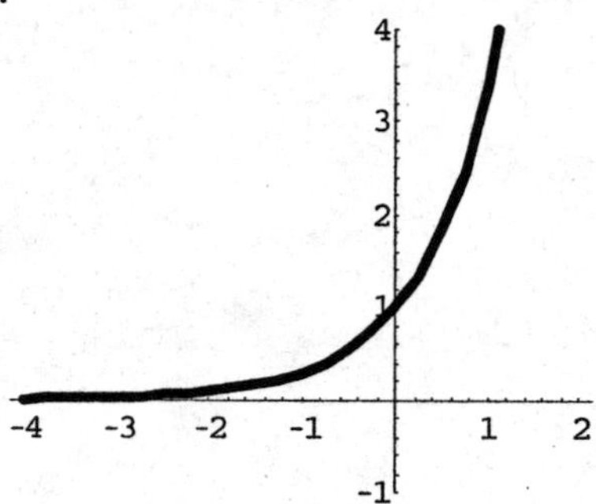

20. Sketch the graph of $y = 2 - e^{-x}$.

Answer:

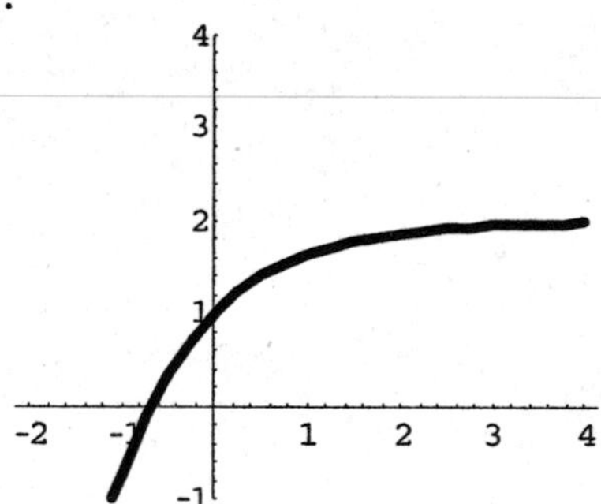

21. Sketch the graph of $y = \dfrac{e^{x} - e^{-x}}{2}$.

Answer:

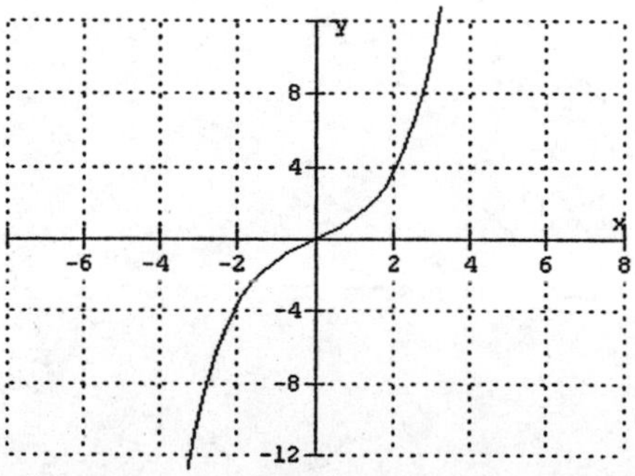

22. Sketch the graph of $y = x^2 + e^x$.

Answer:

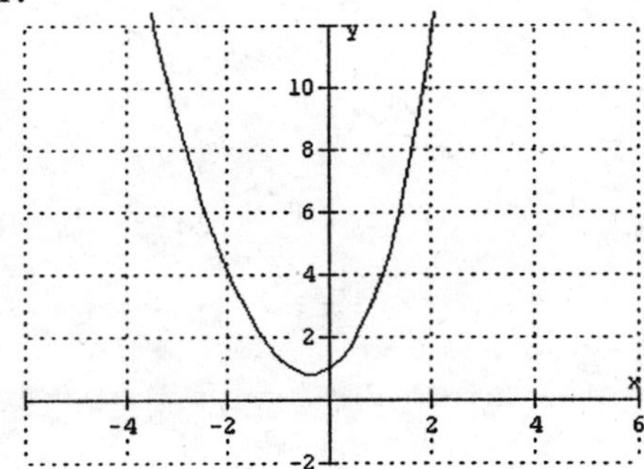

23. Sketch the graph of $y = \dfrac{e^x + e^{-x}}{2}$.

Answer:

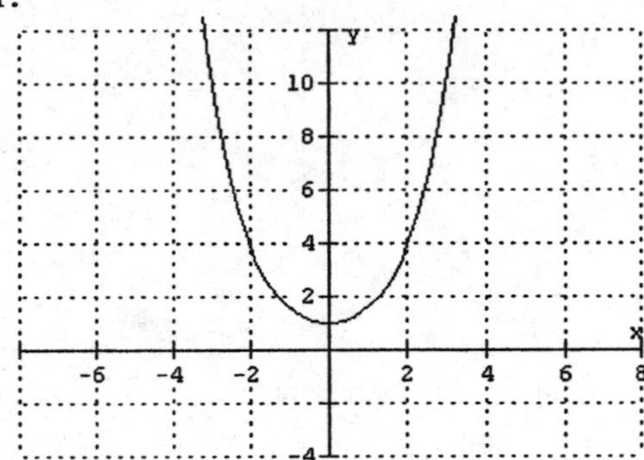

Section 5.2

1. Express in logarithmic form: $4^2 = 16$.
   Answer: $\log_4 16 = 2$

2. Express in logarithmic form: $\left(\frac{1}{3}\right)^4 = \frac{1}{81}$.

   Answer: $\log_{1/3} \frac{1}{81} = 4$

3. Express in logarithmic form: $3^{-2} = \frac{1}{9}$.

   Answer: $\log_3 \frac{1}{9} = -2$

4. Express in logarithmic form: $81^{3/4} = 27$.
   Answer: $\log_{81} 27 = \frac{3}{4}$

5. Express in logarithmic form: $32^{-2/5} = 0.25$.
   Answer: $\log_{32} 0.25 = -\frac{2}{5}$

6. Use the fact that $\log_6 5 = 0.8982$ and $\log_6 3 = 0.6131$ to find $\log_6 15$.
   Answer: 1.5113

7. Use the fact that $\log_6 5 = 0.8982$ and $\log_6 3 = 0.6131$ to find $\log_6 \frac{5}{3}$.

   Answer: 0.2851

8. Use the fact that $\log_6 5 = 0.8982$ and $\log_6 3 = 0.6131$ to find $\log_6 9$.
   Answer: 1.2262

9. Use the fact that $\log_6 5 = 0.8982$ and $\log_6 3 = 0.6131$ to find $\log_6 75$.
   Answer: 2.4095

10. Use the fact that $\log_6 5 = 0.8982$ and $\log_6 3 = 0.6131$ to find $\log_6 \sqrt{5}$.
    Answer: 0.4491

11. Use the laws of logarithms to expand and simplify the expression: $\log x(x-1)^2$.
    Answer: $\log(x) + 2\log(x-1)$

12. Use the laws of logarithms to expand and simplify the expression: $\log \dfrac{\sqrt{x-2}}{x^2-3}$.

Answer: $\dfrac{1}{2}\log(x-2)-\log(x^2-3)$

13. Use the laws of logarithms to simplify the expression: $\log x^3\left(x^3+2\right)^{1/3}$.

Answer: $3\log x+\dfrac{1}{3}\log\left(x^3+2\right)$

14. Use the laws of logarithms to expand and simplify the expression: $\ln(xe^x)$.
Answer: $\ln x + x$

15. Use the laws of logarithms to simplify the expression: $\ln\left(\dfrac{3e^x}{x}\right)$.

Answer: $\ln 3 + x - \ln x$

16. Sketch the graph of $f(x) = \log_2 x$.
Answer:

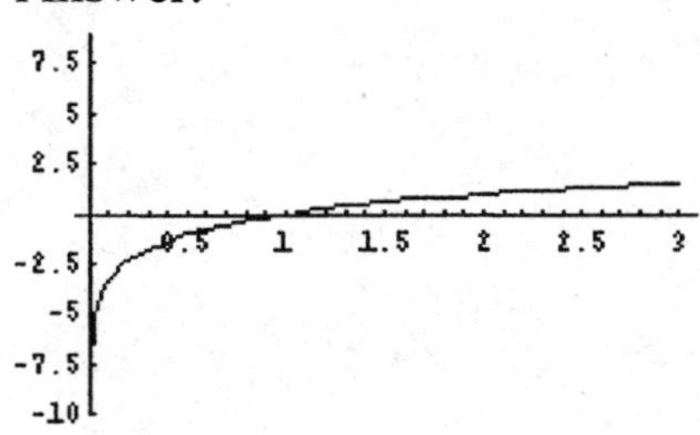

17. Sketch the graph of $g(x) = \ln 3x$.
Answer:

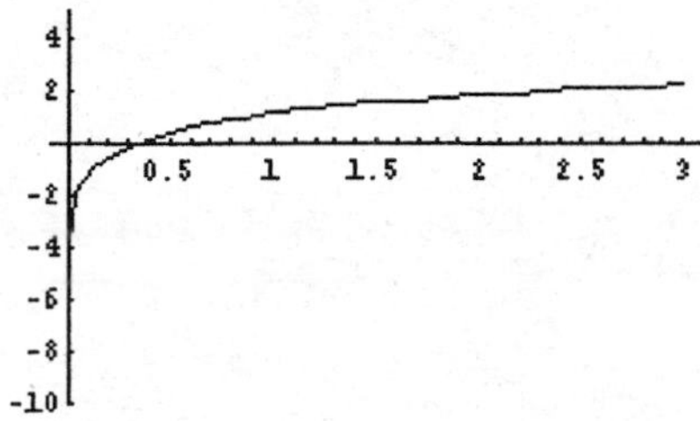

18. Sketch the graph of $g(x) = \log_{2/5} x$.

Answer:

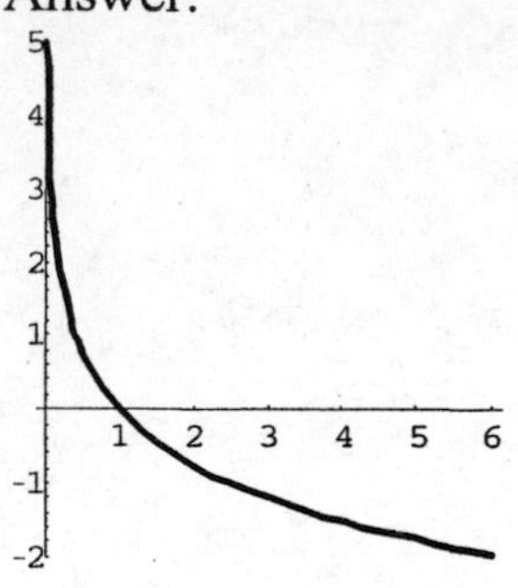

19. Use the laws of logarithms to solve the equation $\log_3 x = 3$.

Answer: $x = 27$

20. Use the laws of logarithms to solve the equation $\log_2 \frac{1}{4} = x$.

Answer: $x = -2$

21. Use the laws of logarithms to solve the equation $\log_x 9 = 2$.

Answer: $x = 3$

22. Use the laws of logarithms to solve the equation $\log(x+2) + \log(3) = 1$.

Answer: $x = \frac{4}{3}$

23. Use the laws of logarithms to solve the equation $\log(x+2) - \log(x-1) = \log 4$.

Answer: $x = 2$

24. Use the laws of logarithms to solve the equation $e^{3x-1} = 5$.

Answer: $x = \frac{1}{3} + \frac{1}{3}\ln 5$

25. Use the laws of logarithms to solve the equation $e^{3x+6} = 9$.

Answer: $x = \frac{1}{3}\ln 9 - 2$

26. Use the laws of logarithms to solve the equation $7e^{3t-1} = 7$.

Answer: $t = \frac{1}{3}$

27. Use the laws of logarithms to solve the equation $5e^{-0.3t} - 3 = 7$.

Answer: $t = -\frac{10\ln 2}{3}$

28. Use the laws of logarithms to solve the equation $\frac{40}{1+2e^{0.3t}} = 10$.

Answer: $t = \frac{10}{3}\ln(3/2)$

29. Use the laws of logarithms to solve the equation $3e^{2-3x} = 19$.

Answer: $x = \frac{2}{3} - \frac{1}{3}\ln 19 + \frac{1}{3}\ln 3$

30. The temperature of a mug of coffee after t minutes is given by $T = 80 + 100e^{-0.182t}$, where T is measured in degrees Fahrenheit.
(a) What is the initial temperature of the coffee?

Answer: 180° F

(b) When (to the nearest hundredth of a minute) will the coffee be at 100°?

Answer: after 8.84 minutes

Section 5.3

1. What is the interest on $20,000, invested at 6.5% for 7 years, and compounded annually?
   Answer: $11,079.73

2. What is the interest on $1 million, invested at 18% for 4 years, and compounded annually?
   Answer: $938,777.76

3. What is the future value of $1250, invested at 9.5% for 5 years, if it is compounded semiannually?
   Answer: $1988.16

4. What is the future value of $4500, invested at 15% for 20 years, if it is compounded quarterly?
   Answer: $85,558.06

5. What is the future value of $20,000, invested at 6.5% for 7 years, if it is compounded monthly?
   Answer: $31,484.79

6. What is the future value of $1 million, invested at 18% for 4 years, if it is compounded daily?
   Answer: $2,054,068.63

7. What is the present value of $25,000 in 2 years, if it is invested at 12% compounded monthly?
   Answer: $19,689.15

8. Find the accumulated amount after 5 years if $1800 is invested at 8% per year compounded quarterly.
   Answer: $2674.71

9. Find the accumulated amount after 5 years if $3200 is invested at 7% per year compounded continuously.
   Answer: $4541.02

10. Find the accumulated amount after 12 years if $800 is invested at 15% per year compounded continuously.
    Answer: $4839.72

11. Find the effective rate of interest corresponding to a nominal rate of 6% compounded quarterly.
    Answer: 6.14%

12. A father wants to be able to provide his newborn baby with a college education. To do this, the father estimates that he will need $120,000 when his child turns 18. How much money should the father invest in an account that pays 7% interest per year compounded daily so that the account is worth $120,000 in 18 years?
Answer: $34,042.60

13. Compute the future value after 10 years on $2000 invested at 8% interest compounded annually.
Answer: $4317.85

14. What interest rate would double your money in 10 years if you earned interest compounded monthly?
Answer: 6.95%

15. Find the effective rate of interest corresponding to a nominal rate of 17.5% per year compounded monthly (round to the nearest hundredth of one percent).
Answer: 18.97% per year

16. Find the effective rate of interest corresponding to a nominal rate of 11.5% per year compounded monthly (round to the nearest hundredth of one percent).
Answer: 12.13% per year

17. Find the effective rate of interest corresponding to a nominal rate of 15.5% per year compounded monthly (round to the nearest hundredth of one percent).
Answer: 16.65% per year

18. Find the effective rate of interest corresponding to a nominal rate of 6.5% per year compounded monthly (round to the nearest hundredth of one percent).
Answer: 6.7% per year

19. Find the time, in years, that it will take for an investment to double in value at a rate of 7% per year compounded daily (round to the nearest tenth of a year).
Answer: 9.9 years

20. Find the time, in years, that it will take for an investment to triple in value at a rate of 6% per year compounded daily (round to the nearest tenth of a year).
Answer: 18.3 years

21. How long will it take $800 to grow to $1800 if the investment earns interest at a rate of 10% compounded monthly?
Answer: 8.1 years

22. How long will it take $2500 to grow to $40000 if the investment earns interest at a rate of 16% compounded quarterly?
Answer: 17.7 years

Section 5.4

1. Find the derivative of the function $f(x) = e^{4x}$.

   Answer: $4e^{4x}$

2. Find the derivative of the function $f(x) = 3e^x - x^4$.

   Answer: $3e^x - 4x^3$

3. Find the derivative of the function $f(x) = e^{-3x}$.

   Answer: $-3e^{-3x}$

4. Find the derivative of the function $f(x) = x^2 e^{4x}$.

   Answer: $4x^2 e^{4x} + 2xe^{4x}$

5. Find the derivative of the function $f(x) = \dfrac{2x}{e^{2x}}$.

   Answer: $\dfrac{2-4x}{e^{2x}}$

6. Find the derivative of the function $f(t) = 18e^{0.5t} + 2$.

   Answer: $9e^{0.5t}$

7. Find the derivative of the function $f(x) = \dfrac{e^x + 2}{e^x}$.

   Answer: $-2e^{-x}$

8. Find the derivative of the function $f(x) = 3e^{2x+2}$.

   Answer: $6e^{2x+2}$

9. Find the derivative of the function $f(x) = 2e^{-3/x}$.

   Answer: $\dfrac{6}{x^2} e^{-3/x}$

10. Find the derivative of the function $f(x) = \left(e^{2x} + 1\right)^{12}$.

    Answer: $24e^{2x}\left(e^{2x} + 1\right)^{11}$

11. Find the derivative of the function $f(x) = \dfrac{e^{2x} + 1}{e^{2x} - 1}$.

Answer: $-4\dfrac{e^{2x}}{\left(e^{2x}-1\right)^2}$

12. Find the derivative of the function $f(t)=\dfrac{e^{-2t}}{1+4t}$.

Answer: $\dfrac{-2(1+4t)e^{-2t}-4e^{-2t}}{\left(1+4t\right)^2}$

13. Find the second derivative of the function $f(t)=3e^{-3t}+4e^{-2t}$.

Answer: $27e^{-3t}+16e^{-2t}$

14. Find the interval(s) where $h(x)=xe^x$ is increasing and the interval(s) where it is decreasing.

Answer: Increasing: $(-1,\infty)$; decreasing: $(-\infty,-1)$

15. Find the absolute maximum and the absolute minimum of $g(x)=e^x-x$ on $[-1,1]$.

Answer: Absolute maximum: $g(1)=e-1$; absolute minimum: $g(0)=1$

16. Find the absolute extrema of $f(x)=e^{-x^2+4x}$ on $[0,3]$.

Answer: Absolute maximum: $f(2)=e^4$; absolute minimum: $f(0)=1$

17. Find the equation of the tangent line to the graph of the function $y=e^{3x-1}$ at the point $(1/3,1)$.

Answer: $y=3x$

18. Sketch the graph of $f(t)=t-e^{-2t}$.

Answer:

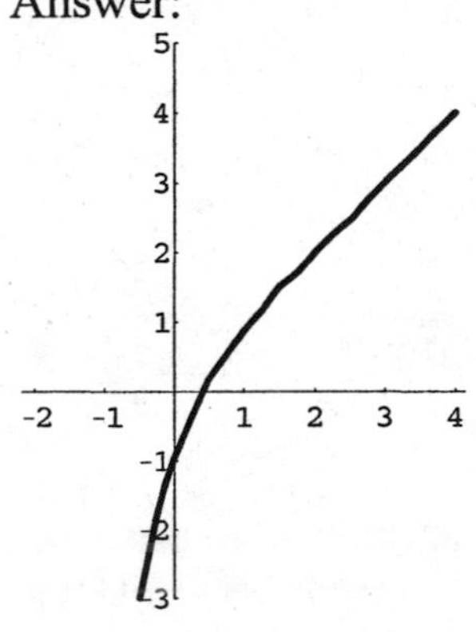

Section 5.5

1. Find the derivative of the function $f(x) = \ln(x^2 + 3)$.

   Answer: $\dfrac{2x}{x^2 + 3}$

2. Find the derivative of the function $f(x) = \dfrac{1}{\ln x}$.

   Answer: $\dfrac{-1}{x(\ln x)^2}$

3. Find the derivative of the function $f(x) = x^2 \ln x$.

   Answer: $x + 2x \ln x$

4. Find the derivative of the function $f(x) = \ln\left(\dfrac{2}{3x^5}\right)$.

   Answer: $\dfrac{-5}{x}$

5. Find the derivative of the function $f(t) = 8\ln\left(t^6\right)$.

   Answer: $\dfrac{48}{t}$

6. Find the derivative of the function $f(x) = e^{2x} \ln(x+2)$.

   Answer: $\dfrac{e^{2x}}{x+2} + 2e^{2x} \ln(x+2)$

7. Find the second derivative of the function $f(x) = \ln 3x$.

   Answer: $\dfrac{-1}{x^2}$

8. Find the second derivative of the function $f(x) = \dfrac{1}{\ln x}$.

   Answer: $\dfrac{2 + \ln x}{x^2 (\ln x)^3}$

9. Find the second derivative of the function $f(x) = \dfrac{1}{(\ln x)^2}$.

Answer: $\dfrac{6+2\ln x}{x^2(\ln x)^4}$

10. Use logarithmic differentiation to find the derivative of the function $y=(2x+1)^2(x+3)^3$.

Answer: $5(2x+3)(2x+1)(x+3)^2$

11. Use logarithmic differentiation to find the derivative of the function $y=7^x$.

Answer: $7^x \ln 7$

12. Use logarithmic differentiation to find the derivative of the function $y=\sqrt[3]{x+4}(2x+3)^3$.

Answer: $\sqrt[3]{x+4}(2x+3)^3\left[\dfrac{1}{3(x+4)}+\dfrac{6}{2x+3}\right]$

13. Use logarithmic differentiation to find the derivative of the function $y=(x-8)^3(x+2)^5$.

Answer: $(8x-34)(x-8)^2(x+2)^4$

14. Use logarithmic differentiation to find the derivative of the function $y=x^{(\ln x)^2}$.

Answer: $\dfrac{3(\ln x)^2 x^{(\ln x)^2}}{x}$

15. Find the interval(s) on which $f(x)=x-\ln x$ is increasing and the interval(s) on which it is decreasing.

Answer: Increasing: $(1,\infty)$; decreasing: $(0,1)$

16. Find the absolute maximum and the absolute minimum of $g(x)=2\ln x-x$ on $[1,3]$

Answer: Absolute maximum $g(2)=2\ln 2-2$; absolute minimum $g(1)=-1$

17. Let $f(x)=xe^{2x}$.

(a) Find the interval(s) on which $f(x)$ is concave upward.

Answer: $(-1,\infty)$

(b) Find the interval(s) on which $f(x)$ is concave downward.
Answer: $(-\infty,-1)$

(c) Find the x-coordinate(s) of any point(s) of inflection of f.
Answer: $x=-1$

18. Let $f(x)=e^x-\frac{1}{2}x^2$.

(a) Find the interval(s) on which $f(x)$ is concave upward.
Answer: $(0,\infty)$

(b) Find the interval(s) on which $f(x)$ is concave downward.
Answer: $(-\infty,0)$

(c) Find the x-coordinate(s) of any point(s) of inflection of f.
Answer: $x=0$

Section 5.6

1. A quantity $Q(t)$ is described by the exponential growth function $Q(t) = 1{,}200e^{0.05t}$, where t is measured in minutes.
   (a) What is the growth constant?
   Answer: 0.05
   (b) What quantity is initially present?
   Answer: 1200
   (c) What quantity is present after 10 minutes? (Round your answer to a whole year)
   Answer: 1978

2. A nature preserve is being established. A population biologist has estimated that the population of the deer in the preserve is currently 150 and will increase at an annual growth rate of 5%.
   (a) Find the function $Q(t)$ that expresses the deer population as a function of time t (in years).
   Answer: $Q(t) = 150e^{0.05t}$
   (b) Estimate the deer population in 10 years.
   Answer: 247

3. Wood deposits recovered from an archaeological site contain 35% of the carbon 14 they originally contained. How long ago did the tree from which the wood was obtained die? The decay constant of carbon 14 is $k = 0.00012$.
   Answer: 8749 years

4. A radioactive element has a half-life of 400 years. What is the decay constant? (in 5-decimal places)
   Answer: 0.001732868

5. During a flu epidemic, the number of children in a school district who contracted influenza after t days is given by $Q(t) = \dfrac{1500}{1 + 229e^{-0.5t}}$.
   (a) How many children had contracted influenza after the first day?
   Answer: 11
   (b) How many children had contracted influenza after five days?
   Answer: 76

6. A town had a population of 600 when it built a new school building. Ten years after the school was built, the population of the town was 900. Assuming the same rate of exponential growth, what will be the population of the town twenty years after the school was built?
   Answer: 1350

7. A city currently has a population of 150,000. A city planner estimates that the population of the city will be 200,000 in 15 years. If this is true, what is the annual rate of population growth?
Answer: 0.019 or 1.9%

8. A new car depreciates according to the function $V(t) = 18{,}000e^{-0.6t}$, where $V(t)$ represents the value of the car in dollars t years after it was purchased. How fast will the value of the car be changing three years after purchase?
Answer: Decreasing at a rate of $1785.23 per year

9. The population growth of a certain rodent is approximately 3% per month. Find the time it takes for the population to triple.
Answer: $\approx$ 36.6 months

10. A radioactive substance has a half-life of 20 years. If 200 g of the substance are present initially, find
(a) the amount present after 18 years.
Answer: ≈ 107.2 g
(b) the rate at which the substance will be decaying 18 years later.
Answer: ≈ -3.71 g/year

Exam 5A

Name:
Instructor:
Section:

Write your work as neatly as possible.

1. Evaluate

(a) $\left(\frac{1}{2}\right)^{-4} \cdot 2^{-3}$

(b) $\left(3x^2y^6\right)^3$

2. Sketch the graph of $f(x) = 2 - \left(\frac{1}{3}\right)^x$.

3. Sketch the graph of $f(x) = e^{-x}$.

4. Express in logarithmic form: $49^{-1/2} = \frac{1}{7}$.

5. What is the future value of \$7800, invested at 9% for 3 years, if it is compounded monthly?

6. What is the future value of \$200, invested at 5.5% for 7 years, if it is compounded continuously?

7. Use the laws of logarithms to expand and simplify the expression: $\log x\sqrt{x+2}$.

8. Use the laws of logarithms to expand and simplify the expression: $\ln x^2e^{2x}$.

9. Use the laws of logarithms to solve the equation $\log_4 16 = x$.

10. Use the laws of logarithms to solve the equation $\log_3 x = -2$.

11. Sketch the graph of $h(x) = \log_{1/2} x$.

12. Use the laws of logarithms to solve the equation $e^{3x+1} = 18$.

13. Find the derivative of the function $f(x) = e^{7x}$.

14. Find the derivative of the function $f(x) = x \ln x$.

15. Find the absolute maximum and the absolute minimum of $g(x) = \dfrac{\ln x}{x}$ on $[1,3]$.

16. Use logarithmic differentiation to find the derivative of the function $y = (x+7)^4 (x-9)^5$.

17. A quantity $Q(t)$ is described by the exponential growth function $Q(t) = 220e^{0.08t}$, where t is measured in months.
   (a) What is the growth constant?

   (b) What quantity is initially present?

18. A radioactive element has a half-life of 1700 years. What is the decay constant?

19. The population of rabbits in a park is initially 120 and is expected to increase at an annual rate of 5%. Find the expected population in 5 years.

20. How long will it take \$600 to grow to \$1300 if the money is in an account that pays interest at a rate of 6% compounded quarterly?

Exam 5B

Name:
Instructor:
Section:

Write your work as neatly as possible.

1. Simplify

 (a) $\left(6x^{8}\right)\left(3x^{-4}\right)$

 (b) $\dfrac{3a^{-5}}{27a^{-7}}$

2. Sketch the graph of $f(x)=3-3^{x}$.

3. Sketch the graph of $f(x)=e^{2x}$.

4. Express in logarithmic form: $\left(\dfrac{1}{4}\right)^{1/2}=\dfrac{1}{2}$.

5. Use the fact that $\log_c a=0.1101$ and $\log_c b=2.3444$ to find $\log_c ab$.

6. Use the fact that $\log_c a=2.6667$ and $\log_c b=0.5141$ to find $\log_c\left(\dfrac{a}{b}\right)$.

7. Use the laws of logarithms to expand and simplify the expression: $\log\dfrac{x}{3x+1}$.

8. Use the laws of logarithms to expand and simplify the expression: $\ln\sqrt{e^{x}}$.

9. Use the laws of logarithms to solve the equation $\log_5 \frac{1}{25} = x$.

10. Use the laws of logarithms to solve the equation $\log_x 64 = 3$.

11. Sketch the graph of $h(x) = -\ln x + 2$.

12. Use the laws of logarithms to solve the equation $e^{4x-1} = 6$.

13. A quantity $Q(t)$ is described by the exponential growth function $Q(t) = 410e^{0.0035t}$, where t is measured in minutes.
    (a) What quantity is initially present?

    (b) What quantity is present in 50 minutes?

14. A radioactive element has a half-life of 52 years. What is the decay constant?

15. The population of rabbits in a park is initially 700 and is expected to increase at an annual rate of 4%. Find the expected population in 12 years.

16. A town has a population of 1000. In 7 years, the population is expected to be 1400. What is the annual rate of population growth?

17. What interest rate would double your money in 12 years if you earned interest compounded monthly?

18. Find the derivative of the function $f(x) = \ln\left(x^3 + 2x\right)$.

19. Find the derivative of the function $f(x) = \sqrt{x+1}\left(e^3\right)$.

20. Use logarithmic differentiation to find the derivative of the function $y = e^x x^{2\ln x}$.

Exam 5C

Name:
Instructor:
Section:

Write your work as neatly as possible.

1. Solve the equation $6.3^{2-3x} = 6.3^{x}$ for x.

2. Sketch the graph of $f(x) = 3^{0.5x}$.

3. Sketch the graph of $g(x) = 1 - \frac{1}{2}e^{-x}$.

4. Express in logarithmic form: $64^{-2/3} = \frac{1}{16}$.

5. Use the fact that $\log_c a = 0.475$ and $\log_c b = 0.223$ to find $\log_c a^2 b$.

6. Use the fact that $\log_c a = 0.111$ and $\log_c b = 0.845$ to find $\log_c \sqrt{ab}$.

7. Use the laws of logarithms to expand and simplify the expression: $\log \frac{\sqrt{x}}{x+1}$.

8. Use the laws of logarithms to expand and simplify the expression: $\ln \frac{e^x}{x}$.

9. Use the laws of logarithms to solve the equation $\log_9 1 = x$.

10. Use the laws of logarithms to solve the equation $\log_{1/5} \frac{1}{25} = x$.

11. Sketch the graph of $h(x) = \log_3(x+2)$.

12. Compute the future value after 50 years on \$5 invested at 8% interest compounded monthly.

13. Use the laws of logarithms to solve the equation $e^{1-3x} = 9$.

14. A quantity $Q(t)$ is described by the exponential growth function $Q(t) = 1000e^{0.007t}$, where t is measured in hours.

    (a) What is the initial quantity?

    (b) What quantity is present after 5 hours?

15. A radioactive element has a half-life of 900 years. What is the decay constant?

16. The population of rabbits in a park is initially 500 and is expected to increase at an annual rate of 7%. Find the expected population in 8 years.

17. A town has a population of 600. In 9 years, the population is expected to be 1000. What is the annual rate of population growth?

18. Find the derivative of the function $f(x) = \ln(x^2 + 1)$.

19. Find the derivative of the function $f(x) = \sqrt{3}\left(e^{x+1}\right)$.

20. Use logarithmic differentiation to find the derivative of the function $y = 12^x$.

Exam 5D

Name:
Instructor:
Section:

Write your work as neatly as possible.

1. Solve the equation $7^{3x+2} = \frac{1}{49}^{-2}$ for x.

2. Sketch the graph of $f(x) = \left(\frac{1}{2}\right)^x$.

3. Sketch the graph of $g(x) = 2 - \frac{1}{3}e^x$.

4. Express in logarithmic form: $\left(\frac{1}{5}\right)^{-4} = 625$.

5. Use the fact that $\log_c b = 0.9922$ and $\log_c a = 3.2211$ to find $\log_c ab$.

6. Use the fact that $\log_c a = 1.15$ and $\log_c b = 2.46$ to find $\log_c \frac{b}{a}$.

7. Use the laws of logarithms to expand and simplify the expression: $\log\left(\frac{\sqrt[3]{x}}{x^2+1}\right)$.

8. Use the laws of logarithms to expand and simplify the expression: $\ln\left(x^3 e^{2x}\right)$.

9. Use the laws of logarithms to solve the equation $\log_{1/2} 8 = x$.

10. Use the laws of logarithms to solve the equation $\log_x 1000 = -3$.

11. Sketch the graph of $h(x) = \ln(xe)$.

12. What is the interest from $2 million, invested at 12% for 4 years, and compounded annually?

13. Use the laws of logarithms to solve the equation $e^{x/3} = 4$.

14. A quantity $Q(t)$ is described by the exponential growth function $Q(t) = 170e^{0.15t}$, where t is measured in years.
(a) What quantity is initially present?

(b) What quantity is present after 4 years?

15. A radioactive element has a half-life of 9.7 minutes. What is the decay constant?

16. The population of rabbits in a park is initially 800 and is expected to increase at an annual rate of 12%. Find the expected population in 14 years.

17. A radioactive substance has a half-life of 10 years. If 50 g of the substance are present initially, find
(a) the amount present after 8 years.
(b) the rate at which the substance will be decaying 8 years later.

18. Find the derivative of the function $f(x) = \ln\sqrt{x}$.

19. Find the derivative of the function $f(x) = \dfrac{x}{e^x + 1}$.

20. Use logarithmic differentiation to find the derivative of the function $y = x^{1/2}(x^2 + 1)^{5/2}$.

Answers to Chapter 5 Exams

Exam 5A

1. (a) 2

   (b) $27x^6y^{18}$

2.

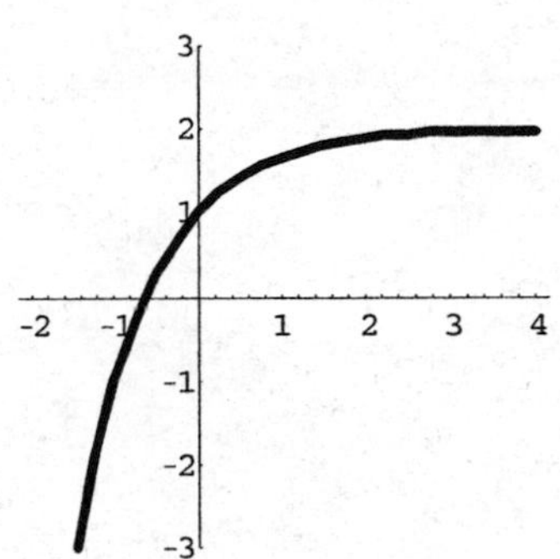

3.

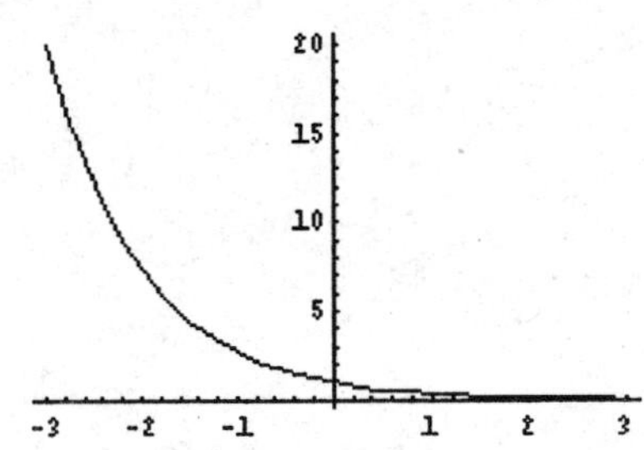

4. $\log_{49}\dfrac{1}{7}=-\dfrac{1}{2}$

5. \$10207.43

6. \$11.51

7. $\log x+\dfrac{1}{2}\log(x+2)$

8. $2\ln x+2x$

9. $x=2$

10. $x=\dfrac{1}{9}$

Exam 5B

1. (a) $18x^4$

   (b) $a^2/9$

2.

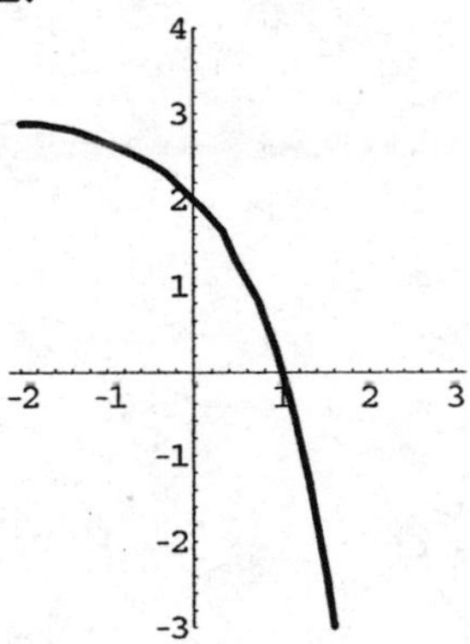

3.

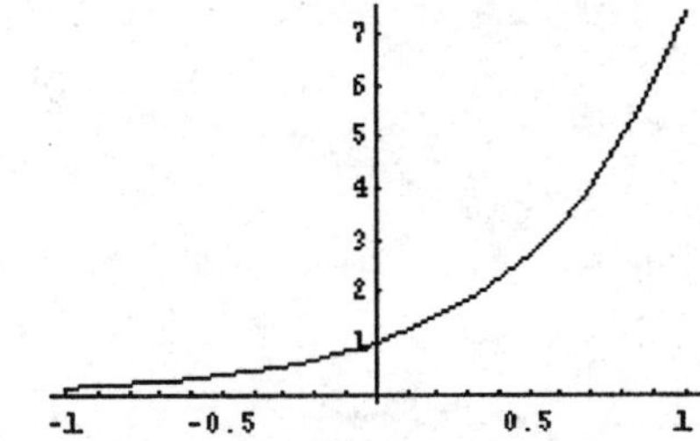

4. $\log_{1/4}\dfrac{1}{2}=\dfrac{1}{2}$

5. 2.4505

6. 2.1526

7. $\log x-\log(3x+1)$

8. $\dfrac{1}{2}x$

9. $x=-2$

10. $x=4$

11.

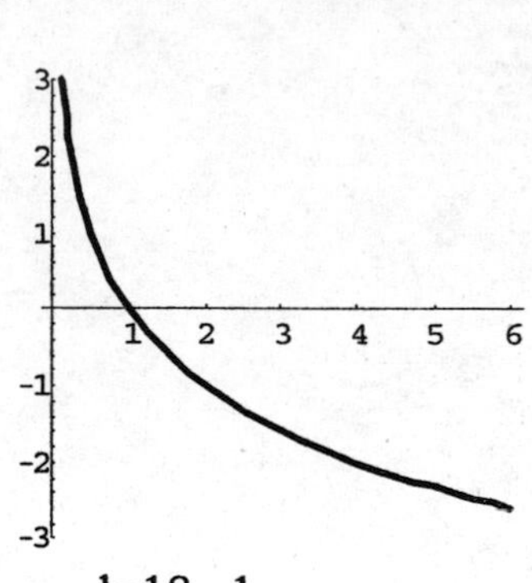

12. $x = \dfrac{\ln 18 - 1}{3}$

13. $7e^{7x}$

14. $1 + \ln x$

15. Absolute maximum $g(e) = \dfrac{1}{e}$; absolute minimum $g(1) = 0$

16. $(9x-1)(x+7)^3(x-9)^4$

17. (a) 0.08

(b) 220

18. 0.00042

19. 154

20. ≈ 13 years

11.

12. $x = \dfrac{1}{4} + \dfrac{1}{4}\ln 6$

13. (a) 410

(b) about 488

14. 0.01333

15. 1131

16. 0.048 or 4.8%

17. 5.79%

18. $\dfrac{3x^2 - 2}{x^3 - 2x}$

19. $\dfrac{e^3}{2\sqrt{x+1}}$

20. $\dfrac{e^x x^{2\ln x}(x + 4\ln x)}{x}$

Exam 5C

1. $x = 1/2$
2.

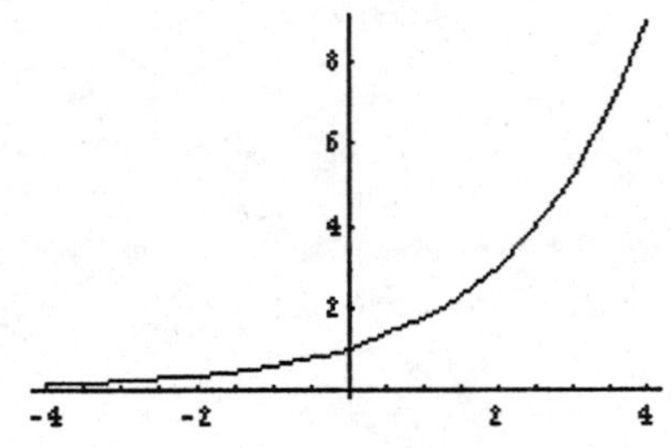

3.

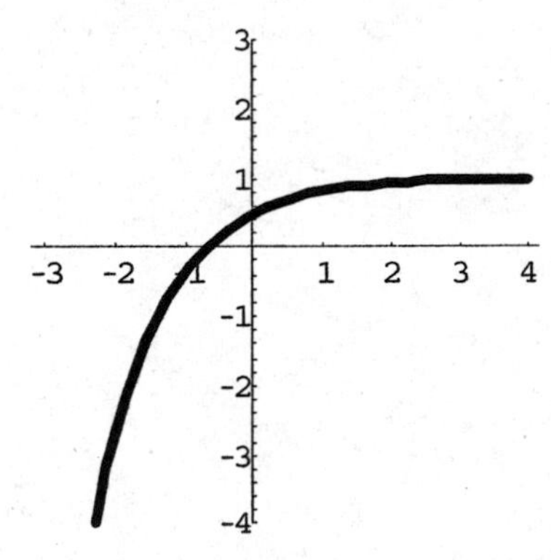

4. $\log_{64} \frac{1}{16} = -\frac{2}{3}$

5. 1.173

6. 0.478

7. $\frac{1}{2}\log x - \log(x+1)$

8. $x - \ln x$

9. $x = 0$

10. $x = 2$

Exam 5D

1. $x = 2/3$
2.

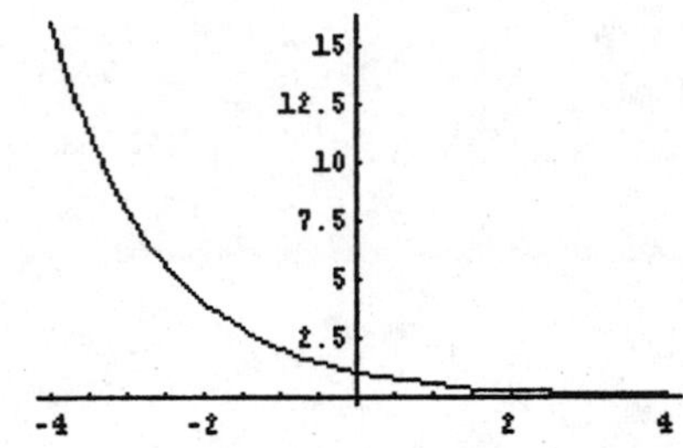

3.

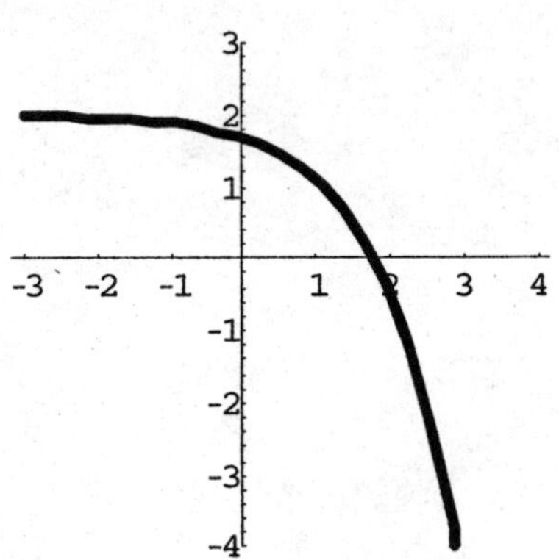

4. $\log_{1/5} 625 = -4$

5. 4.2133

6. 1.31

7. $\frac{1}{3}\log x - \log(x^2+1)$

8. $3\ln x + 2x$

9. $x = -3$

10. $x = \frac{1}{10}$

11.

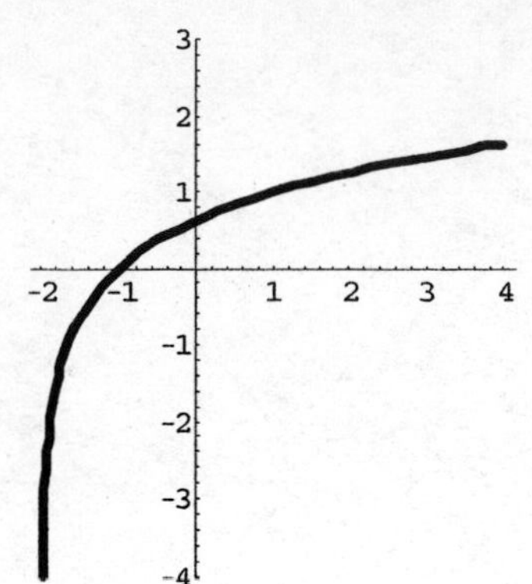

12. \$269.39

13. $x = \dfrac{1 - \ln 9}{3}$

14. (a) 1000
(b) 1036

15. 0.0007702

16. 875

17. 0.057 or 5.7%

18. $\dfrac{2x}{x^2 + 1}$

19. $\sqrt{3}\left(e^{x+1}\right)$

20. $12^x \ln 12$

11.

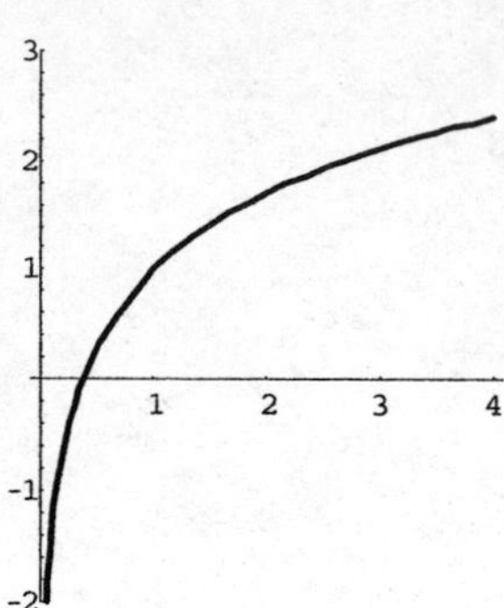

12. \$1.147 million

13. $x = 3\ln 4$

14. (a) 170
(b) 310

15. 0.07146

16. 4292

17. (a) 28.72g (b) -2 g/yr

18. $\dfrac{1}{2x}$

19. $\dfrac{e^x + 1 - xe^x}{\left(e^x + 1\right)^2}$

20. $\dfrac{(11x^2 + 1)(x^2 + 1)^{3/2}}{2x^{1/2}}$

Chapter 6 ■ Integration

Section 6.1

1. Find the indefinite integral $\int 3dx$.

   Answer: $3x+C$

2. Find the indefinite integral $\int \sqrt{5}dx$.

   Answer: $\sqrt{5}x+C$

3. Find the indefinite integral $\int 2x^3dx$.

   Answer: $\frac{1}{2}x^4+C$

4. Find the indefinite integral $\int 4t^{-6}dt$.

   Answer: $-\frac{4}{5}t^{-5}+C$

5. Find the indefinite integral $\int x^{5/3}dx$.

   Answer: $\frac{3}{8}x^{8/3}+C$

6. Find the indefinite integral $\int 2x^{-2/3}dx$.

   Answer: $6x^{1/3}+C$

7. Find the indefinite integral $\int e\sqrt{t}dt$.

   Answer: $\frac{2}{3}et^{3/2}+C$

8. Find the indefinite integral $\int \left(1+2x+4x^2\right)dx$.

   Answer: $x+x^2+\frac{4}{3}x^3+C$

9. Find the indefinite integral $\int \left(0.4t^3-0.3t^2+1.5\right)dt$.

   Answer: $0.1t^4-0.1t^3+1.5t+C$

10. Find the indefinite integral $\int 3e^x dx$.

Answer: $3e^x + C$

11. Find the indefinite integral $\int \left(2+\sqrt{x}+2x+e^x\right)dx$.

Answer: $2x+\frac{2}{3}x^{3/2}+x^2+e^x+C$

12. Find the indefinite integral $\int \left(u^{7/2}+2u^{5/2}-u\right)du$.

Answer: $\frac{2}{9}u^{9/2}+\frac{4}{7}u^{7/2}-\frac{1}{2}u^2+C$

13. Find the indefinite integral $\int \left(\sqrt[5]{x^2}-\frac{1}{x^3}\right)dx$.

Answer: $\frac{5}{7}x^{7/5}+\frac{1}{2}x^{-2}+C$

14. Find the indefinite integral $\int (2y+3)(3y-2)dy$.

Answer: $2y^3+\frac{5}{2}y^2-6y+C$

15. Find the indefinite integral $\int \sqrt{y}\left(y^2-y+1\right)dy$.

Answer: $\frac{2}{7}y^{7/2}-\frac{2}{5}y^{5/2}+\frac{2}{3}y^{3/2}+C$

16. Find the indefinite integral $\int \left(2e^x+x^{2e}\right)dx$.

Answer: $2e^x+\frac{1}{2e+1}x^{2e+1}+C$

17. Find the indefinite integral $\int \frac{x^5+\sqrt[5]{x}}{x^2}dx$.

Answer: $\frac{1}{4}x^4-\frac{5}{4}x^{-4/5}+C$

18. Find the indefinite integral $\int \frac{y^3-5y^2-y}{y}dy$.

Answer: $\frac{y^3}{3}-\frac{5}{2}y^2-y+C$

19. Find the indefinite integral $\int \frac{(\sqrt{x}+1)^2}{x^3}dx$.

Answer: $-x^{-1}-\frac{4}{3}x^{-3/2}-\frac{1}{2}x^{-2}+C$

20. Find the indefinite integral $\int (e^t + t^\pi)dx$.

Answer: $e^t + \frac{1}{\pi+1}t^{\pi+1} + C$

21. Find the function $f(x)$ if $f'(x) = 6x^2 - 4x + 7$ and $f(1) = 3$.

Answer: $2x^3 - 2x^2 + 7x - 4$

22. Find the function $f(x)$ if $f'(x) = 3x^2 + e^x$ and $f(0) = 3$.

Answer: $x^3 + e^x + 2$

23. Find the function $f(x)$ if $f'(x) = 4x - 2$ and $f(1) = 1$.

Answer: $f = 2x^2 - 2x + 1$

24. Find the function $f(x)$ if $f'(x) = \sqrt[5]{x^2} - \frac{1}{x^3}$ and $f(1) = 2$

Answer: $\frac{5}{7}x^{7/5} + \frac{1}{2}x^{-2} + \frac{11}{14}$

25. Find the function $f(x)$ if $f'(x) = \frac{x-3}{x}$ and $f(1) = 2$.

Answer: $f = x - 3\ln x + 1$

26. A ball is thrown straight up into the air. Its velocity t seconds after being thrown is given by the function $f(t) = 64 - 32t$. Find the ball's position $s(t)$ at any time t, assuming its position is 0 when $t = 0$.

Answer: $s(t) = 64t - 16t^2$

27. A study conducted by Mega-Byte Ltd. estimates that the number of online service subscribers will grow at a rate of $250 + 200t^{5/6}$ new subscribers per month t months from the start date of the service. If 4000 customers signed up for the service initially, how many subscribers will there be 18 months later?

Answer: 30,333

28. The rate of growth of a particular type of pest can be approximated by the function $20+20t^{2/3}$ pests/month. If there are initially 20 pests present, how many will there be 8 months from beginning?
Answer: 584

29. A ball is thrown straight up into the air. Its velocity t seconds after being thrown is given by the function $f(t) = 64 - 32t$. Find the ball's position $s(t)$ at any time t, assuming its position is 100 when $t = 0$.
Answer: $s(t) = 64t - 16t^2 + 100$

30. A ball is thrown straight up into the air. Its velocity t seconds after being thrown is given by the function $f(t) = 64 - 32t$. Find the ball's position $s(t)$ at any time t, assuming its position is -50 when $t = 0$.
Answer: $s(t) = 64t - 16t^2 - 50$

Section 6.2

1. Find the indefinite integral $\int 2x\sqrt{x^2+3}dx$.

   Answer: $\frac{2}{3}\left(x^2+3\right)^{3/2}+C$

2. Find the indefinite integral $\int 6(6x+4)^3\,dx$.

   Answer: $\frac{1}{4}(6x+4)^4+C$

3. Find the indefinite integral $\int\left(x^3+7x\right)^4\left(3x^2+7\right)dx$.

   Answer: $\frac{1}{5}\left(x^3+7x\right)^5+C$

4. Find the indefinite integral $\int\frac{3x^2}{\left(x^3+3\right)^4}dx$.

   Answer: $\frac{-1}{3\left(x^3+3\right)^3}+C$

5. Find the indefinite integral $\int\frac{3x}{3x^2+5}dx$.

   Answer: $\frac{1}{2}\ln\left(3x^2+5\right)+C$

6. Find the indefinite integral $\int\frac{3x^2+3}{\left(x^3+3x\right)^4}dx$.

   Answer: $\frac{-1}{3\left(x^3+3\right)^3}+C$

7. Find the indefinite integral $\int 4x\left(x^2-4\right)^{12}dx$.

   Answer: $\frac{2}{13}\left(x^2-4\right)^{13}+C$

8. Find the indefinite integral $\int\frac{x^3}{\sqrt{x^4+4}}dx$.

   Answer: $\frac{1}{2}\sqrt{x^4+4}+C$

9. Find the indefinite integral $\int \frac{2x+2}{x^2+2x+3}dx$.

Answer: $\ln\left|x^2+2x+3\right|+C$

10. Find the indefinite integral $\int \frac{x^3+2x}{x^4+4x^2+2}dx$.

Answer: $\frac{1}{4}\ln\left|x^4+4x^2+2\right|+C$

11. Find the indefinite integral $\int e^{3x}dx$.

Answer: $\frac{1}{3}e^{3x}+C$

12. Find the indefinite integral $\int \left(2e^x+3e^{-x}\right)dx$.

Answer: $2e^x-3e^{-x}+C$

13. Find the indefinite integral $\int \left(x+\frac{1}{2}\right)e^{x^2+x}dx$

Answer: $\frac{1}{2}e^{x^2+x}+C$

14. Find the indefinite integral $\int x^4 e^{x^5-2}dx$.

Answer: $\frac{1}{5}e^{x^5-2}+C$

15. Find the indefinite integral $\int \frac{\ln x}{5x}dx$.

Answer: $\frac{1}{10}(\ln x)^2+C$

16. Find the indefinite integral $\int \frac{e^{-2/x}}{x^2}dx$.

Answer: $\frac{1}{2}e^{-2/x}+C$

17. Find the indefinite integral $\int \frac{4e^x}{2+e^x}dx$.

Answer: $4\ln(2+e^x)+C$

18. Find the indefinite integral $\int \frac{1}{x(\ln x)^2}\,dx$.

Answer: $\frac{-1}{\ln x}+C$

19. Find the indefinite integral $\int \frac{2}{t(\ln t)}\,dt$.

Answer: $2\ln(\ln t)+C$

20. Find the indefinite integral $\int \frac{(\ln x)^4}{x}\,dx$.

Answer: $\frac{1}{5}(\ln x)^5+C$

21. Find the function $f(x)$ if $f'(x)=4(3x-2)^5$ and f passes through the point (1,1).

Answer: $f=\frac{2}{9}(3x-2)^6+\frac{7}{9}$

Section 6.3

1. Let $f(x) = x^2$ and compute the Riemann sum of f over the interval $[1,3]$ using four subintervals of equal length ($n = 4$). Choose the representative point in each subinterval to be the midpoint of the subinterval.
Answer: 8.625

2. Let $f(x) = x^2$ and compute the Riemann sum of f over the interval $[1,3]$ using four subintervals of equal length ($n = 4$). Choose the representative point in each subinterval to be the left endpoint of the subinterval.
Answer: 6.75

3. Let $f(x) = 4x+1$ and compute the Riemann sum of f over the interval $[0,3]$ using six subintervals of equal length ($n = 6$). Choose the representative point in each subinterval to be the left endpoint of the subinterval.
Answer: 18

4. Let $f(x) = 4x+1$ and compute the Riemann sum of f over the interval $[0,3]$ using six subintervals of equal length ($n = 6$). Choose the representative point in each subinterval to be the right endpoint of the subinterval.
Answer: 24

5. Let $f(x) = x^2$ and compute the Riemann sum of f over the interval $[1,3]$ using four subintervals of equal length ($n = 4$). Choose the representative point in each subinterval to be the right endpoint of the subinterval.
Answer: 10.75

6. Let $f(x) = x^4$ and compute the Riemann sum of f over the interval $[2,4]$ using four subintervals of equal length ($n = 4$). Choose the representative point in each subinterval to be the midpoint of the subinterval.
Answer: 196.0703125

7. Let $f(x) = x^4$ and compute the Riemann sum of f over the interval $[1,3]$ using four subintervals of equal length ($n = 4$). Choose the representative point in each subinterval to be the left endpoint of the subinterval.
Answer: 143.0625

8. Let $f(x) = x^4$ and compute the Riemann sum of f over the interval $[1,3]$ using four subintervals of equal length ($n = 4$). Choose the representative point in each subinterval to be the right endpoint of the subinterval.
Answer: 263.0625

9. Let $f(x) = 2x^2 + 2$ and compute the Riemann sum of f over the interval $[0,1]$ using four subintervals of equal length ($n = 4$). Choose the representative point in each subinterval to be the midpoint of the subinterval.
Answer: 2.65625

10. Let $f(x) = \frac{e^x}{x}$ and compute the Riemann sum of f over the interval $[0,1]$ using four subintervals of equal length ($n = 4$). Choose the representative point in each subinterval to be the midpoint of the subinterval.
Answer: about 4.669

11. Find the area of the region under the graph of the function $f(x) = 4x + 5$ on the interval $[-1,2]$.
Answer: 21

12. Find the area of the region under the graph of the function $f(x) = 11$ on the interval $[-2,4]$.
Answer: 66

13. Find the area of the region under the graph of the function $f(x) = x^2$ on the interval $[-1,2]$.
Answer: 3

14. Find the area of the region under the graph of the function $f(x) = 4x^3$ on the interval $[1,3]$.
Answer: 80

15. Find the area of the region under the graph of the function $f(x) = \frac{1}{x}$ on the interval $[2,8]$.
Answer: 2 (ln2)

16. Find the area of the region under the graph of the function $f(x) = 2 + \sqrt[3]{x}$ on the interval $[0,8]$.
Answer: 28

Section 6.4

1. Evaluate the definite integral $\int_1^2 4dx$.

   Answer: 4

2. Evaluate the definite integral $\int_1^2 2xdx$.

   Answer: 3

3. Evaluate the definite integral $\int_{-2}^3 (4x+3)dx$.

   Answer: 25

4. Evaluate the definite integral $\int_1^5 \frac{1}{x}dx$.

   Answer: ln(5)

5. Evaluate the definite integral $\int_4^9 \frac{3}{\sqrt{x}}dx$.

   Answer: 6

6. Evaluate the definite integral $\int_{-1}^1 (3-2x)dx$.

   Answer: 6

7. Evaluate the definite integral $\int_0^1 (t-t^2)^2\,dt$.

   Answer: $\frac{1}{30}$

8. Evaluate the definite integral $\int_5^7 \frac{3}{x-4}dx$.

   Answer: 3 ln 3

9. Evaluate the definite integral $\int_1^4 \frac{3}{x^4}dx$.

   Answer: $\frac{63}{64}$

10. Evaluate the definite integral $\int_1^4 \left(1+\frac{1}{x^2}+\frac{1}{x^4}\right)dx$.

    Answer: $\frac{261}{64}$

11. Evaluate the definite integral $\int_1^8 \left(\sqrt[3]{x} - \frac{1}{\sqrt[3]{x}}\right) dx$.

Answer: $\frac{27}{4}$

12. Find the area of the region R under the graph of $y = x^2 + 1$ and above x-axis from $x = -1$ to $x = 2$.

Answer: 6.

13. Find the area of the region bounded by $y = x$ and $y = x^3$ from $x = 0$ to $x = 1$.

Answer: 0.25.

14. Find the area of the region bounded by $y = x$ and $y = \sqrt{x}$ from $x = 0$ to $x = 1$.

Answer: $\frac{1}{6} = 0.1\overline{6}$

15. Find the area of the region R under the graph of $y = x^2$ on the interval [0, 1].

Answer: $\frac{1}{3}$

16. Find the area of the region bounded by $y = x^2$ and $y = -x^2 + 18$ from $x = -3$ to $x = 3$.

Answer: 72.

Section 6.5

1. Evaluate the definite integral $\int_0^4 2x\sqrt{x^2+9}dx$.

   Answer: $\frac{196}{3}$

2. Evaluate the definite integral $\int_0^1 \frac{3e^x}{e^x+2}dx$.

   Answer: $3\ln(e+2)-3\ln 3$

3. Evaluate the definite integral $\int_0^3 e^{3x}dx$.

   Answer: $\frac{1}{3}e^9-\frac{1}{3}$

4. Evaluate the definite integral $\int_0^2 xe^{x^2+2}dx$.

   Answer: $\frac{1}{2}e^6-\frac{1}{2}e^2$

5. Evaluate the definite integral $\int_2^3 x^4e^{x^5-2}dx$.

   Answer: $\frac{1}{5}e^{241}-\frac{1}{5}e^{30}$

6. Evaluate the definite integral $\int_2^4 \frac{\ln x}{5x}dx$.

   Answer: $\frac{3}{10}(\ln 2)^2$

7. Evaluate the definite integral $\int_{-4}^{-2} \frac{e^{-2/x}}{x^2}dx$.

   Answer: $\frac{1}{2}e-\frac{1}{2}\sqrt{e}$

8. Evaluate the definite integral $\int_{12}^{16} \frac{1}{x(\ln x)^2}dx$.

   Answer: $\frac{1}{\ln 12}-\frac{1}{\ln 16}$

9. Evaluate the definite integral $\int_1^{32} x^{-2/5}dx$.

   Answer: $\frac{35}{3}$

10. Evaluate the definite integral $\int_1^2 \frac{6x^4 + 4x^3 + 2}{x^2} dx$.

Answer: 21

11. Evaluate the definite integral $\int_e^{e^2} \frac{(\ln x)^4}{x} dx$.

Answer: $\frac{31}{5}$

12. Evaluate the definite integral $\int_0^1 2x^2 (x^3 + 2)^2 dx$.

Answer: $4\frac{2}{9}$

13. Evaluate the definite integral $\int_0^2 \frac{x}{\sqrt{4x^2 + 9}} dx$.

Answer: $\frac{1}{2}$

14. Evaluate the definite integral $\int_0^3 (e^{-x} + 1) dx$.

Answer: $4 - e^{-3}$

15. Find the average value of the function $f(x) = x^2 + 3$ over the interval $[1,5]$.

Answer: $\frac{40}{3}$

16. Find the average value of the function $f(x) = 10 - 2x$ over the interval $[1,3]$.

Answer: 6

17. Find the average value of the function $f(x) = \sqrt{x}$ over the interval $[1,9]$.

Answer: $\frac{13}{6}$

18. Find the average value of the function $f(x) = e^x$ over the interval $[0,10]$.

Answer: $\frac{1}{10}e^{10} - \frac{1}{10}$

19. Find the average value of the function $f(x) = \frac{1}{x+2}$ over the interval $[-1,3]$.

Answer: $\frac{1}{4}\ln 5$

Section 6.6

1. Find the area of the region bounded by the graphs of the functions $f(x) = x^2$ and $g(x) = 10$ and the vertical lines $x = 0$ and $x = 2$.

   Answer: $\frac{52}{3}$

2. Find the area of the shaded region below where y = $f(x) = x^3 - 4x^2$.

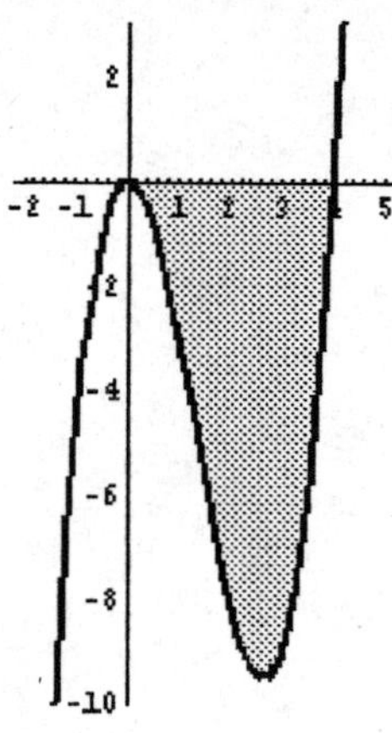

   Answer: $\frac{64}{3}$

3. Find the area of the region bounded by the graphs of the functions $f(x) = x^3$ and $g(x) = x^{2/3}$ (shaded below).

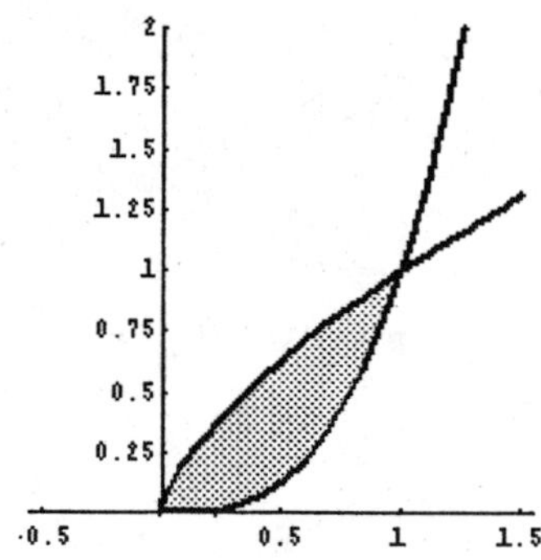

   Answer: $\frac{7}{20}$

4. Find the area of the region bounded by the graphs of the functions $f(x) = 2 + x^2$ and $g(x) = 1$ and the vertical lines $x = 1$ and $x = 3$.

   Answer: $\frac{32}{3}$

5. Find the area of the region bounded by the graphs of the functions $f(x) = e^{x-2}$ and $g(x) = 0$ and the vertical lines $x = -2$ and $x = 2$.

   Answer: $1 - e^{-4}$

6. Find the area of the region bounded by the graphs of the functions $f(x) = -x^2 + 4x$ and $g(x) = 2x - 8$.

   Answer: 36

7. Find the area of the region completely enclosed by the graphs of the functions $f(x) = x^3$ and $g(x) = x$.

   Answer: $\frac{1}{2}$

8. Find the area of the region completely enclosed by the graphs of the functions $f(x) = x$ and $g(x) = x^2 - 2x$.

   Answer: $\frac{9}{2}$

9. Find the area of the region completely enclosed by the graphs of the functions $f(x) = 4x$ and $g(x) = x^2 - 2x$.

   Answer: 36

10. Find the area of the region completely enclosed by the graph of the function $f(x) = x(x^2 - 9)$ and x-axis.

    Answer: 40.5.

11. Find the area of the region completely enclosed by the graph of the function $f(x) = x^3 - 25x$ and x-axis.

    Answer: 312.50.

Section 6.7

1. Find the amount of an annuity if \$225/month is paid into it for a period of 15 years earning interest at the rate of 8%/year compounded continuously.
   Answer: \$78,303.95

2. Find the amount of an annuity if \$350/month is paid into it for a period of 35 years earning interest at the rate of 12%/year compounded continuously.
   Answer: \$2,299,021.59

3. Estimate the present value of an annuity if payments are \$600 monthly for 25 years and the account earns interest at the rate of 9%/year compounded continuously.
   Answer: \$71,568.06

4. Estimate the present value of an annuity if payments are \$1100 monthly for 12 years and the account earns interest at the rate of 6%/year compounded continuously.
   Answer: \$112,914.50

5. Suppose that for a certain product, the demand equation is $p = 500 - 10x$ and the supply equation is $p = 0.5x^2 + 100$. The price is set at the equilibrium price.
   (a) Find the consumer surplus.
   Answer: \$2000
   (b) Find the producer surplus.
   Answer: \$2667

6. A particular profession's income distribution is given by $f(x) = \frac{7}{8}x^2 + \frac{1}{8}x$.
   Compute the coefficient of inequality for the Lorentz curve.
   Answer: $\frac{7}{24}$

Exam 6A

Name:
Instructor:
Section:

Write your work as neatly as possible.

1. Find the indefinite integral $\int \sqrt{7}\,dx$.

2. Find the indefinite integral $\int \left(x^{3/2} + 2\right)dx$.

3. Find the indefinite integral $\int \left(x^{-2} + x^2\right)dx$.

4. Find the function $f(x)$ if $f'(x) = x^2 - x + 1$ and $f(0) = 2$.

5. Find the indefinite integral $\int 12xe^{x^2}\,dx$.

6. Find the indefinite integral $\int \frac{x+2}{x^2+4x+3}\,dx$.

7. Find the indefinite integral $\int 5x\sqrt{3x^2+1}\,dx$.

8. Let $f(x) = x^2$ and compute the Riemann sum of f over the interval $[1,3]$ using four subintervals of equal length ($n = 4$). Choose the representative point in each subinterval to be the midpoint of the subinterval.

9. Find the area of the region under the graph of the function $f(x) = x^3$ on the interval $[0,2]$.

10. Evaluate the definite integral $\int_{-1}^{2} \left(2x^3 - 2\right)dx$.

11. Evaluate the definite integral $\int_1^e \frac{(\ln x)^2}{x} dx$.

12. Evaluate the definite integral $\int_{\sqrt{2}}^{\sqrt{7}} 3x\sqrt{x^2+2}dx$.

13. Find the average value of the function $f(x) = 2 - x^2$ over the interval $[1, 5]$.

14. Find the area of the region bounded by the graphs of the functions $f(x) = x^2 + 16$ and $g(x) = x$ and the vertical lines $x = 0$ and $x = 2$.

15. The demand function for a certain product is given by $p = -0.01x^2 - 0.3x + 6$, where p represents the unit price in dollars and x is the quantity demanded measured in units of a thousand. Determine the consumer surplus if the price is set at \$2.

16. Find the amount of an annuity if \$375/month is paid into it for a period of 10 years earning interest at the rate of 11%/year compounded continuously.

Exam 6B

Name:
Instructor:
Section:

Write your work as neatly as possible.

1. Find the indefinite integral $\int (25x^4 + 4x - 3)\,dx$.

2. Find the indefinite integral $\int \frac{x^3 - 2x^2}{2x}\,dx$.

3. Find the indefinite integral $\int \left(x^{1/4} + \frac{1}{x^{1/4}} \right) dx$.

4. Find the function $f(x)$ if $f'(x) = 8x - 3$ and $f(1) = 2$.

5. Find the indefinite integral $\int \frac{1}{x \ln x}\,dx$.

6. Find the indefinite integral $\int \frac{2x+1}{x^2+x-1}\,dx$.

7. Find the indefinite integral $\int \frac{6x^5 - 4}{\sqrt{x^6 - 4x}}\,dx$.

8. Let $f(x) = x^3$ and compute the Riemann sum of f over the interval $[1,3]$ using four subintervals of equal length ($n = 4$). Choose the representative point in each subinterval to be the midpoint of the subinterval.

9. Find the area of the region under the graph of the function $f(x) = 10 + x^3$ on the interval $[0, 4]$.

10. Evaluate the definite integral $\int_{-1}^{4}(6x)\,dx$.

11. Evaluate the definite integral $\int_{0}^{1} e^{4x+1}\,dx$.

12. Evaluate the definite integral $\int_{0}^{1}(2x+1)\sqrt{x^2+x}\,dx$.

13. Find the average value of the function $f(x)=4-x^2$ over the interval $[0,2]$.

14. Find the area of the region bounded by the graphs of the functions $f(x)=16-x^2$ and $g(x)=7$.

15. The demand function for a certain product is given by $p=-0.01x^2-0.2x+10$, where p represents the unit price in dollars and x is the quantity demanded measured in units of a thousand. Determine the consumer surplus if the price is set at $2.

16. Find the amount of an annuity if $800/month is paid into it for a period of 20 years earning interest at the rate of 7%/year compounded continuously.

Exam 6C

Name:
Instructor:
Section:

Write your work as neatly as possible.

1. Find the indefinite integral $\int \pi^2 dx$.

2. Find the indefinite integral $\int \left(x - \frac{3}{\sqrt{x}} \right) dx$.

3. Find the indefinite integral $\int \left(x^{-3} + x + 1 \right) dx$.

4. Find the function $f(x)$ if $f'(x) = 2x + 3$ and $f(0) = 2$

5. Find the indefinite integral $\int \frac{(\ln x + 2)^2}{x} dx$.

6. Find the indefinite integral $\int \frac{8x}{1 - x^2} dx$.

7. Find the indefinite integral $\int x^2 \sqrt{x^3 + 1} dx$.

8. Let $f(x) = x^3 + 1$ and compute the Riemann sum of f over the interval $[0,2]$ using four subintervals of equal length ($n = 4$). Choose the representative point in each subinterval to be the midpoint of the subinterval.

9. Find the area of the region under the graph of the function $f(x) = 4 - x^2$ on the interval $[0,2]$.

10. Evaluate the definite integral $\int_{-1}^{4} (3x - 2) dx$.

11. Evaluate the definite integral $\int_0^1 \frac{e^x}{1+e^x} dx$.

12. Evaluate the definite integral $\int_0^{\sqrt{2}} x\sqrt{x^2+2}dx$.

13. Find the average value of the function $f(x)=3x^2-1$ over the interval $[0,2]$.

14. Find the area of the region bounded by the graphs of the functions $f(x)=9-x^2$ and $g(x)=x$ and the vertical lines $x=0$ and $x=2$.

15. The demand function for a certain product is given by $p=-0.01x^2-0.2x+12$, where p represents the unit price in dollars and x is the quantity demanded measured in units of a thousand. Determine the consumer surplus if the price is set at $4.

16. Estimate the present value of an annuity if payments are $300 monthly for 35 years and the account earns interest at the rate of 9%/year compounded continuously.

Exam 6D

Name:
Instructor:
Section:

Write your work as neatly as possible.

1. Find the indefinite integral $\int(5x^4 - x + 7)dx$.

2. Find the indefinite integral $\int(\sqrt[4]{t} + t^{-2})dx$.

3. Find the indefinite integral $\int\left(\frac{4}{x^3} + \frac{x^3}{4}\right)dx$.

4. Find the function $f(x)$ if $f'(x) = 3x^2 + 2$ and $f(1) = -1$

5. Find the indefinite integral $\int\frac{e^x}{e^x - 3}dx$.

6. Find the indefinite integral $\int(3x^2 + 5x)^6(6x + 5)dx$.

7. Find the indefinite integral $\int\frac{x}{\sqrt{x^2 - 1}}dx$.

8. Let $f(x) = x^3$ and compute the Riemann sum of f over the interval $[0,2]$ using four subintervals of equal length ($n = 4$). Choose the representative point in each subinterval to be the midpoint of the subinterval.

9. Find the area of the region under the graph of the function $f(x) = 4x^2 - 2x^3$ on the interval $[0,2]$.

10. Evaluate the definite integral $\int_1^3(3x^2 - 2x)dx$.

11. Evaluate the definite integral $\int_0^{e-1} \frac{1}{x+1} dx$.

12. Evaluate the definite integral $\int_0^1 2x\sqrt{3x^2+1}dx$.

13. Find the average value of the function $f(x) = e^x + 1$ over the interval $[0,3]$.

14. Find the area of the region bounded by the graphs of the functions $f(x) = x^2 - 2$ and $g(x) = x$ and the vertical lines $x = 0$ and $x = 2$.

15. The demand function for a certain product is given by $p = -0.01x^2 - 0.3x + 8$, where p represents the unit price in dollars and x is the quantity demanded measured in units of a thousand. Determine the consumer surplus if the price is set at \$4.

16. Estimate the present value of an annuity if payments are \$2000 monthly for 6 years and the account earns interest at the rate of 10%/year compounded continuously.

Answers to Chapter 6 Exams

Exam 6A

1. $\sqrt{7}x + C$
2. $\frac{2}{5}x^{5/2} + 2x + C$
3. $-\frac{1}{x} + \frac{1}{3}x^3 + C$
4. $\frac{x^3}{3} - \frac{x^2}{2} + x + 2$
5. $6e^{x^2} + C$
6. $\frac{1}{2}\ln\left|x^2 + 4x + 3\right| + C$
7. $\frac{5}{9}\left(3x^2 + 1\right)^{3/2} + C$
8. 8.625
9. 4
10. 1.5
11. $\frac{1}{3}$
12. 19
13. $-\frac{25}{3}$
14. $\frac{98}{3}$
15. \$21,667
16. \$81988.61

Exam 6B

1. $5x^5 + 2x^2 - 3x + C$
2. $\frac{1}{6}x^3 - \frac{1}{2}x^2 + C$
3. $\frac{4}{5}x^{5/4} + \frac{4}{3}x^{3/4} + C$
4. $4x^2 - 3x + 1$
5. $\ln(\ln x) + C$
6. $\ln\left|x^2 + x - 1\right| + C$
7. $2\sqrt{x^6 - 4x} + C$
8. 19.75
9. 104
10. 45
11. $\frac{1}{4}\left(e^5 - e\right)$
12. $\frac{4\sqrt{2}}{3}$
13. $\frac{8}{3}$
14. 36
15. \$93,333
16. \$418,998.85

Exam 6C

1. $\pi^2 x + C$
2. $\frac{1}{2}x^2 - 6x^{1/2} + C$
3. $-\frac{1}{2x^2} + \frac{1}{2}x^2 + x + C$
4. $x^2 + 3x + 2$
5. $\frac{1}{3}(\ln x + 2)^3 + C$
6. $-4\ln\left|1 - x^2\right| + C$
7. $\frac{2}{9}\left(x^3 + 1\right)^{3/2} + C$
8. 5.875
9. $\frac{16}{3}$
10. 12.5
11. $\ln\left(\frac{1+e}{2}\right)$
12. $\frac{1}{3}\left(8 - 2^{3/2}\right)$
13. 3
14. $\frac{40}{3}$
15. \$93,333
16. \$38,285.91

Exam 6D

1. $x^5 - \frac{x^2}{2} + 7x + C$
2. $\frac{4}{5}t^{5/4} - \frac{1}{t} + C$
3. $-\frac{2}{x^2} + \frac{x^4}{16} + C$
4. $x^3 + 2x - 4$
5. $\ln\left(e^x - 3\right) + C$
6. $\frac{\left(3x^2 + 5x\right)^7}{7} + C$
7. $\sqrt{x^2 - 1} + C$
8. 3.875
9. $\frac{8}{3}$
10. 18
11. 1
12. $\frac{14}{9}$
13. $\frac{e^3 + 2}{3}$
14. 4.5
15. \$21,667
16. \$108,285.21

Chapter 7 ■ Additional Topics in Integration

Section 7.1

1. Find the indefinite integral $\int xe^{3x}dx$.

   Answer: $\frac{1}{3}xe^{3x}-\frac{1}{9}e^{3x}+C$

2. Find the indefinite integral $\int x\ln x dx$.

   Answer: $\frac{1}{2}x^2\ln x-\frac{1}{4}x^2+C$

3. Find the indefinite integral $\int 12xe^{4x}dx$.

   Answer: $3xe^{4x}-\frac{3}{4}e^{4x}+C$

4. Find the indefinite integral $\int\left(e^{-x}+2x\right)^2dx$.

   Answer: $-\frac{1}{2}e^{-2x}-4xe^{-x}-4e^{-x}+\frac{4}{3}x^3+C$

5. Find the indefinite integral $\int\ln x dx$.

   Answer: $x\ln x-x+C$

6. Find the indefinite integral $\int(t+2)e^t dt$.

   Answer: $e^t(t+1)+C$

7. Find the indefinite integral $\int t^2\ln t dt$.

   Answer: $\frac{1}{9}t^3(3\ln t-1)+C$

8. Find the indefinite integral $\int t(t-2)^{-3}dt$.

   Answer: $-\frac{1}{t-2}-\frac{1}{(t-2)^2}+C$

9. Find the indefinite integral $\int t^3e^t dt$.

   Answer: $(t^3-3t^2+6t-6)e^t+C$

10. Find the indefinite integral $\int x\sqrt{x-11}dx$.

Answer: $\frac{2}{5}(x-11)^{5/2}+\frac{22}{3}(x-11)^{3/2}+C$

11. Find the indefinite integral $\int x\ln 3x dx$.

Answer: $\frac{1}{2}x^2\ln 3x-\frac{1}{4}x^2+C$

12. Find the indefinite integral $\int \ln(8x)dx$.

Answer: $x\ln(8x)-x+C$

13. the indefinite integral $\int x^2\ln 4x dx$.

Answer: $\frac{1}{3}x^3\ln 4x-\frac{1}{9}x^3+C$

14. Find the indefinite integral $\int x^3e^{x^2}dx$.

Answer: $\frac{1}{2}e^{x^2}(x^2-1)+C$

15. Find the indefinite integral $\int \sqrt[3]{x}\ln x dx$.

Answer: $\frac{3}{4}x^{4/3}\ln x-\frac{9}{16}x^{4/3}+C$

16. Find the indefinite integral $\int (2x+3)e^x dx$.

Answer: $(2x+1)e^x+C$

17. Find the indefinite integral $\int \frac{\ln x}{x^{5/2}}dx$.

Answer: $\frac{-2\ln x}{3x^{3/2}}-\frac{4}{9x^{3/2}}+C$

18. Evaluate the definite integral $\int_0^1 te^{-t}dt$.

Answer: $1-\frac{2}{e}$

19. Evaluate the definite integral $\int_0^3 2te^{-t}\,dt$.

Answer: $2-\frac{8}{e^3}$

20. Evaluate the definite integral $\int_1^4 \sqrt{t}\ln t\,dt$.

Answer: $\frac{32}{3}\ln 2-\frac{28}{9}$

21. Evaluate the definite integral $\int_0^1 x^2e^{-x}\,dx$.

Answer: $2-\frac{5}{e}$

22. Evaluate the definite integral $\int_1^4 \ln\sqrt{x}\,dx$.

Answer: $4\ln 2-\frac{3}{2}$

Section 7.2

1. Use a table of integrals to find $\int \frac{3x}{2+5x}\,dx$.

   Answer: $\frac{3}{5}x - \frac{6}{25}\ln|2+5x| + C$

2. Use a table of integrals to find $\int \frac{4x^2}{2+5x}\,dx$.

   Answer: $\frac{2}{5}x^2 - \frac{8}{25}x + \frac{16}{125}\ln|2+5x| + C$

3. Use a table of integrals to find $\int x^2\sqrt{16+9x^2}\,dx$.

   Answer: $\frac{1}{36}(8+9x^2)\sqrt{16+9x^2} - \frac{32}{27}\ln\left|3x+\sqrt{16+9x^2}\right| + C$

4. Use a table of integrals to find $\int \frac{dx}{x\sqrt{1+9x}}$.

   Answer: $\ln\left|\frac{\sqrt{1+9x}-1}{\sqrt{1+9x}+1}\right| + C$

5. Use a table of integrals to find $\int \frac{xdx}{\sqrt{4+3x}}$.

   Answer: $\frac{2}{27}(3x-8)\sqrt{4+3x} + C$

6. Use a table of integrals to evaluate $\int_0^3 \frac{dx}{\sqrt{16+9x^2}}$.

   Answer: $\frac{1}{3}\ln\left(9+\sqrt{97}\right) - \frac{2}{3}\ln 2$

7. Use a table of integrals to find $\int \frac{dx}{\left(4-x^2\right)^{3/2}}dx$.

   Answer: $\frac{x}{4\sqrt{4-x^2}} + C$

8. Use a table of integrals to find $\int x^2\sqrt{x^2-9}dx$.

Answer: $\frac{x}{8}\left(2x^2-9\right)\sqrt{x^2-9}-\frac{81}{8}\ln\left|x+\sqrt{x^2-9}\right|+C$

9. Use a table of integrals to find $\int x^2\sqrt{15+x^2}\,dx$.

Answer: $\frac{x}{8}\left(15+2x^2\right)\sqrt{15+x^2}-\frac{225}{8}\ln\left|x+\sqrt{15+x^2}\right|+C$

10. Use a table of integrals to find $\int xe^{5x}dx$.

Answer: $\frac{1}{5}xe^{5x}-\frac{1}{25}e^{5x}+C$

11. Use a table of integrals to find $\int\frac{xdx}{\left(x^2-1\right)\ln\left(x^2-1\right)}$.

Answer: $\frac{1}{2}\ln\left|\ln\left(x^2-1\right)\right|+C$

12. Use a table of integrals to find $\int\frac{e^{2x}dx}{\sqrt{16+e^{4x}}}$.

Answer: $\frac{1}{2}\ln\left(e^{2x}+\sqrt{16+e^{4x}}\right)+C$

13. Use a table of integrals to find $\int\frac{\ln x}{x(1+4\ln x)}dx$.

Answer: $\frac{1}{16}\left[4\ln x-\ln|1+4\ln x|\right]+C$

14. Use a table of integrals to find $\int\frac{\ln x}{x(3+2\ln x)}dx$.

Answer: $\frac{1}{4}\left[3+2x-3\ln|3+2\ln x|\right]+C$

15. Use a table of integrals to find $\int\frac{2x}{\left(x^2+1\right)\ln\left(x^2+1\right)}dx$.

Answer: $\ln\left|\ln(x^2+1)\right|+C$

16. Use a table of integrals to find $\int x^4e^x dx$.

Answer: $e^x\left(x^4-4x^3+12x^2-24x+24\right)+C$

17. Use a table of integrals to find $\int x^4 \ln x dx$.

Answer: $\frac{1}{5}x^5 \ln x - \frac{1}{25}x^5 + C$

18. Use a table of integrals to find $\int (\ln x)^2 \, dx$.

Answer: $x\left[(\ln x)^2 - 2\ln x + 2\right] + C$

19. Find $\int \frac{dx}{x^{1/3} + x^{1/2}}$.

Answer: $2x^{1/2} - 3x^{1/3} + 6x^{1/6} - 6\ln(1 + x^{1/6}) + C$

20. Find $\int \frac{6u^3}{1+u} du$.

Answer: $2u^3 - 3u^2 + 6u - 6\ln|1+u| + C$

21. Find $\int \frac{dx}{1+e^x}$.

Answer: $-\ln(1+e^{-x}) + C$

22. Find $\int 5x^2 \sqrt{3x^2+1} dx$.

Answer: $-\frac{5\sqrt{3}\ln\left|\sqrt{3x^2+1} + \sqrt{3}x\right|}{72} - \frac{5x\sqrt{3x^2+1}(6x^2+1)}{24} + C$

Section 7.3

1. Use the Trapezoidal Rule to approximate $\int_0^1 te^{-t}\,dt$ with $n = 4$.

   Answer: 0.2590

2. Use the Trapezoidal Rule to approximate $\int_1^4 \sqrt{t}\ln t\,dt$ with $n = 6$.

   Answer: 4.2792

3. Use the Trapezoidal Rule to approximate $\int_0^1 x^2e^{-x}\,dx$ with $n = 8$.

   Answer: 0.1611

4. Use the Trapezoidal Rule to approximate $\int_1^4 \left(x^2+1\right)dx$ with $n = 6$.

   Answer: 22.375

5. Use Simpson's Rule to approximate $\int_1^4 \left(x^2+1\right)dx$ with $n = 6$.

   Answer: 24

6. Use the Trapezoidal Rule to approximate $\int_1^4 \ln\sqrt{x}\,dx$ with $n = 6$.

   Answer: 1.2649

7. Use the Trapezoidal Rule to approximate $\int_0^1 \sqrt{1+t^4}\,dt$ with $n = 4$.

   Answer: 1.0968

8. Use the Trapezoidal Rule to approximate $\int_1^2 \sqrt{2+t^2}\,dt$ with $n = 4$.

   Answer: 2.0724

9. Use the Trapezoidal Rule to approximate $\int_0^2 \frac{dx}{\sqrt{x^4+1}}$ with $n = 6$.

   Answer: 1.3550

10. Use the Trapezoidal Rule to approximate $\int_2^3 \frac{2dx}{x^2}$ with $n = 4$.

    Answer: 0.3352

11. Use the Trapezoidal Rule to approximate $\int_0^3 e^{-x^2}\,dx$ with $n = 8$.

    Answer: 0.8862

12. Use the Trapezoidal Rule to approximate $\int_1^4 x^{-3/2}e^x dx$ with $n = 4$.

Answer: 11.0558

13. Use Simpson's Rule to approximate $\int_0^1 te^{-t}dt$ with $n = 4$.

Answer: 0.2642

14. Use Simpson's Rule to approximate $\int_2^3 \frac{2dx}{x^2}$ with $n = 4$.

Answer: 0.3334

15. Use Simpson's Rule to approximate $\int_1^2 \sqrt{2+t^2}dt$ with $n = 4$.

Answer: 2.0712

16. Use Simpson's Rule to approximate $\int_1^4 \sqrt{t}\ln t dt$ with $n = 6$.

Answer: 4.2825

17. Use Simpson's Rule to approximate $\int_0^1 x^2e^{-x}dx$ with $n = 8$.

Answer: 0.1606

18. Use Simpson's Rule to approximate $\int_1^4 \ln\sqrt{x}dx$ with $n = 6$.

Answer: 1.2723

19. Use Simpson's Rule to approximate $\int_0^1 \sqrt{1+t^4}dt$ with $n = 4$.

Answer: 1.0894

20. Use Simpson's Rule to approximate $\int_0^2 \frac{dx}{\sqrt{x^4+1}}$ with $n = 6$.

Answer: 1.3566

21. Use the Simpson's Rule to approximate $\int_0^3 e^{-x^2}dx$ with $n = 8$.

Answer: 0.8862

22. Use the Simpson's Rule to approximate $\int_1^4 x^{-3/2}e^x dx$ with $n = 4$.

Answer: 10.8143

23. Find a bound on the error in approximating $\int_1^3 (2x^5 - 4)\,dx$ using the trapezoidal rule with $n = 8$.
Answer: 11.25

24. Find a bound on the error in approximating $\int_1^3 (2x^5 - 4)\,dx$ using Simpson's rule with $n = 8$.
Answer: 0.3125

25. Find a bound on the error in approximating $\int_0^2 \frac{e^{-2x}}{4}\,dx$ using the trapezoidal rule with $n = 6$.
Answer: 0.01852

26. Find a bound on the error in approximating $\int_0^2 \frac{e^{-2x}}{4}\,dx$ using Simpson's rule with $n = 6$.
Answer: 0.0005487

Section 7.4

1. Find the area of the region under the curve $y = \dfrac{3}{x^2}$ for $x \geq 4$.

   Answer: $\dfrac{3}{4}$

2. Find the area of the region under the curve $y = \dfrac{1}{(x-3)^2}$ for $x \geq 4$.

   Answer: 1

3. Find the area of the region under the curve $y = \dfrac{1}{x^{5/2}}$ for $x \geq 3$.

   Answer: $\dfrac{2\sqrt{3}}{27}$

4. Find the area of the region under the curve $y = \dfrac{1}{(x-1)^{3/2}}$ for $x \geq 2$.

   Answer: 2

5. Find the area of the region under the curve $y = e^{3x}$ for $x \leq 0$.

   Answer: $\dfrac{1}{3}$

6. Evaluate the improper integral $\int_2^\infty \dfrac{2}{x^5}dx$ if it is convergent.

   Answer: $\dfrac{1}{32}$

7. Evaluate the improper integral $\int_4^\infty \dfrac{3}{x^{5/2}}dx$ if it is convergent.

   Answer: $\dfrac{1}{4}$

8. Evaluate the improper integral $\int_1^\infty \dfrac{3}{\sqrt[3]{x}}dx$ if it is convergent.

   Answer: Not convergent

9. Evaluate the improper integral $\int_5^\infty \dfrac{6}{x}dx$ if it is convergent.

   Answer: Not convergent

10. Evaluate the improper integral $\int_{-\infty}^{1} \frac{2}{(x-3)^3} dx$ if it is convergent.

Answer: $-\frac{1}{4}$

11. Evaluate the improper integral $\int_{2}^{\infty} \frac{1}{(3x-1)^{3/2}} dx$ if it is convergent.

Answer: $\frac{2\sqrt{5}}{15}$

12. Evaluate the improper integral $\int_{1}^{\infty} e^{-x} dx$ if it is convergent.

Answer: $\frac{1}{e}$

13. Evaluate the improper integral $\int_{0}^{\infty} e^{-x/5} dx$ if it is convergent.

Answer: 5

14. Evaluate the improper integral $\int_{-\infty}^{1} e^{3x} dx$ if it is convergent.

Answer: $\frac{1}{3}e^3$

15. Evaluate the improper integral $\int_{2}^{\infty} \frac{e^{\sqrt{x}}}{\sqrt{x}} dx$ if it is convergent.

Answer: Not convergent

16. Evaluate the improper integral $\int_{0}^{\infty} xe^{-3x} dx$ if it is convergent.

Answer: $\frac{1}{9}$

17. Evaluate the improper integral $\int_{-\infty}^{\infty} 2x^5 dx$ if it is convergent.

Answer: Not convergent

18. Evaluate the improper integral $\int_{0}^{\infty} x^3 \left(1+x^4\right)^{-2} dx$ if it is convergent.

Answer: $1/4$

19. Evaluate the improper integral $\int_0^\infty x\left(x^2+9\right)^{-3/2} dx$ if it is convergent.

Answer: 1/3

20. Evaluate the improper integral $\int_{-\infty}^\infty x^3\left(1+x^4\right)^{-2} dx$ if it is convergent.

Answer: 0

21. Evaluate the improper integral $\int_{-\infty}^\infty x\left(x^2+3\right)^{-3/2} dx$ if it is convergent.

Answer: 0

22. Evaluate the improper integral $\int_0^\infty xe^{2-x^2} dx$ if it is convergent.

Answer: $\frac{1}{2}e^2$

23. Evaluate the improper integral $\int_0^\infty \left(x-\frac{1}{2}\right)e^{-x^2+x+1} dx$ if it is convergent.

Answer: $\frac{1}{2}e$

24. Evaluate the improper integral $\int_0^\infty \frac{e^{-x}}{1+e^{-x}} dx$ if it is convergent.

Answer: ln 2

25. Evaluate the improper integral $\int_{-\infty}^0 \frac{e^{-x}}{1+e^{-x}} dx$ if it is convergent.

Answer: Not convergent

26. Evaluate the improper integral $\int_0^\infty \frac{xe^{-x^2}}{1+e^{-x^2}} dx$ if it is convergent.

Answer: $\frac{1}{2}\ln 2$

Section 7.5

1. A scholarship fund is being set up in the name of a deceased math teacher. If the scholarship is to award \$1800/year and the fund earns interest at a rate of 7% compounded continuously, find the required amount for the endowment.
   Answer: \$25,714.29

2. A scholarship fund is being set up in the name of a deceased math teacher. If the scholarship is to award \$1000/year and the fund earns interest at a rate of 12% compounded continuously, find the required amount for the endowment.
   Answer: \$8333.33

3.
   (a) Determine the value of the constant k such that the function $f(x) = k(3 - x)$ is a probability density function on the interval $[0,3]$.
   Answer: $\frac{2}{9}$
   (b) If x is a continuous random variable with the probability density function given in part (a), compute the probability that x will assume a value between $x = 1.5$ and $x = 2.5$.
   Answer: $\frac{2}{9}$

4. Determine k so that $f(x) = k\left(x^3 + 1\right)$ is a probability density function on [0,2].
   Answer: 1/6

5. Determine k so that $f(x) = k(7 - 4x)$ is a probability density function on [0,2].
   Answer: 1/6

6. If a continuous random variable x is exponentially distributed with probability density function $f(x) = 0.025e^{-0.025x}$ $(0 \le x < \infty)$ find the expected value of x.
   Answer: 40

7. The amount of time (in minutes) it takes for a particular child to brush his teeth is a continuous random variable with probability density function
   $f(x) = \frac{32}{63t^3}$ $\left(\frac{1}{2} \le t \le 4\right)$.
   (a) Find the probability that the boy will take less than 2 minutes to brush.
   Answer: $\frac{20}{21}$
   (b) Find the probability that the boy will take between 1 and 2 minutes to brush.
   Answer: $\frac{4}{21}$

Exam 7A

Name:
Instructor:
Section:

Write your work as neatly as possible.

1. Find the indefinite integral $\int 2xe^{x+1}dx$.

2. Find the indefinite integral $\int t^3 \ln(t^2)dt$.

3. Find the indefinite integral $\int x(x-3)^{-3/2}\,dx$.

4. Evaluate the definite integral $\int_1^4 t^{3/2} \ln t\,dt$.

5. Use a table of integrals to find $\int x^2\sqrt{16+9x^2}\,dx$.

6. Use a table of integrals to find $\int \frac{1}{1+5e^{3x}}dx$.

7. Use a table of integrals to find $\int x^5 \ln x\,dx$.

8. Use the Trapezoidal Rule to approximate $\int_2^4 (x^2-2)dx$ with $n = 4$.

9. Use Simpson's Rule to approximate $\int_0^2 \frac{dx}{\sqrt{x^5+1}}dx$ with $n = 6$.

10. Find the area of the region under the curve $y = \frac{1}{(x-1)^{3/2}}$ for $x \geq 3$.

11. A scholarship fund being set up in the name of a deceased math teacher. If the scholarship is to award $2200/year and the fund earns interest at a rate of 7% compounded continuously, find the required amount for the endowment.

12. Evaluate the improper integral $\int_{1}^{\infty} \frac{1}{2x+1} dx$ if it is convergent.

13. Evaluate the improper integral $\int_{-\infty}^{\infty} x\left(x^2+3\right)^{-2} dx$ if it is convergent.

14. Evaluate the improper integral $\int_{-\infty}^{0} \frac{e^x}{1+e^{-x}} dx$ if it is convergent.

15. Find the value of k so that $f(x) = k\left(x^2+3\right)$ is a probability density function on the interval [0, 1].

Exam 7B

Name:
Instructor:
Section:

Write your work as neatly as possible.

1. Find the indefinite integral $\int x \ln x^2 \, dx$.

2. Find the indefinite integral $\int t(t+2)^{-6} \, dt$.

3. Find the indefinite integral $\int \sqrt[5]{x} \ln x \, dx$.

4. Evaluate the definite integral $\int_0^1 xe^{x/3} dx$.

5. Use a table of integrals to find $\int \frac{dx}{x\sqrt{1+16x}}$.

6. Use a table of integrals to find $\int \frac{dx}{x \ln x \sqrt{4+(\ln x)^2}}$.

7. Use a table of integrals to find $\int \frac{(\ln x)^2}{4} \, dx$.

8. Use the Trapezoidal Rule to approximate $\int_0^1 \frac{dx}{\sqrt{x^6+1}}$ with $n = 6$.

9. Find a bound on the error in approximating $\int_0^2 \sqrt{4x+1} dx$ using Simpson's rule with $n = 8$.

10. Use Simpson's Rule to approximate $\int_0^4 e^{-x^2} dx$ with $n = 8$.

11. Find the area of the region under the curve $y = e^{4x}$ for $x \le 0$.

12. Evaluate the improper integral $\int_{-\infty}^{1} \frac{2}{(x-4)^3} dx$ if it is convergent.

13. Evaluate the improper integral $\int_{0}^{\infty} e^{-x} dx$ if it is convergent.

14. Evaluate the improper integral $\int_{0}^{\infty} xe^{4-x^2} dx$ if it is convergent.

15. A scholarship fund being set up in the name of a famous biologist. If the scholarship is to award \$1000/year and the fund earns interest at a rate of 7.5% compounded continuously, find the required amount for the endowment.

16. Determine k so that $f(x) = k(9-2x)$ is a probability density function on [1,3].

Exam 7C

Name:
Instructor:
Section:

Write your work as neatly as possible.

1. Find the indefinite integral $\int \frac{xe^{4x}}{8} dx$.

2. Find the indefinite integral $\int t^4 e^t \, dt$.

3. Find the indefinite integral $\int x^2 \ln(6x) dx$.

4. Evaluate the definite integral $\int_4^9 \ln\sqrt{x} dx$.

5. Use a table of integrals to evaluate $\int_0^2 \frac{dx}{\sqrt{4+x^2}}$.

6. Use a table of integrals to find $\int \frac{dx}{2+8e^{6x}}$.

7. Use the Trapezoidal Rule to approximate $\int_2^3 te^{-t} dt$ with $n = 4$.

8. Use Simpson's Rule to approximate $\int_2^4 \sqrt{t}(\ln t)^2 \, dt$ with $n = 6$.

9. Find a bound on the error in approximating $\int_1^5 \frac{1}{6x} dx$ using the trapezoidal rule with $n = 8$.

10. Find a bound on the error in approximating $\int_0^2 e^{-x/2} dx$ using Simpson's rule with $n = 6$.

11. Find the area of the region under the curve $y = \dfrac{2}{x^2}$ for $x \geq 2$.

12. Find the area of the region bounded by the x-axis and the graph of the function $f(x) = \dfrac{e^x}{\left(1+e^x\right)^2}$.

13. Evaluate the improper integral $\int_2^{\infty} \dfrac{1}{(3x-2)^{3/2}}\,dx$ if it is convergent.

14. Evaluate the improper integral $\int_{-\infty}^{\infty} x^8\,dx$ if it is convergent.

15. Evaluate the improper integral $\int_0^{\infty} (x-2)e^{-x^2+4x+3}\,dx$ if it is convergent.

16. (a) Determine the value of the constant k such that the function $f(x) = k(5-x)$ is a probability density function on the interval $[0,5]$.

(b) If x is a continuous random variable with the probability density given in part (a), compute the probability that x will assume a value between $x = 1.5$ and $x = 3.5$.

17. If a continuous random variable x is exponentially distributed with probability density function $f(x) = 0.005e^{-0.005x}$ $(0 \leq x < \infty)$ find the expected value of x.

Exam 7D

Name:
Instructor:
Section:

Write your work as neatly as possible.

1. Find the indefinite integral $\int (e^x + 2x)^2\,dx$.

2. Find the indefinite integral $\int x \ln 2x\,dx$.

3. Find the indefinite integral $\int \frac{\ln x}{x^{5/3}}\,dx$.

4. Use a table of integrals to find $\int \frac{dx}{x\sqrt{49 - x^2}}$.

5. Use a table of integrals to find $\int \frac{\ln x}{x(1 + 2\ln x)}\,dx$.

6. Use the Trapezoidal Rule to approximate $\int_2^3 te^{-t}\,dt$ with $n = 4$.

7. Use Simpson's Rule to approximate $\int_4^9 \sqrt{t}\ln t\,dt$ with $n = 6$.

8. Find a bound on the error in approximating $\int_0^1 xe^x\,dx$ using the trapezoidal rule with $n = 6$.

9. Find a bound on the error in approximating $\int_1^4 \left(x^{7/2} + 5x^2\right)dx$ using Simpson's rule with $n = 4$.

10. Find the area of the region under the curve $y = \dfrac{1}{(x-4)^2}$ for $x \geq 6$.

11. Evaluate the improper integral $\int_2^{\infty} \dfrac{7}{x^6}\,dx$ if it is convergent.

12. Evaluate the improper integral $\int_1^{\infty} e^{-3x}\,dx$ if it is convergent.

13. Evaluate the improper integral $\int_0^{\infty} x^4 \left(1+x^5\right)^{-2} dx$ if it is convergent.

14. Evaluate the improper integral $\int_0^{\infty} \dfrac{e^{-2x}}{1+e^{-2x}}\,dx$ if it is convergent.

15. (a) Determine the value of the constant k such that the function $f(x) = k(k-x)$ is a probability density function on the interval $[0, k]$.

    (b) If x is a continuous random variable with the probability density given in part (a), compute the probability that x will assume a value between $x = \dfrac{1}{3}k$ and $x = \dfrac{2}{3}k$.

16. If a continuous random variable x is exponentially distributed with probability density function $f(x) = 0.1e^{-0.1x}$ $(0 \leq x < \infty)$ find the probability that x is between 10 and 50.

Answers to Chapter 7 Exams

Exam 7A

1. $2e^{x+1}(x-1)+C$
2. $\frac{1}{4}t^4\ln(t^2)-\frac{1}{8}t^4+C$
3. $2(x-3)^{1/2}-6(x-3)^{-1/2}+C$
4. $\frac{128}{5}\ln 2-\frac{124}{25}$
5. $\frac{1}{27}\left[\frac{3x}{8}(16+18x^2)\sqrt{16+9x^2}-32\ln\left|3x+\sqrt{16+9x^2}\right|\right]+C$
6. $x-\frac{1}{3}\ln\left(1+5e^{3x}\right)+C$
7. $\frac{1}{6}x^6\ln|x|-\frac{1}{36}x^6+C$
8. 14.75
9. 1.3138496
10. $\sqrt{2}$
11. \$31,428.57
12. Not convergent
13. 0
14. $1-\ln 2$
15. $k=\frac{3}{10}$

Exam 7B

1. $\frac{1}{2}x^2\ln(x^2)-\frac{1}{2}x^2+C$
2. $-\frac{1}{4(t+2)^4}+\frac{2}{5(t+2)^5}+C$
3. $\frac{5}{6}x^{6/5}\ln x-\frac{25}{36}x^{6/5}+C$
4. $9-6e^{1/3}$
5. $\ln\left|\frac{\sqrt{1+16x}-1}{\sqrt{1+16x}+1}\right|+C$
6. $-\frac{1}{2}\ln\left|\frac{\sqrt{4+(\ln x)^2}+2}{\ln x}\right|+C$
7. $\frac{x(\ln x)^2}{4}-\frac{x\ln x-x}{2}+C$
8. 0.9449085
9. 0.010417
10. 0.886196
11. $\frac{1}{4}$
12. $-\frac{1}{9}$
13. 1
14. $\frac{1}{2}e^4$
15. \$13,333.33
16. $k=\frac{1}{10}$

Exam 7C

1. $\left(\frac{x}{32}-\frac{1}{128}\right)e^{4x}+C$
2. $\left(t^4-4t^3+12t^2-24t+24\right)e^t+C$
3. $\frac{x^3}{3}\ln(6x)-\frac{x^3}{9}+C$
4. $9\ln 3-4\ln 2-\frac{5}{2}$
5. $\ln\left(\sqrt{2}+1\right)$
6. $\frac{1}{2}\left[x-\frac{1}{6}\ln\left(1+4e^{6x}\right)\right]+C$
7. 0.2070446
8. 4.2929681
9. 0.02778
10. 0.000008573
11. 1
12. 1
13. $\frac{1}{3}$
14. Not Convergent
15. $\frac{e^3}{2}$
16. (a) $\frac{2}{25}$ (b) $\frac{2}{5}$
17. 200

Exam 7D

1. $\frac{e^{2x}}{2}+4xe^x-4e^x+\frac{4}{3}x^3+C$
2. $\frac{1}{2}x^2\ln 2x-\frac{1}{4}x^2+C$
3. $-\frac{3}{2x^{2/3}}\ln x-\frac{9}{4x^{2/3}}+C$
4. $-\frac{1}{7}\ln\left|\frac{7+\sqrt{49-x^2}}{x}\right|+C$
5. $\frac{1}{2}\ln x-\frac{1}{4}\ln\left|1+2\ln x\right|+C$
6. 0.222208
7. 23.7120118
8. 0.01062
9. 0.03461
10. $\frac{1}{2}$
11. $\frac{7}{160}$
12. $\frac{1}{3e^3}$
13. $\frac{1}{5}$
14. $\frac{\ln 2}{2}$
15. (a) $\sqrt[3]{2}$ (b) $\frac{1}{3}$
16. 0.36114

Chapter 8 ■ Calculus of Several Variables

Section 8.1

1. Let $f(x, y) = xy^2 + 4x$. Compute $f(2,4)$.
   Answer: 40

2. Let $f(x, y) = 3x + y^2$. Compute $f(2,3)$, $f(3,2)$, and $f(1,1)$.
   Answer: 15, 13, 4

3. Let $f(x, y) = x^2y^3 + 3x$. Compute $f(-1,2)$.
   Answer: 5

4. Let $f(x, y) = x^2y^2 - 3x$. Compute $f(-1,3)$.
   Answer: 12

5. Let $f(x, y) = 2x + 5y - 7$. Compute $f(1,3)$ and $f(0,5)$.
   Answer: 10; 18

6. Let $h(p, r) = \dfrac{3p + 3r}{p^2 - r^2}$. Compute $h(3,2)$, $h(2,3)$, and $h(0,1)$.
   Answer: 3, -3, -3

7. Let $f(r, t) = \dfrac{3 + r}{t - r}$. Compute $f(3,2)$ and $f(7,5)$.
   Answer: -6; -5

8. Let $f(x, y) = 3x\sqrt{y} - y\sqrt{x}$. Compute $f(0,0)$, $f(1,4)$, and $f(4,1)$.
   Answer: 0, 2, 10

9. Let $h(x, y) = \dfrac{x}{y}e^{x/y}$. Compute $h(1,1)$, $h(2,1)$, and $h(1,2)$.
   Answer: e, $2e^2$, $\dfrac{1}{2}\sqrt{e}$

10. Let $g(u, v, w) = \dfrac{ue^v + ve^w + we^u}{uvw}$. Compute $g(1,2,3)$ and $g(3,2,1)$.
    Answer: $\dfrac{1}{6}(2e^3 + e^2 + 3e)$, $\dfrac{1}{6}(e^3 + 3e^2 + 2e)$

11. Find the domain of the function $f(x, y) = 2x - y$.
Answer: The set of all points (x, y) in the xy-plane

12. Find the domain of the function $f(x, y) = e^{7x-y}$.
Answer: The set of all points (x, y) in the xy-plane

13. Find the domain of the function $f(x, y, z) = x^2 + y^2 + \dfrac{1}{z^2}$.
Answer: The set of all points (x, y, z) in the xyz-space except those lying on the xy-plane

14. Find the domain of the function $f(x, y) = e^{-x^2/y}$.
Answer: The set of all points (x, y) in the xy-plane except those lying on the x-axis

15. Find the domain of the function $f(x, y) = x^3 - y^3$.
Answer: The set of all points (x, y) in the xy-plane

16. Find the domain of the function $f(x, y) = \dfrac{3}{x+y}$.
Answer: The set of all points (x, y) in the xy-plane except those lying on the line $y = -x$.

17. Find the domain of the function $f(x, y) = \sqrt{4 - x^2 - y^2}$.
Answer: The set of all points (x, y) in the xy-plane lying on and inside the circle $x^2 + y^2 = 4$.

18. Find the domain of the function $g(x, y) = \ln(3x + y - 4)$.
Answer: The set of all points (x, y) in the xy-plane that satisfy $y > -3x + 4$.

19. Find the domain of the function $f(x, y) = x^2 + 2y^2$.
Answer: The set of all points (x, y) in the xy-plane

20. Find the domain of the function $f(x, y) = \dfrac{4}{x-y}$.
Answer: The set of all points (x, y) in the xy-plane except those lying on the line $y = x$.

21. Find the domain of the function $f(x, y) = 3x^2y^2 - 4x^3$.
Answer: The set of all points (x, y) in the xy-plane

22. Sketch the level curves of the function $f(x, y) = x + y$ corresponding to the values $z = -2,\ 0,\ 2$.
Answer:

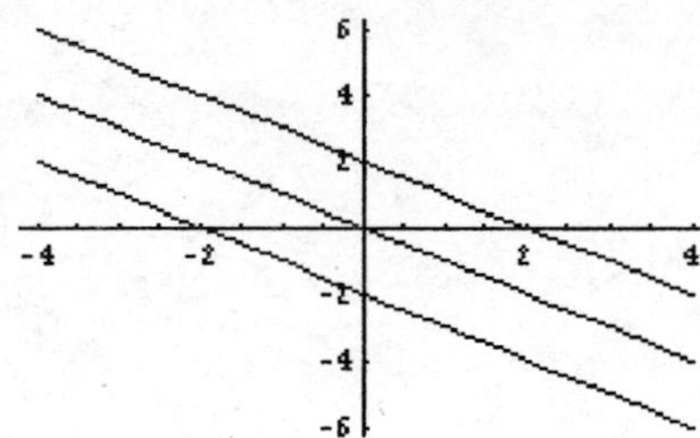

23. Sketch the level curves of the function $f(x, y) = e^{-x} - y$ corresponding to the values $z = -2,\ 0,\ 2$.
Answer:

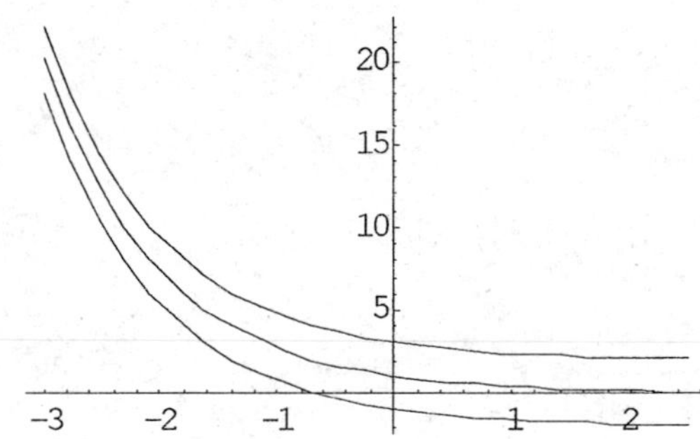

24. Sketch the level curves of the function $f(x, y) = x - y^2$ corresponding to the values $z = -2,\ 0,\ 2$.
Answer:

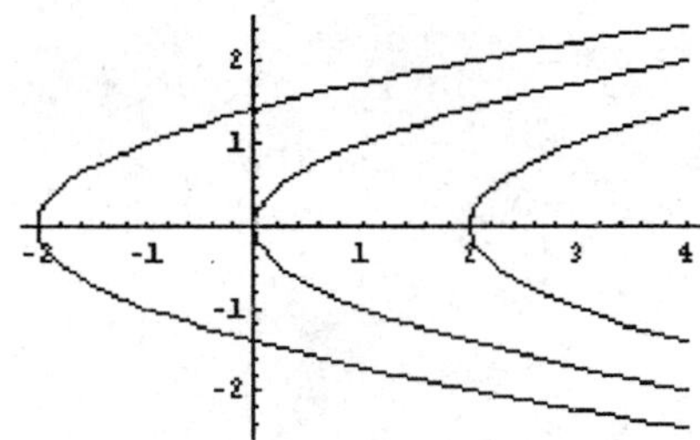

25. The IQ (intelligence quotient) of a person whose mental age is m years and whose chronological age is c years is defined as $f(m, c) = \dfrac{100m}{c}$. What is the IQ of a ten-year old child who has a mental age of 12.5 years?
Answer: 125

26. If a principal of P dollars is deposited in an account earning interest at the rate of r per year compounded continuously, then the accumulated amount at the end of t years is given by $A = f(P, r, t) = Pe^{rt}$ dollars. Find the accumulated amount at the end of three years if a sum of \$5000 is deposited in an account bearing interest at the rate of 8% per year.
Answer: \$6356.25

27. The monthly payment P that amortizes a loan of A dollars in t years at an interest rate of r per year is given by $P(A, r, t) = \dfrac{A\left(\frac{r}{12}\right)}{1-\left(1+\frac{r}{12}\right)^{-12t}}$.
Find the monthly payment for a loan of \$75,000 that will be amortized over 15 years at 5%, compounded monthly.
Answer: \$593.10

28. The volume of a cylinder with radius r and height h is given by the function $V(r,h) = \pi r^2 h$. Find the volume of a cylinder with a radius of 3 inches and a height of 2 inches.
Answer: 18π cubic inches

29. The volume of a cylinder with radius r and height h is given by the function $V(r,h) = \pi r^2 h$. Find the volume of a cylinder with a radius of 2 inches and a height of 3 inches.
Answer: 12π cubic inches

30. The volume of a cylinder with radius r and height h is given by the function $V(r,h) = \pi r^2 h$. Find the volume of a cylinder with a radius of 3 inches and a height of 4 inches.
Answer: 36π cubic inches

31. The volume of a cylinder with radius r and height h is given by the function $V(r,h) = \pi r^2 h$. Find the volume of a cylinder with a radius of 2 inches and a height of 1 inch.
Answer: 4π cubic inches

Section 8.2

1. Let $f(x,y)=3x^2y-2y$. Find $\frac{\partial f}{\partial y}$.

   Answer: $3x^2-2$

2. Find the first partial derivatives of $f(x,y)=3xy$.
   Answer: $f_x=3y;\ f_y=3x$

3. Find the first partial derivatives of $f(x,y)=10x-7y$.
   Answer: $f_x=10;\ f_y=-7$

4. Find the first partial derivatives of $g(m,n)=\frac{m}{n+2}$.

   Answer: $g_m=\frac{1}{n+2};\ g_n=\frac{-m}{(n+2)^2}$

5. Find the first partial derivatives of $f(x,y)=e^{2xy}$.
   Answer: $f_x=2ye^{2xy};\ f_y=2xe^{2xy}$

6. Let $f(x,y)=4xy^2+3x$. Find $\frac{\partial f}{\partial x}$.

   Answer: $4y^2+3$

7. Let $f(x,y)=8x^3y^2+2xy$. Find $\frac{\partial f}{\partial y}$.

   Answer: $16x^3y+2x$

8. Let $f(x,y)=\frac{3x}{y}-e^{xy}$. Find f_x.

   Answer: $\frac{3}{y}-ye^{xy}$

9. Let $f(x,y)=\frac{4y}{x}-\ln(xy)$. Find f_y.

   Answer: $\frac{4}{x}-\frac{1}{y}$

10. Let $f(x,y)=2y\ln(xy)$. Find f_y.
    Answer: $2+2\ln(xy)$

11. Let $f(x,y)=\dfrac{\ln y}{2xy^2}$. Find f_x.

Answer: $-\dfrac{\ln y}{2x^2y^2}$

12. Evaluate the first partial derivatives of $f(x,y)=2x^2y+4x$ at the point (1,2).
Answer: $f_x(1,2)=12;\ f_y(1,2)=2$

13. Evaluate the first partial derivatives of $f(x,y,z)=y+4xz^3$ at the point (1,0,3).
Answer: $f_x(1,0,3)=108;\ f_y(1,0,3)=1;\ f_z(1,0,3)=108$

14. Let $f(x,y,z)=4x^2yz^3+3xz$. Find f_{xz}.

Answer: $24xyz^2+3$

15. Let $f(x,y,z)=3xyz+2x^2yz^3$. Find f_{zx}.

Answer: $3y+12xyz^2$

16. Let $f(x,y,z)=3xyz+2x^2yz^3$. Find f_{zy}.

Answer: $3x+6x^2z^2$

17. Let $f(x,y,z)=4x^2yz^3+3xz$. Find f_{xy}.

Answer: $8xz^3$

18. Let $f(x,y)=e^{xy}$. Find $f_{yy}(2,0)$.
Answer: 4

19. Let $f(x,y)=xe^{xy}$. Find $f_{xx}(0,3)$.
Answer: 6

20. Let $f(x,y)=x^2e^{2y}$. Find $f_{yy}(2,0)$.
Answer: 16

21. Let $f(x,y)=e^{x^2y}$. Find $f_{xx}(2,2)$.
Answer: $68e^8$

22. Let $f(x,y)=2x^2+3y$.

(a) Find $\dfrac{\partial f}{\partial x}$.

Answer: $4x$

(b) Find $\frac{\partial f}{\partial y}$

Answer: 3

23. Let $g(a,b,c) = ab^2 + bc^3 - abc$.

(a) Find $\frac{\partial g}{\partial a}$.

Answer: $b^2 - bc$

(b) Find $\frac{\partial g}{\partial c}$

Answer: $3bc^2 - ab$

24. Let $f(x,y) = 3x^2y^3 + xy^2$. Find $f_x(2,1)$.

Answer: 13

25. Let $f(x,y) = e^{xy} - \ln(xy)$. Find $f_y(1,1)$.

Answer: $e - 1$

26. Let $f(x,y,z) = e^{xz} + xyz^2$. Find $\frac{\partial^2 f}{\partial z^2}$.

Answer: $x^2e^{xz} + 2xy$

27. Let $f(x,y) = 3x^2y^3$. Find $\frac{\partial^2 f}{\partial y^2}$.

Answer: $18x^2y$

28. Let $f(x,y) = 3x^6y^8$. Find $\frac{\partial^2 f}{\partial x \partial y}$.

Answer: $144x^5y^7$

29. Let $f(x,y) = 4x^2y^5$. Find $\frac{\partial^2 f}{\partial y^2}$.

Answer: $80x^2y^3$

30. Let $g(a,b) = a^2b^5$. Find g_{ab}.

Answer: $10ab^4$

Section 8.3

1. The productivity of a country is given by the function $f(x,y)=30x^{2/5}y^{3/5}$, where x units of labor and y units of capital are used. Find the marginal productivity of capital when $x=32$ and $y=243$.
Answer: 8

2. The productivity of a country is given by the function $f(x,y)=60x^{1/3}y^{2/3}$, where x units of labor and y units of capital are used. Find the marginal productivity of labor when $x=8$ and $y=64$.
Answer: 80

3. The productivity of a country is given by the function $f(x,y)=32x^{1/4}y^{3/4}$, where x units of labor and y units of capital are used. Find the marginal productivity of capital when $x=16$ and $y=81$.
Answer: 16

4. The productivity of a country is given by the function $f(x,y)=30x^{2/5}y^{3/5}$, where x units of labor and y units of capital are used.
(a) Find the marginal productivity of labor when $x=32$ and $y=243$.
Answer: $\frac{81}{2}$
(b) Find the marginal productivity of capital when the amount expended on labor is 243 units and the amount expended on capital is 32 units.
Answer: $\frac{81}{2}$
(c) If the amounts actually expended on labor and capital are currently 243 units and 32 units, respectively, then should the government encourage increased expenditure on labor or on capital to increase productivity the most?
Answer: Capital

5. Find any critical points of the function $f(x,y)=x^2-xy+y^2+1$.
Answer: (0, 0)

6. Find any critical points of the function $f(x,y)=3x-4yx$.
Answer: (0, 3/4)

7. Find any critical points of the function $f(x,y)=y^2+xy-x^2-5y+2$.
Answer: (1, 2)

8. Find any critical points of the function $f(x,y)=x^2+xy-y^2+5x+2$.
Answer: $(-2,-1)$

9. Find any critical points of the function $f(x,y) = 4x^2 + 3y^2 - 2$.
Answer: (0, 0)

10. Find any critical points of the function $f(x,y) = 3x^2 + xy - y^2 + 26x - 2$.
Answer: $(-4,-2)$

11. Find any critical points of the function $f(x,y) = 3x^2 + 6y^2 - 2$.
Answer: $(0,0)$

12. Find any critical points of the function $f(x,y) = e^{x^2+x+y^2}$.
Answer: $\left(-\frac{1}{2},0\right)$

13. Identify any relative extrema or saddle points of the function $f(x,y) = x^2 + y^2 - 10$.
Answer: Relative minimum at (0, 0)

14. Identify any relative extrema or saddle points of the function $f(x,y) = 2x^2 + 3xy - 5y^2 - 12x$.
Answer: Saddle point at $\left(\frac{120}{49},\frac{36}{49}\right)$

15. Identify any relative extrema or saddle points of the function $f(x,y) = -x^2 - 2y^2 + 8x + 12y - 3$.
Answer: Relative maximum at (4, 3)

16. Identify any relative extrema or saddle points of the function $f(x,y) = 4y^3 + x^2 - 12y^2 - 36y - 4$.
Answer: Saddle point at $(0,-1)$; relative minimum at (0, 3)

17. Identify any relative extrema or saddle points of the function $f(x,y) = 3x^2 + 3y^2 + 4xy - 8x + 4y + 2$.
Answer: Relative minimum at $\left(\frac{16}{5},-\frac{14}{5}\right)$

18. Identify any relative extrema or saddle points of the function $f(x,y) = \frac{1}{e^{x^2+y^2}}$.
Answer: Relative maximum at (0, 0)

19. Identify any relative extrema or saddle points of the function $f(x, y) = x^2 + xy + y^3$.

Answer: Saddle point at (0, 0), Relative minimum at $\left(-\frac{1}{12}, \frac{1}{6}\right)$

20. Let $f(x, y) = x^2 + y^2 + 2x - 4y + 2$.
(a) Find any critical points of f.
Answer: $(-1,2)$

(b) For any critical points found in part (a), use the Second Derivative Test to classify the critical points as relative extrema, if possible.
Answer: $(-1,2)$: relative minimum

21. Let $f(x, y) = x^3 + y^2 - 12x - 6y + 2$.
(a) Find any critical points of f.
Answer: $(2,3)$, $(-2,3)$

(b) For any critical points found in part (a), use the Second Derivative Test to classify the critical points as relative extrema, if possible.
Answer: $(2,3)$: relative minimum, $(-2,3)$: saddle point

22. Let $f(x, y) = 2y^3 - x^2 - 12y^2 + 4x - 30y + 15$.
(a) Find any critical points of f.
Answer: $(2, -1), (2, 5)$

(b) If there were any critical points found in part (a), use the Second Derivative Test to classify the critical points as relative extrema, if possible.
Answer: $(2, 5)$: saddle point, $(2, -1)$: relative maximum

23. A company has a revenue function of $R(x) = 2x^2 + 4y^2 + 6x + 12y + 300$ and a cost function of $C(x) = 3x^2 + 6y^2 + 100$, where R and C are measured in dollars and x and y represent the number of units of two types of products which are produced and sold.
(a) Find the profit function $P(x)$.
Answer: $P(x) = -x^2 - 2y^2 + 6x + 12y + 200$

(b) Find the values of x and y which result in a maximum profit.
Answer: $x = 3, y = 3$

(c) What is the maximum profit?
Answer: $227

24. A company produces two products. Its revenue R in hundreds of dollars from selling x hundred units of product A and y hundred units of product B is given by the function of $R(x, y) = -2x^2 - 20y^2 + 68x + 73y - 2xy$. Determine how many of each product should be sold to maximize the revenue. What is the maximum revenue?
Answer: 1650 of A, 100 of B, for a revenue of $59,750

25. A furniture company has found that the labor cost, L, for the production of its finished furniture pieces is the following function of construction time, c, and finishing time, f: $L(c, f) = c^2 + 6cf + 10f^2 - 16c - 52f + 110$. Determine how many hours of each type of time should be used to minimize the labor cost. What is the minimum labor cost?
Answer: 2 hours of construction time, 2 hours of finishing time, for a cost of $42.

Section 8.4

1. Find the equation of the least-squares line for the following data:

x	1	2	3	4
y	3	4	9	6

Answer: $y=\frac{7}{5}x+2$

2. Find the equation of the least-squares line for the following data:

x	1	3	4	6
y	2	2.7	3.5	4.2

Answer: $y=\frac{59}{130}x+\frac{393}{260}$

3. Find the equation of the least-squares line for the following data:

x	1	2	3	4
y	5	6	8	11

Answer: $y=2x+\frac{5}{2}$

4. Find the equation of the least-squares line for the following data:

x	1	3	4	5	7
y	0	3	5	8	13

Answer: $y=\frac{11}{5}x-3$

5. Find the equation of the least-squares line for the following data:

x	2	4	5	7	9
y	7	8	10	13	16

Answer: $y=\frac{197}{146}x+\frac{513}{146}$

Section 8.5

1. Use the Method of Lagrange Multipliers to maximize the function $f(x,y)=3x+2y-x^2-y^2$ subject to the constraint $x+3y-8=0$.

   Answer: $f\left(\frac{37}{20},\frac{41}{20}\right)=\frac{81}{40}$

2. Use the Method of Lagrange Multipliers to maximize the function $f(x,y)=3xy$ subject to the constraint $6x+9y-12=0$.

   Answer: $f\left(1,\frac{2}{3}\right)=2$

3. Use the Method of Lagrange Multipliers to maximize the function $f(x,y,z)=xy+2yz+4xz$ subject to the constraint $xyz=27$.

   Answer: $f(3,6,3/2)=54$

4. Find the points of the rectangular hyperbola $xy=1$ that are closest to the origin (0, 0).
   Answer: (1, 1) and (-1, -1).

5. The plan $x+y+z=12$ intersects the paraboloid $z=x^2+y^2$ in an ellipse. Find the highest and lowest points on this ellipse.
   Answer: (-3, -3, 18) and (2, 2, 8).

6. Find the maximum volume of a rectangular box inscribed in the ellipsoid $\frac{x^2}{a^2}+\frac{y^2}{b^2}+\frac{z^2}{c^2}=1$ with its faces parallel to the coordinate planes.

   Answer: $V=\frac{8}{3\sqrt{3}}abc$

7. Use the Method of Lagrange Multipliers to minimize the function $f(x,y)=x^3+2y^2$ subject to the constraint $x+y-1=0$.

   Answer: $f\left(\frac{2}{3},\frac{1}{3}\right)=\frac{14}{27}$

Section 8.6

1. Evaluate $\iint_R f(x,y)dA$ for $f(x,y)=5+3y-x$, where R is the rectangle defined by $1\le x\le 2$ and $0\le y\le 2$.
   Answer: 13

2. Evaluate $\iint_R f(x,y)dA$ for $f(x,y)=x^2y$, where R is the rectangle defined by $0\le x\le 3$ and $0\le y\le 2$.
   Answer: 18

3. Evaluate $\iint_R f(x,y)dA$ for $f(x,y)=e^x-y$, where R is the rectangle defined by $-1\le x\le 1$ and $0\le y\le 1$.
   Answer: $e-\frac{1}{e}-1$

4. Evaluate $\iint_R f(x,y)dA$ for $f(x,y)=e^{x+y}$, where R is the rectangle defined by $-1\le x\le 1$ and $0\le y\le 1$.
   Answer: $e^2-1-e+\frac{1}{e}$

5. Evaluate $\iint_R f(x,y)dA$ for $f(x,y)=2xy$, where R is bounded by $x=0, x=1, y=0$ and $y=x$.
   Answer: $\frac{1}{4}$

6. Evaluate $\iint_R f(x,y)dA$ for $f(x,y)=3x-4y$, where R is bounded by $x=0, x=2, y=0$ and $y=x^2$.
   Answer: $-\frac{4}{5}$

7. Evaluate $\int_0^2\int_{\sqrt{x}}^{x^2}(xy)dydx$.
   Answer: 4

8. Evaluate $\int_0^2 \int_2^5 10\, dydx$.

Answer: 60

9. Evaluate $\int_0^1 \int_x^{x+2} \left(x^2 - 2y\right) dydx$.

Answer: -5

10. Evaluate $\int_0^3 \int_x^{x+1} \left(e^x\right) dydx$.

Answer: $e^3 - 1$

11. Find the volume of the solid bounded above by $z = f(x,y) = 2y + 2$ and below by $y = 9 - x^2, 0 \le x \le 3$.

Answer: $165\frac{3}{5}$

12. Find the volume of the solid bounded above by $z = f(x,y) = 2e^x + y$ and below by $y = x,\ y = 1,$ and $0 \le x \le 1$.

Answer: $2e - \frac{11}{3}$

13. Find the volume of the solid bounded above by $z = f(x,y) = 2 - y - 2x$ and below by the triangle with vertices in the *xy*-plane at $(0,0), (1,0),$ and $(0,2)$.

Answer: $\frac{2}{3}$

14. Find the average value of $z = f(x,y) = 2y + 2$ over the region bounded by $y = 9 - x^2, 0 \le x \le 3$.

Answer: 9.2

15. Find the average value of $z = f(x,y) = 2 - y - 2x$ over the region bounded by the triangle with vertices in the *xy*-plane at $(0,0), (1,0),$ and $(0,2)$.

Answer: $\frac{2}{3}$

16. Find the average value of $z = f(x, y) = 2xy$, over the region bounded by $x = 0, x = 1, y = 0$ and $y = x$.

Answer: $\frac{1}{2}$

Exam 8A

Name:
Instructor:
Section:

Write your work as neatly as possible.

1. Let $f(x, y) = 4xy^2 + 2xy + y^2$. Compute $f(1, -2)$.

2. Find the domain of the function $f(x, y) = \dfrac{4x + xy}{3x - y + 2}$.

3. Sketch the level curves of the function $f(x, y) = 3x^2 - y$ corresponding to the values $z = -2, 0, 2$

4. The monthly payment P that amortizes a loan of A dollars in t years at an interest rate of r per year is given by $P(A, r, t) = \dfrac{A\left(\dfrac{r}{12}\right)}{1 - \left(1 + \dfrac{r}{12}\right)^{-12t}}$.

   Find the monthly payment for a loan of \$98,000 that will be amortized over 20 years at 6%.

5. Let $f(x, y) = \dfrac{x^3 y}{3} - e^{xy}$. Find $\dfrac{\partial f}{\partial y}$.

6. Let $f(x, y) = \dfrac{3x}{y^2}$. Find $f_x(2, 5)$.

7. Let $f(x, y, z) = 3xy^2 z + 2xy^2 z^3$. Find f_{zx}.

8. Let $f(x, y) = e^{2xy^2}$. Find $f_{yy}(1, 1)$.

9. The productivity of a country is given by the function $f(x, y) = 40x^{1/2} y^{1/2}$, where x units of labor and y units of capital are used. Find the marginal productivity of labor when $x = 16$ and $y = 9$.

10. Let $f(x, y) = 4x^3y^{3/2}$. Find $\dfrac{\partial^2 f}{\partial y^2}$.

11. Find any critical points of the function $f(x, y) = 3x^2 - 2xy + 5y$.

12. Find any critical points of the function $f(x, y) = 2x^2 + xy - 13x - 3y + 21$.

13. Identify any relative extrema or saddle points of the function $f(x, y) = 2x^2 + 3xy - 4y^2 - 8x$.

14. A company has a revenue function of $R(x) = x^2 + y^2 + 12x + 24y + 1000$ and a cost function of $C(x) = 3x^2 + 5y^2 + 200$, where R and C are measured in dollars and x and y represent the number of units of two types of products which are produced and sold.
(a) Find the profit function $P(x)$.

(b) Find the values of x and y which result in a maximum profit.

(c) What is the maximum profit?

15. Find the equation of the least-squares line for the following data:

x	1	3	6	7
y	2	5	8	10

16. Use the Method of Lagrange multipliers to find the minimum and the maximum of $f(x, y) = x^2 y$ subject to the constraint $2x + 3y - 12 = 0$.

17. Evaluate $\iint_R f(x, y)\,dA$ for $f(x, y) = x + 3y$, where R is the rectangle defined by $1 \le x \le 4$ and $0 \le y \le 2$.

18. Evaluate $\int_0^2 \int_x^{x^2} \left(x^3 + 2y\right)\, dydx$.

19. Find the volume of the solid bounded above by $z = f(x, y) = 2xy$ and below by $y = 4 - x^2$, $0 \le x \le 1$.

Exam 8B

Name:
Instructor:
Section:

Write your work as neatly as possible.

1. Let $f(x,y)=\sqrt{xy}+x^3-2y$. Compute $f(4,9)$.

2. Find the domain of the function $f(x,y)=\sqrt{3+x-y}$.

3. Sketch the level curves of the function $f(x,y)=3x+y$ corresponding to the values $z=-2,0,2$

4. The volume of a cylinder with radius r and height h is given by the function $V(r,h)=\pi r^2 h$. Find the volume of a cylinder with a radius of 4 inches and a height of 3 inches.

5. Let $f(x,y)=6x^3y-\dfrac{2x}{y}$. Find $\dfrac{\partial f}{\partial x}$.

6. Let $f(x,y)=\dfrac{4y^2}{x}-\ln(xy)$. Find f_y.

7. Let $f(x,y,z)=3x^2yz+2xy^2z^3$. Find f_{zy}.

8. Let $f(x,y)=xe^{x^2y^2}$. Find $f_{xx}(1,3)$.

9. The productivity of a country is given by the function $f(x,y)=60x^{1/3}y^{2/3}$, where x units of labor and y units of capital are used. Find the marginal productivity of labor when $x=8$ and $y=64$.

10. Find any critical points of the function $f(x,y)=4x^2-2xy+3y-12$.

11. Find any critical points of the function $f(x, y) = 3x^2 + 4y^2 - 4$.

12. Identify any relative extrema or saddle points of the function
$f(x, y) = -x^2 - 2y^2 + xy + 4x + 16y - 3$.

13. A company has a revenue function of $R(x) = 2x^2 + 3y^2 + 10x + 8y + 600$ and a cost function of $C(x) = 3x^2 + 5y^2 + 200$, where R and C are measured in dollars and x and y represent the number of units of two types of products which are produced and sold.

(a) Find the profit function $P(x)$.

(b) Find the values of x and y which result in a maximum profit.

(c) What is the maximum profit?

14. Find the equation of the least-squares line for the following data:

x	1	2	3	5
y	10	8	5	4

15. Use the Method of Lagrange Multipliers to minimize the function
$f(x, y) = 2x^2 - xy - y^2$ subject to the constraint $x + y = 4$.

16. Find the average value of $f(x, y) = x + 4y$, over R, where R is the rectangle defined by $1 \le x \le 4$ and $0 \le y \le 1$.

17. Evaluate $\int_0^1 \int_{x^2}^{x} (x^3 + 2y)\, dydx$.

18. Find the volume of the solid bounded above by $z = f(x, y) = 2y + 1$ and below by $y = x^2$, $y = 0$,, $1 \le x \le 2$.

Exam 8C

Name:
Instructor:
Section:

Write your work as neatly as possible.

1. Let $f(x,y)=\dfrac{x^3y-4y}{2x+y}$. Compute $f(-1,3)$.

2. Find the domain of the function $f(x,y)=xe^{xy}-2xy^3$.

3. Sketch the level curves of the function $f(x,y)=e^{-2x}+2y$ corresponding to the values $z=-2,0,2$

4. Let $f(x,y)=3x^2y^2+8y$. Find $\dfrac{\partial f}{\partial x}$.

5. Let $f(x,y)=xy^3+\ln(5xy)$. Find f_y.

6. Let $f(x,y,z)=3xe^x ye^y z$. Find f_{xy}.

7. Let $f(x,y)=x^2e^{3y}$. Find $f_{yy}(3,1)$.

8. The productivity of a country is given by the function $f(x,y)=32x^{1/4}y^{3/4}$, where x units of labor and y units of capital are used. Find the marginal productivity of labor when $x=16$ and $y=81$.

9. Find any critical points of the function $f(x,y)=x^3+y^2-2xy+7x-8y+4$.

10. Find any critical points of the function $f(x,y)=6x^2+4y^2+3$.

11. Identify any relative extrema or saddle points of the function $f(x, y) = -x^2 - y^2 + 4$.

12. Identify any relative extrema or saddle points of the function $f(x, y) = 2y^3 - x^2 + 12y^2 + 4x - 30y + 15$.

13. A company has a revenue function of $R(x) = x^2 + 2y^2 + 10x + 4y + 800$ and a cost function of $C(x) = 2x^2 + 3y^2 + 100$, where R and C are measured in dollars and x and y represent the number of units of two types of products which are produced and sold.

    (a) Find the profit function $P(x)$.

    (b) Find the values of x and y which result in a maximum profit.

    (c) What is the maximum profit?

14. Find the equation of the least-squares line for the following data:

x	1	3	4	6	9
y	2	3	6	8	9

15. Use the Method of Lagrange Multipliers to minimize the function $f(x, y, z) = xyz$ subject to the constraint $x + 2y + z = 60$.

16. Find the average value of $f(x, y) = 2x + 3y$, over R, where R is the rectangle defined by $-1 \le x \le 3$ and $0 \le y \le 1$.

17. Evaluate $\int_0^1 \int_{x^2}^x (x^3 3y^2)\, dydx$.

18. Find the volume of the solid bounded above by $z = f(x, y) = 5$ and below by $y = 25 - x^2$, $0 \le x \le 1$.

Exam 8D

Name:
Instructor:
Section:

Write your work as neatly as possible.

1. Let $f(x,y,z)=x^2z+2xy+z^3$. Compute $f(1,-1,2)$.

2. Find the domain of the function $g(x,y)=\ln(4x-y+1)$.

3. Sketch the level curves of the function $f(x,y)=x^2y$ corresponding to the values $z=-2,-1,1,2$

4. The IQ of a person whose mental age is m years and whose chronological age is c years is defined as $f(m,c)=\dfrac{100m}{c}$. What is the IQ of a twelve-year old child who has a mental age of 14.5 years?

5. Let $f(x,y)=8x^3y^4+2x^2y$. Find $\dfrac{\partial f}{\partial y}$.

6. Let $f(x,y)=\dfrac{\ln y}{2x^2y}$. Find f_x.

7. Let $f(x,y,z)=3x^2y^2z^2+3xz$. Find f_{xz}.

8. Let $f(x,y)=7x^3y^2+2xy-4x$. Find $f_{xx}(1,3)$.

9. Let $f(x,y)=4e^{y^3}x$. Find $\dfrac{\partial^2 f}{\partial y^2}$.

10. Find any critical points of the function $f(x,y)=3x^2+xy-y^2+26x-2$.

11. Find any critical points of the function $f(x,y)=3x^2+6y^2-2$.

12. Identify any relative extrema or saddle points of the function $f(x,y)=2x^2+2y^2+3xy-6x+2y+3$.

13. A company has a revenue function of $R(x)=3x^2+4y^2+6x+12y+300$ and a cost function of $C(x)=4x^2+5y^2+100$, where R and C are measured in dollars and x and y represent the number of units of two types of products which are produced and sold.
    (a) Find the profit function $P(x)$.

    (b) Find the values of x and y which result in a maximum profit.

    (c) What is the maximum profit?

14. Find the equation of the least-squares line for the following data:

x	1	3	5	8	11
y	0	1	3	4	7

15. Use the Method of Lagrange Multipliers to minimize the function $f(x,y,z)=xy+3yz+6xz$ subject to the constraint $xyz=144$.

16. Evaluate $\iint_R f(x,y)dA$ for $f(x,y)=x+9y$, where R is the rectangle defined by $2\le x\le 4$ and $0\le y\le 1$.

17. Evaluate $\int_0^1\int_{x^2}^{x}\left(x^3+2y^2\right)dydx$.

18. Find the volume of the solid bounded above by $z=f(x,y)=2y$ and below by $y=9-x^2$, $0\le x\le 3$.

Answers to Chapter 8 Exams

Exam 8A

1. 16
2. The set of all points (x, y) in the xy-plane such that $y \neq 3x+2$
3. 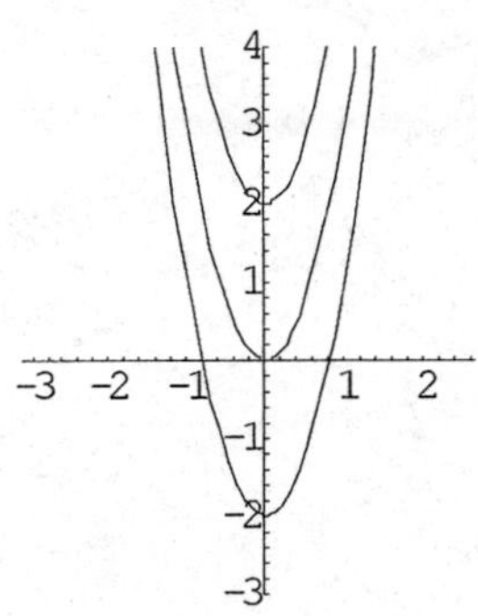
4. \$702.10
5. $\dfrac{x^3}{3} - xe^{xy}$
6. 3/25
7. $3y^2 + 6y^2z^2$
8. $20e^2$
9. 15
10. $\dfrac{3x^3}{\sqrt{y}}$
11. $\left(\dfrac{5}{2}, \dfrac{15}{2}\right)$
12. (3, 1)
13. Saddle point at $\left(\dfrac{64}{41}, \dfrac{24}{41}\right)$
14. (a) $P(x) = -2x^2 - 4y^2 + 12x + 24y + 800$
    (b) $x = 3, y = 3$
    (c) \$854
15. $y = \dfrac{115}{91}x + \dfrac{80}{91}$

Exam 8B

1. 52
2. The set of all points (x, y) in the xy-plane such that $y \leq x+3$
3. 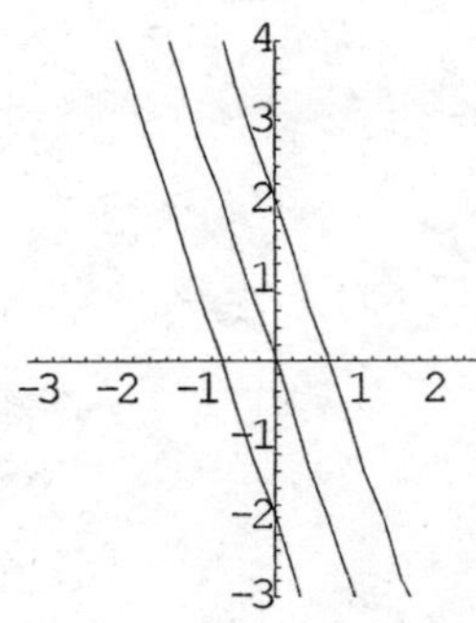
4. 48π cubic inches
5. $18x^2y - \dfrac{2}{y}$
6. $\dfrac{8y}{x} - \dfrac{1}{y}$
7. $3x^2 + 12xyz^2$
8. $378e^9$
9. 80
10. $\left(\dfrac{3}{2}, 6\right)$
11. (0, 0)
12. Relative maximum at $\left(\dfrac{32}{7}, \dfrac{36}{7}\right)$
13. (a) $P(x) = -x^2 - 2y^2 + 10x + 8y + 400$
    (b) $x = 5, y = 2$
    (c) \$433
14. $y = -\dfrac{53}{35}x + \dfrac{382}{35}$
15. $f(-1, 5) = -18$

16. Minimum at (0,4) and maximum at $\left(4, \frac{4}{3}\right)$
17. 33
18. 8
19. $\frac{37}{6}$

16. 4.5
17. $\frac{1}{6}$
18. $\frac{128}{15}$

Exam 8C

1. -15
2. The set of all points (x, y) in the xy-plane
3. 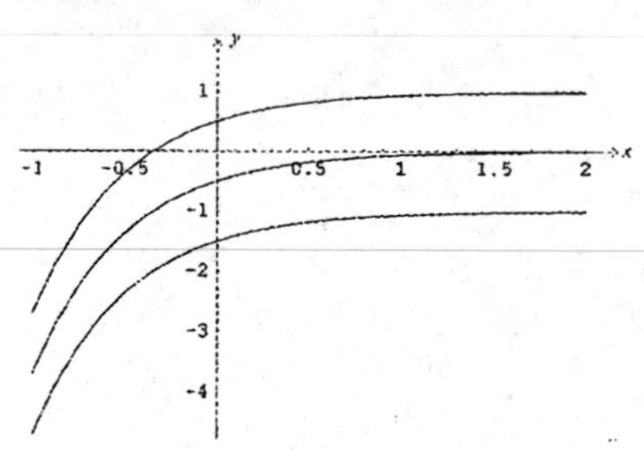
4. $6xy^2$
5. $3x^2y + 1/y$
6. $3(x+1)(y+1)ze^x e^y$
7. $81e^3$
8. 27
9. $(1, 5)$ and $\left(-\frac{1}{3}, \frac{11}{3}\right)$
10. $(0, 0)$
11. Relative maximum at $(0, 0)$
12. Saddle point at $(2, 1)$ relative maximum at $(2, -5)$

Exam 8D

1. 8
2. The set of all points (x, y) in the xy-plane such that $y < 4x + 1$
3. 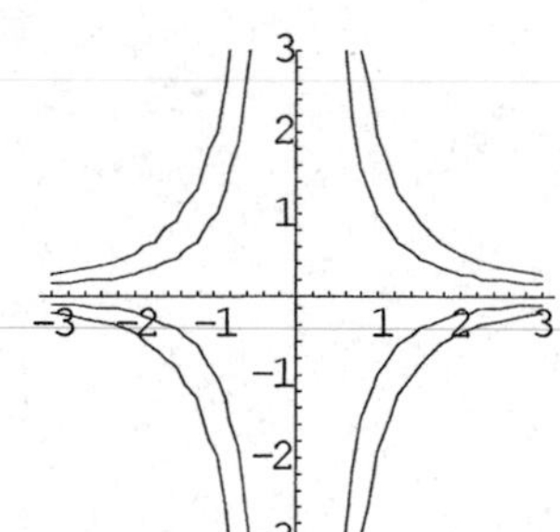
4. ≈ 121
5. $32x^3y^3 + 2x^2$
6. $-\frac{\ln y}{x^3 y}$
7. $12xy^2z + 3$
8. 378
9. $24xye^{y^3} + 36xy^4e^{y^3}$
10. $(-4, -2)$
11. $(0, 0)$
12. Relative minimum at $\left(\frac{30}{7}, -\frac{26}{7}\right)$
13. (a)

13. (a)
$P(x) = -x^2 - y^2 + 10x + 4y + 700$
(b) $x = 5, y = 2$
(c) \$729

14. $y = \frac{88}{93}x + \frac{116}{93}$

15. $f(20, 10, 20) = 4000$

16. 14

17. $\frac{3}{70}$

18. $\frac{370}{3}$

$P(x) = -x^2 - y^2 + 6x + 12y + 200$
(b) $x = 3, y = 6$
(c) \$245

14. $y = \frac{215}{316}x - \frac{64}{79}$

15. Max: $f(6,12,2) = 216$;

16. 15

17. $\frac{11}{105}$

18. $\frac{648}{5}$

Chapter 9 ■ Differential Equations

Section 9.1

1. Verify by substitution that the function $y = x^3 + 7$ is a solution of the differential equation $y' = 3x^2$.

2. Verify by substitution that the function $y = \dfrac{1}{1+x^2}$ is a solution of the differential equation $y' + 2xy^2 = 0$.

3. Verify by substitution that the function $y = -\dfrac{1}{x+c}$ is a solution of the differential equation $y' = y^2$.

4. Show that $y = C(1+x) - 1$ is the general solution of $y' = \dfrac{1+y}{1+x}$ and find a particular solution of the differential equation that satisfies $y(1) = 3$.

   Answer: $y = 2x + 1$

5. Show that $y = \dfrac{C}{1-x^2}$ is the general solution of $(1-x^2)y' - 2xy = 0$ and find a particular solution of the differential equation that satisfies $y(0) = 2$.

   Answer: $y = \dfrac{2}{1-x^2}$.

6. Show that $y = \dfrac{1}{x}(\ln x + C)$ is the general solution of $x^2y' + xy - 1 = 0$ and find a particular solution of the differential equation that satisfies $y(1) = 3$.

   Answer: $y = \dfrac{\ln x + 3}{x}$

7. Show that $y = C_1 + C_2e^{-x} + \dfrac{1}{2}x^2 - x$ is the general solution of $y'' + y' - x = 0$ and find a particular solution of the differential equation that satisfies $y(0) = 1,\ y'(0) = 0$.

Answer: $y = 2 - e^{-x} + \frac{1}{2}x^2 - x$

8. Show that $y = \frac{C_1}{x} + C_2x^2$ is the general solution of $x^2y'' - 2y = 0$ and find a particular solution of the differential equation that satisfies $y(1) = -1,\ y'(1) = 4$.

Answer: $y = -\frac{2}{x} + x^2$

9. The slope of the tangent line of the graph of g at the point (x, y) is the sum of x and y. Formulate the problem in terms of a differential equation.

Answer: $\frac{dy}{dx} = x + y$

10. The rate of change of a population P with respect to time, t, is proportional to the square root of P. Formulate the problem in terms of a differential equation.

Answer: $\frac{dP}{dt} = k\sqrt{P}$

11. The accelertion $\frac{dv}{dt}$ of a Lamborghini is proportional to the difference between 250 km/h and the velocity of the car. Formulate the problem in terms of a differential equation.

Answer: $\frac{dv}{dt} = 250 - v$

Section 9.2

1. Find the general solution of $y^2 \dfrac{dy}{dx} = x$.

   Answer: $2y^3 - 3x^2 = C$

2. Find the general solution of $y\dfrac{dy}{dx} = 2\sqrt{x}$.

   Answer: $3y^2 - 8x^{3/2} = C$

3. Find the general solution of $2x(y+1) - yy' = 0$.

   Answer: $\ln|y+1| + x^2 - y = C$.

4. Find the general solution of $\dfrac{dy}{dx} = 6x(y-1)^{\frac{2}{3}}$.

   Answer: $y(x) = 1 + (x^2 + C)^3$

5. Find the general solution of $y\dfrac{dy}{dx} - 4x\sqrt{y^2+1} = 0$.

   Answer: $\sqrt{y^2+1} - 2x^2 = C$

6. Find the general solution of $y\dfrac{dy}{dx} - x\sqrt{1-y^2} = 0$.

   Answer: $x^2 + 2\sqrt{1-y^2} = C$

7. Find the general solution of $\dfrac{dy}{dx} = \dfrac{x^2 y}{1+2y^2}$.

   Answer: $3\ln|y| + 3y^2 - x^3 = C$

8. Solve the initial value problem $y\dfrac{dy}{dx} = x,\ y(1) = 2$.

   Answer: $y^2 - x^2 = 3$

9. Solve the initial value problem $(y+1)\frac{dy}{dx} = x^2$, $y(1) = -1$.

Answer: $-3y^2 - 6y + 2x^3 = 5$.

10. Solve the initial value problem $\frac{dy}{dx} = 2xy$, $y(0) = 2$.

Answer: $y = 2e^{x^2}$

11. Solve the initial value problem $\frac{dy}{dx} = 2x(y-1)$, $y(0) = 2$.

Answer: $y = 1 + e^{x^2}$

12. Solve the initial value problem $\frac{dy}{dx} = (y-2)(3x+1)$, $y(0) = 5$.

Answer: $y = 2 + 3e^{\frac{3}{2}x^2 + x}$

13. Solve the initial value problem $\frac{dy}{dx} = \frac{4-2x}{3y^2-5}$, $y(1) = 3$.

Answer: $y^3 - 5y = -x^2 + 4x + 9$

14. Solve the initial value problem $\frac{dy}{dx} = y^2e^x$, $y(0) = \frac{1}{2}$.

Answer: $y = \frac{1}{3 - e^x}$

15. Solve the initial value problem $\frac{dy}{dx} = -2x + xy + y - 2$, $y(0) = 3$

Answer: $y = 2 + e^{\frac{x^2}{2}} + x$

16. Find the general solution of the differential equation $xy^2 + 3y^2 - x^2y' = 0$.

Answer: $y = \frac{x}{3 - Cx - x\ln x}$

17. Find the general solution of the differential equation $3y + x^4 y' = 2xy$.

Answer: $y(x) = Ce^{x^{-3} - x^{-2}}$

18. Find the general solution of the differential equation $3x^5 y^2 + x^3 y' = 2y^2$.

Answer: $y(x) = \dfrac{x^2}{x^5 + Cx^2 + 1}$

19. Find the general solution of the differential equation $9x^2 y^2 + x^{3/2} y' = y^2$.

Answer: $y(x) = \dfrac{\sqrt{x}}{6x^2 + C\sqrt{x} + 2}$

20. An apple pie is taken out the oven at a temperature of 200^0 F and placed on the counter in a room where the temperature is 70^0 F. If the temperature of the apple pie is 150^0 F after 5 minutes, find the temperature $y(t)$ as a function of time t.

Answer: $y(t) = 70 + 130e^{-0.097t}$.

21. A hemispherical tank has top radius 4 ft and, at time $t = 0$, is full of water. At that moment a circular hole of diameter 1 in. is opened in the bottom of the tank. How long will it take for all the water to drain from the tank? (Hint: Use Torricelli's Law $A(y)\dfrac{dy}{dt} = -a\sqrt{2gy}$, where a is the area of the hole, $A(y)$ denotes the horizontal cross-sectional area of the tank at height y above the hole, and $g = 32$ ft/s^2.)

Answer: It takes slightly less than 36 minutes (35 minutes and 50 seconds) for the tank to drain.

22. A specimen of charcoal found at Stonehenge contains 63% as much ^{14}C as a sample of present-day charcoal. What is the age of the sample?

Answer: It is about 3800 years.

Section 9.3

1. The resale value of a certain machine decreases at a rate proportional to the machine's purchase price. The machine was purchased at \$100,000 and 2 years later was worth \$64,000.

   a. Find an expression for the resale value of the machine at any time t.

   b. Find the value of the machine after 5 years

   Answer: a. $P(t) = 100{,}000(0.8)^t$
   b. $P(5) = 100{,}000(0.8)^5 = 32{,}768$.

2. A corporation invests P dollars/year (assume this is done on a frequent basis in small deposits over the year so that it is essentially continuous) into a fund earning interest at a rate of r % per year compounded continuously. The size of the fund A grows at a rate given by $\frac{dA}{dt} = rA + P$. Suppose $A = 0$ when $t = 0$. Determine the size of the fund after t years. What is the size of the fund after 5 years if $P =$ \$50,000 and $r =$ 12%.

   Answer: $A(t) = \frac{P}{r}\left(e^{rt} - 1\right)$. The size of the fund after 5 years if $P =$ \$50,000 and $r =$ 12% will be \$342,549.50.

3. A ball is dropped from the top of a building 400 feet high. How long does it take to reach the ground? With what speed does the ball strike the ground?

   Answer: It takes 5 minutes to reach the ground. The speed is 160 ft/second (velocity is – 160 ft/second) when the ball strikes the ground.

4. In May 1993 the world population had reached 5.5 billion and was increasing then at the rate of 250 thousand persons each day. Assuming constant birth and death rates, when should a world population of 11 billion be expected?

   Answer: At year 2035.

5. Use Newton's law of cooling $\frac{dT}{dt} = k(A - T)$ to solve the following problem.
   A 4-lb roast, initially at 50^0 F, is placed in a 375^0F oven at 5:00 P.M. After 75 mimutes it is found that the temperature of the roast is 125^0 F. When will the roast be 150^0 F?

   Answer: It is about 6:45 P.M.

6. A pitcher of buttermilk initially at $25^0\ C$ is to be cooled by setting it on the frount porch, where the temperature is $0^0\ C$. Suppose that the temperature of the bettermilk has dropped to $15^0\ C$ after 20 minutes. When will it be at $5^0\ C$?

Answer: It is about 63 minutes.

7. Upon the birth of their first child, a couple deposited \$5000 in an account that pays 8% interest compound continuously. How much will the account contain on the child's eighteenth birthday?

Answer: \$21,103.48.

8. The Brentano-Stevens law, which describes the rate of change of a response R to a stimulus S, is given by $\frac{dR}{dS} = k \cdot \frac{R}{S}$, where k is a positive constant. Solve this equation.

Answer $R = AS^k$.

9. The rate at which a drug is absorbed into the blood system is given by $\frac{db}{dt} = \alpha - \beta b$, where $b(t)$ is the concentration of the drug in the bloodstream at time t. Solve this equation, assuming $b(0) = 0$.

Answer: $b(t) = \frac{\alpha}{\beta}\left(1 - e^{-\beta t}\right)$

10. The slope of the graph of g at the point (x, y) is given by $g' = y^2(1 + x^3)$ and the graph of g passes through the point (0, 5). Find the function g.

Answer $g(x) = \frac{-20}{20x + 5x^4 - 4}$.

11. The American Court Reporting Institute finds that the average student taking the Advance Stenotype course will progress at a rate given by $\frac{dQ}{dt} = k(120 - Q)$. In a 20-week course, where $Q(t)$ measure the number of words of dictation the student can take per minute after t week in the course. [Assume $Q(0) = 60$.] If the average student can take 90 words of dictation per minute after 10 weeks in the course, how many words per minute can the average student take after completing the course?

Answer: $Q(t) = 120 - 60e^{-\frac{\ln 2}{10}t}$; $Q(20) = 120 - 60e^{-\frac{\ln 2}{10}\cdot 20} = 105$.

Section 9.4

1. Use Euler's method with $n = 10$ to obtain an approximation of the initial value problem $\frac{dy}{dx} = x + y, \quad y(0) = 1$ over the interval [0, 1].

Answer:

n	x_n	Estimate y_n	Actual $y(x_n)$	Error $y(x_n) - y_n$	Percent Error $\frac{y(x_n) - y_n}{y(x_n)}$
0	0	1.0000	1.0000	0.0000	0.00%
1	0.1	1.1000	1.1103	0.0103	0.93%
2	0.2	1.2200	1.2428	0.0228	1.84%
3	0.3	1.3620	1.3997	0.0337	2.69%
4	0.4	1.5282	1.5836	0.0554	3.50%
5	0.5	1.7210	1.7974	0.0764	4.25%
6	0.6	1.9431	2.0442	0.1011	4.95%
7	0.7	2.1974	2.3275	0.1301	5.59%
8	0.8	2.4872	2.6511	0.1639	6.18%
9	0.9	2.8159	3.0192	0.2033	6.73%
10	1	3.1875	3.4366	0.2491	7.25%

2. Use Euler's method with $n = 10$ to obtain an approximation of the initial value problem $\frac{dy}{dx} = x^2 + y^2, \quad y(0) = 1$ over the interval [0, 1].

Answer:

n	x_n	y_n
0	0	1
1	0.1	1.1000
2	0.2	1.2220
3	0.3	1.3753
4	0.4	1.5735
5	0.5	1.8371
6	0.6	2.1995
7	0.7	2.7193
8	0.8	3.5078
9	0.9	4.8023
10	1.0	7.1895

3. Use Euler's method with $n = 5$ to obtain an approximation of $y(5)$ of the initial value problem $\frac{dy}{dx} = x + \frac{1}{5}y, y(0) = -3$.

Answer:

n	x_n	y_n
0	0	-3.0000
1	1	-3.6000
2	2	-3.3200
3	3	-1.9840
4	4	0.69120
5	5	4.74304

4. Use Euler's method with $n = 5$ to obtain an approximation of $y(0.5)$ of the initial value problem $\frac{dy}{dx} = x + y^2, y(0) = 1$.

Answer:

n	x_n	y_n
0	0	1
1	0.1	1.1000
2	0.2	1.2310
3	0.3	1.4025
4	0.4	1.6292
5	0.5	1.9347

5. Use Euler's method with $n = 5$ to obtain an approximation of $y(0.5)$ of the initial value problem $y' = \sqrt{x} + \sqrt{y},\ y(0) = 1$.

Answer: 1.7535

6. Use Euler's method with $n = 5$ to obtain an approximation of $y(0.5)$ of the initial value problem $y' = xe^y,\ y(0) = 1$.

Answer: 1.3008

7. Use Euler's method with $n = 4$ to obtain an approximation of the initial value problem $y' = \sqrt{y},\ y(0) = 1$ over the interval [0, 2]

Answer:

x	0	0.5	1	1.5	2
y_n	1	1.5	2.1124	2.8391	3.6816

8. Use Euler's method with $n = 4$ to obtain an approximation of the initial value problem $y' = x\sqrt{1+y},\ y(0) = 1$ over the interval [0, 2].

Answer:

x	0	0.5	1	1.5	2
y_n	1	1	1.3536	2.1206	3.4455

9. Use Euler's method with $n = 10$ to obtain an approximation of the initial value problem $y' = x + y,\ y(0) = 2$ over the interval [0, 1].

Answer:

n	0	1	2	3	4	5	6	7	8	9	10
x_n	0	0.1	0.2	0.3	0.4	0.5	0.6	0.7	0.8	0.9	1
y_n	2	2.2	2.43	2.693	2.992	3.332	3.715	4.146	4.631	5.174	5.781

10. Use Euler's method with $n = 10$ to obtain an approximation of the initial value problem $y' = e^{xy},\ y(0) = 1$ over the interval [0, 1].

Answer:

n	0	1	2	3	4	5	6	7	8	9	10
x_n	0	0.1	0.2	0.3	0.4	0.5	0.6	0.7	0.8	0.9	1
y_n	1	1.1	1.212	1.339	1.488	1.670	1.900	2.213	2.684	3.54	5.958

11. Use Euler's method with $n = 10$ to obtain an approximation of the initial value problem $y' = 3x - 2y,\ y(0) = 3$ over the interval [0, 1].

Answer:

n	0	1	2	3	4	5	6	7	8	9	10
x_n	0	0.1	0.2	0.3	0.4	0.5	0.6	0.7	0.8	0.9	1
y_n	3	2.4	1.95	1.62	1.386	1.2288	1.133	1.0864	1.0791	1.1033	1.1527

Exam 9A

Name:
Instructor:
Section:

Write your work as neatly as possible.

1. Show that $y = Ce^{-x} - x + 1$ is the general solution of $y' + y + x = 0$ and find a particular solution of the differential equation that satisfies $y(0) = 5$.

2. Find the general solution of $\frac{dy}{dx} = xy^3$.

3. Find the general solution of $\frac{dy}{dx} = \frac{x\sqrt{1-y^2}}{y}$.

4. Solve the initial value problem $\frac{dy}{dx} = \frac{(2x^2+1)y}{x}$, $y(1) = 1$.

5. Use Euler's method with $n = 4$ to obtain an approximation of $y(1)$ of the initial value problem $y' = y - x,\ y(0) = 2$.

6. A cake is removed from an oven at 210^0 F and left to cool at room temperature, which is 70^0 F. After 30 minutes the temperature of the cake is 140^0 F. When will it be 100^0 F?

Exam 9B

Name:
Instructor:
Section:

Write your work as neatly as possible.

1. Show that $y = (x^2 + C)e^{-3x}$ is the general solution of $y' + 3y = 2xe^{-3x}$ and find a particular solution of the differential equation that satisfies $y(0) = -1$.

2. Find the general solution of $\dfrac{dy}{dx} = 4x^{1/3}y^{1/3}$.

3. Find the general solution of $\dfrac{dy}{dx} = \dfrac{y+1}{x+1}$.

4. Solve the initial value problem $2x^2 \dfrac{dy}{dx} = y^3$, $y(1) = 1$.

5. Use Euler's method with $n = 4$ to obtain an approximation of the initial value problem $y' = x + 2y$, $y(0) = 1$ over the interval [0, 0.4].

6. The resale value of a certain machine decreases at a rate proportional to the machine's price. The machine was purchased at $50,000 and 2 years later was worth $32,000.

   a. Find an expression for the resale value of the machine at any time t.

   b. Find the value of the machine after 5 years.

Exam 9C

Name:
Instructor:
Section:

Write your work as neatly as possible.

1. Show that $y = e^x + Ce^{-2x}$ is the general solution of $y' + 2y = 3e^x$ and find a particular solution of the differential equation that satisfies $y(0) = 3$.

2. Find the general solution of $2xy\dfrac{dy}{dx} = x + 1$.

3. Find the general solution of $\dfrac{dy}{dx} = \dfrac{1+x}{\sqrt{y}}$.

4. Solve the initial value problem $\dfrac{dy}{dx} = \dfrac{x(2+y^2)}{y(4+x^2)}$, $y(0) = 1$.

5. Solve the initial value problem $\dfrac{dy}{dx} + 1 = 2y$, $y(1) = 1$.

6. Use Euler's method with $n = 4$ to obtain an approximation of $y(1)$ of the initial value problem $y' = x + y^2$, $y(0) = 1$.

7. You invest P dollars/year into a fund earning interest at a rate of r % per year compounded continuously. The size of the fund A grows at a rate given by $\dfrac{dA}{dt} = rA + P$. Suppose $A = 0$ when $t = 0$. Determine the size of the fund after t years. What is the size of the fund after 5 years if P = \$10,000 and r = 6%.

Exam 9D

Name:
Instructor:
Section:

Write your work as neatly as possible.

1. Show that $y = 2x^6 + cx^4$ is the general solution of $y' - \frac{4}{x}y = 4x^5$ and find a particular solution of the differential equation that satisfies $y(1) = 3$.

2. Find the general solution of $\frac{dy}{dx} = \left(\frac{x+1}{y}\right)^2$.

3. Find the general solution of $\frac{dy}{dx} + 2xy = 0$..

4. Solve the initial value problem $y\frac{dy}{dx} = x(y^2 + 1)$, $y(0) = 2$.

5. Solve the initial value problem $\frac{dy}{dx} = 4xy(y^2 + 1)^{1/2}$, $y(0) = 1$.

6. Use Euler's method with $n = 4$ to obtain an approximation of the initial value problem $y' = x^2y^2$, $y(0) = 1$ over the interval $[0, 0.4]$.

7. The resale value of an antique clock increases at a rate proportional to the clock's price. The antic clock was purchased at $120 and 2 years later was worth $200.
   (a) Find an expression for the resale value of the antic clock at any time t.

   (b) Find the value of the antic clock after 5 years.

Answers to Chapter 9 Exams

Exam 9A

1. $y = 4e^{-x} - x + 1$
2. $y = \pm(C - x^2)^{-1/2}$
3. $2\sqrt{1-y^2} + x^2 + C = 0$
4. $\ln y = x^2 + \ln x - 1$
5. 4.4414
6. After about 66 minutes and 40 seconds.

Exam 9B

1. $y = (x^2 - 1)e^{-3x}$
2. $y = (2x^{4/3} + C)^{3/2}$
3. $y = C(x+1) - 1$
4. $y = \sqrt{x}$
5.

x	0	0.1	0.2	0.3	0.4
$\tilde{y}_n$	1	1.2	1.45	1.76	2.142

6. a. $50{,}000e^{-0.223144t}$

   b. 16,384

Exam 9C

1. $y = e^x + 2e^{-2x}$
2. $y^2 = x + \ln|x| + C$
3. $y = \left(\frac{3}{4}x^2 + \frac{3}{2}x + C\right)^{2/3}$
4. $4y^2 = 4 + 3x^2$
5. $y = \frac{1}{2} + \frac{1}{2}e^{2(x-1)}$

6. 4.3706

7. $A = \dfrac{P(e^{rt} - 1)}{r}$; 58309.8.

Exam 9D

1. $y = 2x^6 + x^4$

2. $y = \sqrt[3]{(x+1)^3 + C}$

3. $y = Ce^{-x^2}$

4. $y^2 = 5e^{x^2} - 1$

5. $\sqrt{y^2 + 1} = 2x^2 + \sqrt{2}$

6.

x	0	0.1	0.2	0.3	0.4
$\tilde{y}_n$	1	0	1.001	1.005	1.014

7. a. $P(t) = 120e^{0.255413\, t}$
   b. 430.33.

Chapter 10 ■ Probability and Calculus

Section 10.1

1. Show that $f(x) = \frac{1}{6}(x+2)$ is a probability density function on the interval [0, 2].

2. Show that $f(x) = 2(3x^2 - 2x^3)$ is a probability density function on the interval [0, 1].

3. Show that $f(x) = \dfrac{8}{3x^3}$ is a probability density function on the interval [1, 2].

4. Show that $f(x) = \dfrac{1}{2x^{3/2}}$ is a probability density function on the interval $[1, \infty)$.

5. Show that the function $f(x, y) = \dfrac{1}{6}$; $D = \{0 \le x \le 3; 1 \le y \le 3\}$ is a joint probability density function on the given region *D*.

6. Show that the function $f(x, y) = \dfrac{1}{3}xy$; $D = \{0 \le x \le 2; 1 \le y \le 2\}$ is a joint probability density function on the given region *D*.

7. Find the value of the constant *k* so that $f(x) = k\left(\dfrac{1}{3}x + \dfrac{1}{4}x^2\right)$ is a probability density function on the interval [0, 2].

   Answer: $\dfrac{3}{4}$

8. Find the value of the constant *k* so that $f(x) = k(2x^2 - x^3)$ is a probability density function on the interval [0, 1].

   Answer: $\dfrac{12}{5}$

9. Find the value of the constant *k* so that $f(x) = kx^{3/2}$ is a probability density function on the interval [0, 4].

   Answer: $\dfrac{5}{64}$

10. Find the value of the constant k so that $f(x) = \dfrac{kx}{x^2+1}$ is a probability density function on the interval [0, 1].

Answer: $\dfrac{2}{\ln 2}$

11. Find the value of the constant k so that $f(x) = \dfrac{k}{x^{3/2}}$ is a probability density function on the interval $[1, \infty)$.

Answer: $\dfrac{1}{2}$

12. Find the value of the constant k so that $f(x) = \dfrac{ke^{-\sqrt{x}}}{\sqrt{x}}$ is a probability density function on the interval $[1, \infty)$.

Answer: $\dfrac{e}{2}$

13. Find the value of the constant k so that the given function $f(x, y) = k\sqrt{x}(2-y)$ is a joint probability density function on $D = \{0 \le x \le 4; 0 \le y \le 2$.

Answer: $\dfrac{3}{32}$

14. Find the value of the constant k so that the given function $f(x, y) = kxye^{-(x^2+y^2)}$ is a joint probability density function on $D = \{0 \le x < \infty; 0 \le y \le \infty\}$

Answer: $k = 4$

15. Let $f(x) = \dfrac{3}{4}(2x - x^2)$ be a probability density function defined on the interval [0, 2]. Find $P(0 \le x \le 1)$.

Answer: $\dfrac{1}{2}$

16. Let $f(x)=\frac{12}{5}(2x^2-x^3)$ be a probability density function defined on the interval $[0, 1]$. Find $P(0 \le x \le \frac{1}{2})$.

Answer: $\frac{1}{80}$

17. Let $f(x)=\frac{5}{64}x^{3/2}$ be a probability density function defined on the interval $[0, 4]$. Find $P(1 \le x \le 2)$.

Answer: $\frac{1}{32}(4\sqrt{2}-1)$

18. Let $f(x)=\frac{1}{2x^{3/2}}$ be a probability density function defined on the interval $[1,\infty)$. Find $P(x \ge 4)$.

Answer: $\frac{1}{2}$

19. Let $f(x)=2e^{-2x}$ be a probability density function defined on the interval $[0,\infty)$. Find $P(1 \le x \le 4)$.

Answer: 0.135

20. Let $f(x)=2e^{-2x}$ be a probability density function defined on the interval $[0,\infty)$. Find $P(x \ge \frac{1}{2})$.

Answer: 0.368

21. Given $f(x,y)=\frac{1}{12}(x+y)$ is a joint probability density function on the region $D=\{(x,\ y)\,|\,0 \le x \le 2;\ 1 \le y \le 3\}$. Find $P(0 \le x \le 1;\ 1 \le y \le 2)$.

Answer: $\frac{1}{6}$

22. A branch of Fleet Bank in Boston has six tellers available to serve customers. The number of tellers busy with customers is a random variable X. Past records indicate that the probability distribution of X is as shown in the following table.

Number of tellers are busy (x)	0	1	2	3	4	5	6
$P(X = x)$	0.029	0.049	0.078	0.155	0.211	0.261	0.217

a. Find the probability that exactly four tellers are busy.

Answer: 21%

b. Find the probability that at least two tellers are busy.

Answer: 92.2%

c. Find the probability that fewer than five tellers are busy.

Answer: 52.2 %

d. Find the probability that at least two but fewer than five tellers are busy.

Answer: 44.4%

Section 10.2

Use the following data to answer problems 1-3.

The distribution of the number of chocolate chips in a cookie is shown in the following table

Number of chocolate chips x	0	1	2	3	4	5	6	7	8
$P(X = x)$	0.01	0.02	0.04	0.15	0.2	0.28	0.21	0.08	0.01

1. Find the probability distribution for the random variable X.

Answer:

Number of chocolate chips x	0	1	2	3	4	5	6	7	8
$P(X \leq x)$	0.01	0.03	0.07	0.22	0.42	0.70	0.91	0.99	1.00

2. Graph the histogram associated with these data.

Answer:

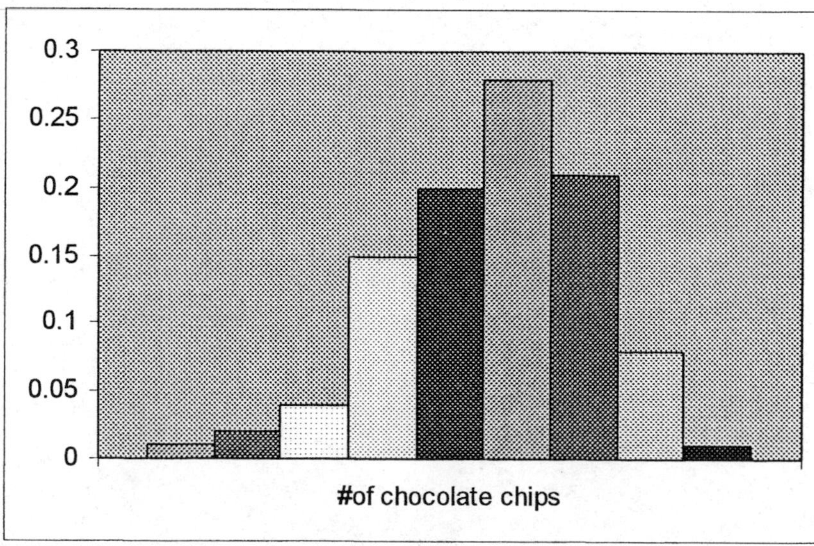

3. Find the mean, variance, and the standard deviation for these data.

Answer: The mean = 4.65; variance = 15.48; and the standard deviation = 3.93.

4. A branch of Fleet Bank in Boston has six tellers available to serve customers. The number of tellers busy with customers is a random variable X. Past records indicate that the probability distribution of X is as shown in the following table.

Number of tellers are busy (x)	0	1	2	3	4	5	6
$P(X = x)$	0.029	0.049	0.078	0.155	0.211	0.261	0.217

Find the mean, variance, and the standard deviation for these data.

Answer: The mean = 4.12, variance = 11.76, and the standard deviation = 3.43.

5. Find the mean, variance, and standard deviation of the random variable x associated with the probability density function $f(x) = \frac{1}{6}(2x+1)$ defined on the interval [0, 2].

Answer: $\frac{11}{9}, \frac{23}{81}, 0.5329$

6. Find the mean, variance, and standard deviation of the random variable x associated with the probability density function $f(x) = \frac{1}{20}(x+3)$ defined on the interval [0, 4].

Answer: $\frac{34}{15}, \frac{284}{225}, 1.1235$

7. Find the mean, variance, and standard deviation of the random variable x associated with the probability density function $f(x) = \frac{8}{3x^3}$ defined on the interval [1, 2].

Answer: $\frac{4}{3}, \frac{8}{9}(3\ln 2 - 2), 0.2657$

8. Find the mean, variance, and standard deviation of the random variable x associated with the probability density function $f(x) = \frac{24}{x^4}$ defined on the interval $[2, \infty)$.

Answer: 3, 3, 1.732

9. Find the mean, variance, and standard deviation of the random variable x associated with the probability density function $f(x) = 2e^{-2x}$ defined on the interval $[0, \infty)$.

   Answer: $\frac{1}{2}, \frac{1}{4}, \frac{1}{2}$

10. The tread life (in thousands of miles) of a certain brand of snow tires is a random variable x with probability density function $f(x) = \frac{1}{15}e^{-x/15}$ on the interval $[0, \infty)$. What is the expected tread life of this brand of tire?

    Answer: 15,000 miles

11. On a typical Monday morning, the time between successive arrivals of planes at JFK airport is an exponentially distributed random variable x with expected value of 12 (minutes).

    a. Find the probability density function associated with x.

       Answer: $f(x) = \frac{1}{12}e^{-\frac{1}{12}x}$

    b. What is the probability that between 6 and 8 minutes will elapse between successive arrivals of planes?

       Answer: 0.09 = 9%

    c. What is the probability that the time between successive arrivals will be more than 15 minutes?

       Answer: 0.20 = 20%

    d. What is the probability that the time between successive arrivals will be less than 10 minutes?

       Answer: 0.57 = 57%

Section 10.3

In the following two problems, (a) sketch the area under the standard normal curve corresponding to the given probability and (b) find the value of the probability of the standard normal variable Z corresponding to this area.

1. $P(-1.65 < z < 1.54)$. Answer: 0.8887

2. $P(-1.5 < z)$. Answer: 0.9332

3. Let Z be the standard normal variable. Find $P(Z < 0.14)$.
   Answer: 0.5557

4. Let Z be the standard normal variable. Find $P(Z > -1.35)$.
   Answer: 0.9115

5. Let Z be the standard normal variable. Find $P(-1.24 < Z < 1.34)$.
   Answer: 0.8024

6. Let Z be the standard normal variable. Find the values of z if z satisfies $P(Z < z) = 0.8869$.
   Answer: 1.21

7. Let Z be the standard normal variable. Find the values of z if z satisfies $P(< -z < Z < z) = 0.7108$.
   Answer: 1.06

8. Let Z be the standard normal variable. Find the values of z if z satisfies $P(Z < z) = 0.9678$.
   Answer: 1.85

9. Let X be a normal random variable with $\mu = 40$ and $\sigma = 5$. Find $P(\text{X} < 50)$.
   Answer: 0.9772

10. Let X be a normal random variable with $\mu = 300$ and $\sigma = 20$. Find $P(280 < \text{X} < 310)$.
    Answer: 0.5328

11. The weights of muffins made by a bakery are normally distributed with a mean of 2 oz and a standard deviation of 0.25 oz. What is the probability that a muffin selected at random will weigh more than 2.5 oz.
    Answer: $0.0228 = 2.28\%$.

12. If the Stanford-Binet IQ test is a normal curve with a mean of 100 and a standard

deviation of 20, what percent of the population has an IQ between 90 and 110?
Answer: 38.3 %.

13. According to the data released by a city's Chamber of Commerce, the weekly wages of factory workers are normally distributed with a mean of $500 and a standard deviation of $40. Find the probability that a worker selected at random from the city has a weekly wage of the following:

a. Less than $400. Answer: 0.0062 = 0.62 %

b. More than $400. Answer: 0.9938 = 99.38%

c. Between $400 and $600. Answer: 0.9876 = 98.76 %

14. The amount of time t (in minutes) it takes to serve a customer at the drive-in window of a fast food restaurant is an exponentially distributed random variable x with an expected value of 2 (minutes). Find the probability that a customer is served in less than 1 minute?
Answer: 0.18 = 18 %

15. Consider IQ's: IQ's are normally distributed with a mean of 100 and a standard deviation of 10. If a person is selected at random, what is the probability that his/her IQ is between 100 and 115?
Answer: There is a 43.42% chance that the person selected has an IQ between 100 and 115.

16. Suppose the weights at birth of newborn babies are normally distributed with mean 7.3 pounds and standard deviation 2.0 pounds. Find the probability that a randomly selected newborn baby weighs:

a. Less than 10 pounds.
Answer: There is a 91.15% probability that a randomly selected newborn baby weighs less than 10 pounds.

b. Between 6 and 8 pounds.
Answer: There is a 37.9% probability that a randomly selected newborn baby weighs between 6 and 8 pounds.

17. A math test has a mean of 75 and a standard deviation of 10 points. Assume the test scour is a normally distributed variable. What percentage of the scores would be between the following?

a. 65 and 85 Answer: 0.6827 = 68.27%

b. 55 and 95 Answer: 0.9545 = 95.45%

c. Above 95 Answer: 0.0228 = 2.28 %

d. Less than 65. Answer: 0.1587 = 15.87 %

Exam 10A

Name:
Instructor:
Section:

Write your work as neatly as possible.

1. Show that $f(x)=\frac{1}{4}\left(x+\frac{1}{2}x^3\right)$ is a probability density function on the interval [0, 2].

2. Find the value of the constant k so that $f(x)=k(x^2-x^3)$ is a probability density function on the interval [0, 1].

3. Find the value of the constant k so that $f(x)=k\left(\frac{2}{x^2}-\frac{1}{x^3}\right)$ is a probability density function on the interval $[1, \infty)$.

4. Find the mean, variance, and standard deviation of the random variable x associated with the probability density function $f(x)=\frac{1}{2}(2-x)$ on the interval [0, 2].

5. The life span of a certain brand of light bulbs is an exponentially distributed random variable x with an expected value of 750 (hours). What is the probability that a randomly chosen bulb will have a life span of less than 500 hours?

6. Let X be a normal random variable with $\mu=150$ and $\sigma=8$. Find $P(140<\mathrm{X}<160)$.

7. If the Stanford-Binet IQ test is a normal curve with a mean of 100 and a standard deviation of 20, what percent of the population has an IQ between 110 and 120?

Exam 10B

Name:
Instructor:
Section:

Write your work as neatly as possible.

1. Show that $f(x)=\frac{6}{5}(x^2+2x^3)$ is a probability density function on the interval [0, 1].

2. Find the value of the constant k so that $f(x)=k(1-x^2)$ is a probability density function on the interval [0, 1].

3. Find the value of the constant k so that $f(x)=kxe^{-2x^2}$ is a probability density function on the interval $[0, \infty)$.

4. Find the mean, variance, and standard deviation of the random variable x associated with the probability density function $f(x)=\dfrac{80}{x^{7/2}}$ on the interval $[4, \infty)$.

5. The life span of a certain brand of light bulbs is an exponentially distributed random variable x with an expected value of 750 (hours). What is the probability that a randomly chosen bulb will have a life span of between 700 and 900 hours?

6. Let X be a normal random variable with $\mu = 3.5$ and $\sigma = 0.5$. Find $P(\text{X} > 3.1)$.

7. The weight of muffins made by a bakery is normally distributed with a mean of 2 oz and a standard deviation of 0.25 oz. What is the probability that a muffin selected at random will weigh between 1.75 oz and 2.25 oz?

Exam 10C

Name:
Instructor:
Section:

Write your work as neatly as possible.

1. Show that $f(x) = 4e^{-4x}$ is a probability density function on the interval $[0, \infty)$.

2. Find the value of the constant k so that $f(x) = kx^{3/2}$ is a probability density function on the interval [0, 4].

3. Find the value of the constant k so that $f(x) = kxe^{-x^2}$ is a probability density function on the interval $[0, \infty)$.

4. Find the mean, variance, and standard deviation of the random variable x associated with the probability density function $f(x) = \frac{1}{4}(3 - x)$ on the interval [0, 2].

5. The life span of a certain brand of light bulbs is an exponentially distributed random variable x with an expected value of 750 (hours). What is the probability that a randomly chosen bulb will have a life span of more than 1000 hours?

6. Let X be a normal random variable with $\mu = 80$ and $\sigma = 5$. Find $P(70 < X < 85)$.

7. If the Stanford-Binet IQ test is a normal curve with a mean of 100 and a standard deviation of 20, what percent of the population has an IQ above 110?

Exam 10D

Name:
Instructor:
Section:

Write your work as neatly as possible.

1. Show that $f(x) = \frac{1}{24}(x + 3\sqrt{x})$ is a probability density function on the interval [0, 4].

2. Find the value of the constant k so that $f(x) = k(2x + x^3)$ is a probability density function in the interval [0, 2].

3. Find the value of the constant k so that $f(x) = \dfrac{k}{x^{4/3}}$ is a probability density function on the interval $[8, \infty)$.

4. Find the mean, variance, and standard deviation of the random variable x associated with the probability density function $f(x) = \dfrac{64}{x^5}$ on the interval $[2, \infty)$.

5. The life span of a certain brand of light bulbs is an exponentially distributed random variable x with an expected value of 750 (hours). What is the probability that a randomly chosen bulb will have a life span of between 800 and 1000 hours?

6. Let X be a normal random variable with $\mu = 360$ and $\sigma = 20$. Find $P(320 < \text{X} < 380)$.

7. The weight of muffins made by a bakery is normally distributed with a mean of 2 oz and a standard deviation of 0.25 oz. What is the probability that a muffin selected at random will weigh less than 2.25 oz?

Answers to Chapter 10 Exams

Exam 10A

2. 12
3. $\frac{2}{3}$
4. $\frac{2}{3}, \frac{2}{9}$, 0.4714
5. 0.4866
6. 0.7888
7. 14.98 percent

Exam 10B

2. $\frac{3}{2}$
3. 4
4. $\frac{20}{3}, \frac{320}{9}$, 5.9628
5. 0.092
6. 0.7881
7. 68.26 percent

Exam 10C

2. $\frac{5}{64}$
3. 2
4. $\frac{5}{6}, \frac{11}{36}$, 0.5528
5. 0.2636
6. 0.8185
7. 30.85 percent

Exam 10D

2. $\frac{1}{8}$
3. $\frac{2}{3}$
4. $\frac{8}{3}, \frac{8}{9}$, 0.9428
5. 0.0806
6. 0.8185
7. 84.13 percent

Chapter 11 ■ Taylor Polynomials and Infinite Series

Section 11.1

1. Find the fourth Taylor polynomial of $f(x)=\frac{1}{x-2}$ at $x=0$.

   Answer: $P_4(x)=-\frac{1}{2}-\frac{1}{4}x-\frac{1}{8}x^2-\frac{1}{16}x^3-\frac{1}{32}x^4$

2. Find the fourth Taylor polynomial of $f(x)=x\ln x$ at $x=1$ and use it to estimate the value of $f(1.1)$ rounded off to five decimal places.

   Answer: $P_4(x)=(x-1)+\frac{1}{2}(x-1)^2-\frac{1}{6}(x-1)^3+\frac{1}{12}(x-1)^4$; 0.104842

3. Use the third Taylor polynomial at $x=0$ to obtain an approximation of the area under the graph of $f(x)=e^{-2x}$ from $x=-0.2$ to $x=0.2$.

   Answer: 0.41075

4. Find a bound in the error incurred in approximating $f(x)=e^{-x/2}$ by the third Taylor polynomial of f at $x=0$ in the interval [0, 1].

   Answer: 0.0026

5. Find the fourth Taylor polynomial of $f(x)=\frac{x}{1-x}$ at $x=0$.

   Answer: $P_4(x)=x+x^2+x^3+x^4$

6. Find the fourth Taylor polynomial of $f(x)=\sqrt{x}$ at $x=4$.

   Answer: $P_4(x)=2+\frac{1}{4}(x-4)-\frac{1}{64}(x-4)^2+\frac{1}{512}(x-4)^3-\frac{5}{16384}(x-4)^4$

7. Find the fourth Taylor polynomial of $f(x)=\frac{1}{2x+3}$ at $x=0$.

   Answer: $P_4(x)=\frac{1}{3}-\frac{2}{9}x+\frac{4}{27}x^2-\frac{8}{81}x^3+\frac{16}{243}x^4$

Section 11.2

1. Write down the first five terms of the sequence $\left\{\frac{n+1}{n^2}\right\}$.

Answer: $2, \frac{3}{4}, \frac{4}{9}, \frac{5}{16}, \frac{6}{25}$

2. Write down the first five terms of the sequence $\left\{\frac{(-1)^{n-1}}{n!}\right\}$.

Answer: $1, -\frac{1}{2}, \frac{1}{6}, -\frac{1}{24}, \frac{1}{120}$

3. Find the general term for the sequence $-\frac{1}{2}, \frac{3}{4}, -\frac{5}{8}, \frac{7}{16}, \ldots$.

Answer: $\left\{\frac{(-1)^n(2n-1)}{2^n}\right\}$

4. Find the general term for the sequence $-\frac{1}{2}, \frac{1}{4}, -\frac{1}{8}, \frac{1}{16}, \ldots$.

Answer: $\left\{\left(-\frac{1}{2}\right)^n\right\}$

5. Determine whether the sequence $\{a_n\}$ where $a_n = \frac{1}{\sqrt{2n+1}}$ converges or diverges. If it converges, find its limit.

Answer: Converges to 0.

6. Determine whether the sequence $\{a_n\}$ where $a_n = \frac{2n+1}{n-1}$ converges or diverges. If it converges, find its limit.

Answer: Converges to 2.

7. Determine whether the sequence $\{a_n\}$ where $a_n = \frac{n^2(n+1)}{n+2}$ converges or diverges. If it converges, find its limit.

Answer: Diverges

8. Determine whether the sequence $\{a_n\}$ where $a_n = \dfrac{n}{\sqrt{n^2+2}}$ converges or diverges. If it converges, find its limit.

Answer: Converges to 1.

9. Find the first 4 terms of the arithmetic sequence with $a_1 = 4$ and $d = \dfrac{1}{2}$.

Answer: $a_1 = 4$, $a_2 = 4\dfrac{1}{2}$, $a_3 = 5$, and $a_4 = 5\dfrac{1}{2}$.

10. Evaluate: $\lim\limits_{n\to\infty} \dfrac{3n+10}{5n+2}$.

Answer: $\dfrac{3}{5}$

11. Evaluate: $\lim\limits_{n\to\infty} \dfrac{\sqrt{9n^6-4}}{5n^3+2}$.

Answer: $\dfrac{3}{5}$

12. Evaluate: $\lim\limits_{n\to\infty} \dfrac{\sqrt{9n^6-4}}{5n^4+2}$.

Answer: 0

13. Evaluate: $\lim\limits_{n\to\infty} \left(\dfrac{1}{n} - \dfrac{1}{n+1}\right)$.

Answer: 0

14. Evaluate: $\lim\limits_{n\to\infty} \dfrac{\sqrt{n^4}+12n}{3n^2-10}$.

Answer: $\dfrac{1}{3}$

Section 11.3

1. Find the sum of the telescoping series $\sum_{n=0}^{\infty}\left(\frac{1}{n+4}-\frac{1}{n+5}\right)$.

   Answer: $\frac{1}{4}$

2. Determine whether the geometric series $\sum_{n=0}^{\infty}\left(-\frac{3}{2}\right)^{n+1}$ is convergent or divergent. If it is convergent, find its sum.

   Answer: Divergent

3. Find the sum of the geometric series $\sum_{n=0}^{\infty}\left(\frac{2^n}{3^{n+1}}\right)$ if it is convergent.

   Answer: 1

4. Find the sum of the geometric series $\sum_{n=0}^{\infty}\left(\frac{4}{\pi}\right)^n$ if it is convergent.

   Answer: Divergent

5. Determine whether the series $\sum_{n=0}^{\infty}\left(\frac{6(3^n)-2^n}{4^n}\right)$ is convergent or divergent. If it is convergent, find its sum.

   Answer: 22

6. Find a rational number that has decimal representation 0.428571428571... .

   Answer: $\frac{3}{7}$

7. Peter and Tracy take turns tossing a pair of dice. The first to throw a 7 wins. If Peter starts the game, then it can be shown that his chances of winning are given by $p=\frac{1}{6}+\left(\frac{1}{6}\right)\left(\frac{5}{6}\right)^2+\left(\frac{1}{6}\right)\left(\frac{5}{6}\right)^4+\cdots$. Find p.

   Answer: $p=\frac{2}{3}$

8. Find the rational number that has decimal representation 0.333333333....

   Answer: $\frac{1}{3}$

Section 11.4

1. Determine whether the series $\sum_{n=0}^{\infty} \frac{2n}{3n-10}$ is convergent or divergent.

   Answer: Divergent.

2. Determine whether the series $\sum_{n=0}^{\infty} \left(\frac{\pi}{2}\right)^n$ is convergent or divergent.

   Answer: Divergent.

3. Determine whether the series $\sum_{n=0}^{\infty} \left(\frac{\pi}{10}\right)^n$ is convergent or divergent.

   Answer: Convergent.

4. Determine whether the series $\sum_{n=0}^{\infty} \frac{2n}{\sqrt{5n^{10}+2}}$ is convergent or divergent.

   Answer: Convergent.

5. Determine whether the series $\sum_{n=0}^{\infty} \frac{3^n}{2^{n+5}}$ is convergent or divergent.

   Answer: Divergent.

6. Use the integral test to determine whether the series $\sum_{n=1}^{\infty} \frac{3}{n+1}$ is convergent or divergent.

   Answer: Divergent

7. Use the integral test to determine whether the series $\sum_{n=27}^{\infty} \frac{3}{n \ln^3 n}$ is convergent or divergent.

   Answer: Convergent.

8. Use the integral test to determine whether the series $\sum_{n=1}^{\infty} \frac{n+10}{n^5}$ is convergent or divergent.

   Answer: Convergent.

9. Use the comparison test to determine whether the series $\sum_{n=1}^{\infty} \frac{3n-10}{5n^2}$ is convergent or divergent.

   Answer: Divergent.

10. Use the comparison test to determine whether the series $\sum_{n=1}^{\infty} \frac{2^n}{5^n+11}$ is convergent or divergent.

    Answer: Convergent.

11. Determine whether the series $\sum_{n=1}^{\infty} \frac{\sqrt{n+1}}{n+1}$ is convergent or divergent.

    Answer: Divergent.

12. Find the value of p for which the series $\sum_{n=2}^{\infty} \frac{1}{n(\ln n)^p}$ is convergent.

    Answer: $p > 1$.

13. Determine whether the series $\sum_{n=1}^{\infty} \frac{1}{4n^3-1}$ is convergent or divergent.

    Answer: Convergent.

14. Determine whether the series $\sum_{n=1}^{\infty} \frac{3}{\sqrt{n}+10}$ is convergent or divergent.

    Answer: Divergent.

15. Determine whether the series $\sum_{n=1}^{\infty} \frac{\sqrt{n^2+2}}{5n+3}$ is convergent or divergent.

    Answer: Divergent.

Section 11.5

1. Find the radius of convergence and the interval of convergence of the power series $\sum_{n=0}^{\infty}\left(\frac{(x+1)^n}{2^n}\right)$.

   Answer: $R = 2$; $(-3, 1)$.

2. Find the radius of convergence and the interval of convergence of the power series $\sum_{n=0}^{\infty}\frac{n}{n+1}(2x)^{n-1}$.

   Answer: $R = \frac{1}{2}$; $(-\frac{1}{2}, \frac{1}{2})$

3. Find the radius of convergence and the interval of convergence of the power series $\sum_{n=0}^{\infty}\frac{n!(x-1)^n}{2^n}$.

   Answer: $R = 0$; Converges only at $x = 1$.

4. Find the radius of convergence and the interval of convergence of the power series $\sum_{n=0}^{\infty}\left(\frac{(-1)^n n^2 (x-1)^n}{2^n}\right)$.

   Answer: $R = 2; (-1, 3)$

5. Find the radius of convergence and the interval of convergence of the power series $\sum_{n=0}^{\infty}\left(\frac{n!}{(2n+1)^3}\right)(x-2)^n$.

   Answer: $\mathrm{R} = 0$. Converges only at $x = 2$.

6. Find the radius of convergence and the interval of convergence of the power series $\sum_{n=0}^{\infty}\left(\frac{2n}{3n+1}\right)x^n$.

   Answer: $R = 1$; $(-1,1)$

Section 11.6

1. Find the Taylor series of $f(x)=e^{-2x}$ at $x=0$ and give its radius and its interval of convergence.

Answer: $\sum_{n=0}^{\infty}\frac{(-1)^n 2^n x^n}{n!}$; $R=\infty$; $(-\infty,\infty)$

2. Find the Taylor series of $f(x)=\frac{3}{2x-1}$ at $x=1$ and give its radius and its interval of convergence.

Answer: $3\sum_{n=0}^{\infty}(-1)^n 2^n (x-1)^n$; $R=\frac{1}{2}$; $(\frac{1}{2},\frac{3}{2})$

3. Find the Taylor series of $f(x)=x^2 e^{-x/2}$ at $x=0$ and give its radius and its interval of convergence.

Answer: $\sum_{n=0}^{\infty}\frac{(-1)^n x^{n+2}}{n!\,2^n}$; $R=\infty$; $(-\infty,\infty)$

4. Use the tenth-degree Taylor polynomial to approximate $\int_0^1 x^2 e^{-x^2}\,dx$.

Answer: 0.19003

5. Find the Taylor series of $f(x)=xe^{-x}$ at $x=0$.

Answer: $x-x^2+\frac{x^3}{2!}-\frac{x^4}{3!}+\cdots+\frac{(-1)^n x^{n+1}}{n!}+\cdots=\sum_{n=0}^{\infty}\frac{(-1)^n x^{n+1}}{n!}$

6. Find the Taylor series of $f(x)=\frac{1}{2}\left(e^x+e^{-x}\right)$ at $x=0$.

Answer: $1+\frac{x^2}{2!}+\frac{x^4}{4!}+\cdots+\frac{x^{2n}}{(2n)!}+\cdots=\sum_{n=0}^{\infty}\frac{x^{2n}}{(2n)!}$

7. Find the Taylor series of $f(x)=\ln(1+\frac{x}{2})$ at $x=0$.

Answer: $\frac{x}{2}-\frac{x^2}{8}+\frac{x^3}{24}-\frac{x^4}{64}+\frac{x^5}{160}-\frac{x^6}{384}+\cdots+\frac{(-1)^{n+1}x^n}{2^n(n)}+\cdots=\sum_{n=1}^{\infty}\frac{(-1)^{n+1}x^n}{2^n(n)}$

Section 11.7

1. Use the Newton-Raphson method to approximate the zero of $f(x) = 2x^3 - 3x + 4$ lying between $x = -2$ and $x = -1$. Continue with the iteration until two successive approximations differ by less than 0.0001.

   Answer: -1.64743

2. Show that $f(x) = 2x^4 - 3x - 5$ has a zero between $x = 1$ and $x = 2$. Then use the Newton-Raphson method to find the zero.

   Answer: 1.47316

3. Make a rough sketch of the graphs of $f(x) = e^x$ and $g(x) = 2 - x^2$. Use your sketch to approximate the point of intersection of the two graphs. Then use the Newton-Raphson method to refine the approximation of the *x*-coordinate of the point of intersection.

   Answer: 0.5373

4. The altitude in feet of a rocket *t* seconds into flight is given by $s = f(t) = -t^3 + 96t^3 + 195t + 5$. Use the Newton-Raphson method to find the time when the rocket hits Earth.

   Answer: $T \approx 97.99$

5. Use the Newton-Raphson method to approximate the zero of $xe^x - 1 = 0$.

   Answer: 0.56714

6. Use the Newton-Raphson method to approximate the zero of $x^2 - 2 = 0$.

   Answer: 1.414241

7. Use the Newton-Raphson algorithm to approximate the zero of $f(x) = x^2 - 3$. Start the iteration with initial guess $x_0 = 1$ and terminate the process when two successive approximation differ by less than 0.00001.

   Answer: 0.73205

Exam 11A

Name:
Instructor:
Section:

Write your work as neatly as possible.

1. Find the third Taylor polynomial of $f(x) = \sqrt{x+1}$ at $x = 3$.

2. Use the second Taylor polynomial of $f(x) = x^{1/3}$ at $x = 8$ to approximate $\sqrt[3]{8.2}$ and find a bound for the error in the approximation.

3. Write down the first five terms of the sequence $\left\{ \frac{(-1)^{n+1}}{n^2} \right\}$.

4. Determine whether the sequence $\left\{ \frac{2n^2+1}{3n^2-1} \right\}$ converges or diverges If the sequence converges, find its limit.

5. Determine whether the geometric series $\sum_{n=0}^{\infty} \left(-\frac{2}{3} \right)^n$ is convergent or divergent. If it is convergent, find its sum.

6. Find a rational number that has decimal representation 0.371371... .

7. Find the radius of convergence and the interval of convergence of the power series $\sum_{n=0}^{\infty} \left(\frac{2n}{3n+1} \right) x^n$.

8. Find the Taylor series of $f(x) = \frac{x^2}{1+3x}$ at $x = 0$ and give its radius and its interval of convergence.

9. Make a rough sketch of the graphs of $f(x) = e^{-x}$ and $g(x) = 3x - 1$ to find an approximation of the x-coordinate of the point of intersection. Then use the Newton-Raphson method to refine the approximation accurate to 5 decimal places.

Exam 11B

Name:
Instructor:
Section:

Write your work as neatly as possible.

1. Find the fourth Taylor polynomial of $f(x)=\sqrt{x}$ at $x=1$.

2. Use the third Taylor polynomial of $f(x)=\dfrac{1}{x+1}$ at $x=0$ to approximate $f(0.2)$ and find a bound for the error in the approximation.

3. Find the general term of the sequence $-\frac{1}{2}, \frac{2}{3}, -\frac{3}{4}, \frac{4}{5}, \ldots$.

4. Determine whether the sequence $\left\{1-\dfrac{2^n}{5^n}\right\}$ converges or diverges If the sequence converges, find its limit.

5. Find the sum of the geometric series $\sum_{n=0}^{\infty}\left(\dfrac{100}{99}\right)^n$ if it is convergent.

6. Determine whether the series $\sum_{n=0}^{\infty}\dfrac{3(2^n)-1}{4^n}$ is convergent or divergent. If it is convergent, find its sum.

7. Find the radius of convergence and the interval of convergence of the power series $\sum_{n=0}^{\infty}\dfrac{2^n(x-1)^n}{n!}$.

8. Find the Taylor series of $f(x)=\dfrac{1}{1+x^2}$ at $x=0$ and give its radius and its interval of convergence.

9. Show that $f(x)=3x^3-2x+4$ has a zero between $x=-2$ and $x=-1$. Then use the Newton-Raphson method to find the zero.

Exam 11C

Name:
Instructor:
Section:

Write your work as neatly as possible.

1. Find the Taylor polynomial of degree 3 of $f(x) = xe^{-x}$ at $x = 0$.

2. Use the second Taylor polynomial of $f(x) = \sqrt{1-x}$ at $x = 0$ to obtain an approximation of $f(-0.1)$ and find a bound for the error in the approximation.

3. Write down the first five terms of the sequence $\left\{\frac{2^{n+1}}{n!}\right\}$.

4. Determine whether the sequence $\left\{\frac{n}{2n+1} - \frac{n+1}{n}\right\}$ converges or diverges If the sequence converges, find its limit.

5. Find the sum of the geometric series $\sum_{n=0}^{\infty}\left(\frac{\pi}{4}\right)^n$ if it is convergent.

6. Determine whether the series $\sum_{n=0}^{\infty}\frac{2(3^n)-1}{2^n}$ is convergent or divergent. If it is convergent, find its sum.

7. Find the radius of convergence and the interval of convergence of the power series $\sum_{n=0}^{\infty}\left(\frac{n!}{(2n+1)^3}\right)(x-2)^n$.

8. Find the Taylor series of $f(x) = x^2e^{-x}$ at $x = 0$ and give its radius and its interval of convergence.

9. Show that $f(x) = 2x^3 - 3x + 2$ has a zero between $x = -2$ and $x = -1$. Then use the Newton-Raphson method to find the zero.

Exam 11D

Name:
Instructor:
Section:

Write your work as neatly as possible.

1. Find the fourth Taylor polynomial of $f(x)=\dfrac{1}{x+1}$ at $x = 1$.

2. Find a bound in the error incurred in approximating $f(x)=\sqrt{x}$ by the third Taylor polynomial of f at $x=1$ in the interval [1, 2].

3. Find the general term of the sequence $\dfrac{2}{3},-\dfrac{4}{9},\dfrac{8}{27},-\dfrac{16}{81},\ldots$.

4. Determine whether the sequence $\left\{\dfrac{2n^3}{(3n+2)^2}\right\}$ converges or diverges. If the sequence converges, find its limit.

5. Find the sum of the telescoping series $\displaystyle\sum_{n=0}^{\infty}\left(\frac{2}{n+1}-\frac{2}{n+2}\right)$.

6. Determine whether the series $\displaystyle\sum_{n=0}^{\infty}\frac{3(2^n)-3^n}{3^n}$ is convergent or divergent. If it is convergent, find its sum.

7. Find the radius of convergence and the interval of convergence of the power series $\displaystyle\sum_{n=0}^{\infty}\left(\frac{(-1)^n n^2(x-1)^n}{2^n}\right)$.

8. Find the Taylor series of $f(x)=\dfrac{x}{1+x}$ at $x=0$ and give its radius and its interval of convergence.

9. Show that $f(x)=2x^4-3x-2$ has a zero between $x=-1$ and $x=0$. Then use the Newton-Raphson method to find the zero.

Answers to Chapter 11 Exams

Exam 11A

1. $2+\frac{1}{4}(x-3)-\frac{1}{64}(x-3)^2+\frac{1}{512}(x-3)^3$
2. 2.01653; 0.00000193
3. $1,-\frac{1}{4},\frac{1}{9},-\frac{1}{16},\frac{1}{25}$
4. $\frac{2}{3}$
5. $\frac{3}{5}$
6. $\frac{371}{999}$
7. $R=1$; $(-1,1)$
8. $\sum_{n=0}^{\infty}(-1)^n 3^n x^{n+2}$; $R=\frac{1}{3}$; $(-\frac{1}{3},\frac{1}{3})$
9. 0.52961

Exam 11B

1. $1+\frac{1}{2}(x-1)-\frac{1}{8}(x-1)^2+\frac{1}{16}(x-1)^3-\frac{5}{128}(x-1)^4$
2. 0.832; 0.0016
3. $\left\{\frac{(-1)^n n}{n+1}\right\}$
4. 1
5. Divergent
6. $\frac{14}{3}$
7. $R=\infty$; $(-\infty,\infty)$
8. $\sum_{n=0}^{\infty}(-1)^n x^{2n}$; $R=1$; $(-1,1)$
9. -1.30068

Exam 11C

1. $x - x^2 + \dfrac{x^3}{2}$
2. 1.04875; 0.000625
3. $4,\ 4,\ \dfrac{4}{3},\ \dfrac{4}{3},\ \dfrac{8}{15}$
4. $-\dfrac{1}{2}$
5. $\dfrac{4}{4-\pi}$
6. Divergent
7. $R = 0$; Converges only at $x = 2$.
8. $\displaystyle\sum_{n=0}^{\infty} \frac{(-1)^n x^{n+2}}{n!}$; $R = \infty$; $(-\infty, \infty)$
9. -1.47569

Exam 11D

1. $\dfrac{1}{2} - \dfrac{1}{4}(x-1) + \dfrac{1}{8}(x-1)^2 - \dfrac{1}{16}(x-1)^3 + \dfrac{1}{32}(x-1)^4$
2. 0.0390625
3. $\dfrac{(-1)^{n+1}2^n}{3^n}$
4. Diverges
5. 2
6. Divergent
7. $R = 2; (-1, 3)$
8. $\displaystyle\sum_{n=0}^{\infty} (-1)^n x^{n+1}$; $R = 1$; $(-1, 1)$
9. -0.58733

Chapter 12 ■ Trigonometric Functions

Section 12.1

1. The angle measure is given in radians. Covert each angle to degree measure and determine the quadrant in which each angle lies.

   a. $\frac{3}{5}\pi$ Answer: 108^0, II

   b. $\frac{11}{9}\pi$ Answer: 220^0, III

   c. -4.65 Answer: -266.43^0, II

2. Find the complement of the angle $\frac{3}{7}\pi$. Answer: $\frac{\pi}{14}$

3. Find the supplement of the angle $\frac{3}{7}\pi$. Answer: $\frac{4\pi}{7}$

4. Convert 120° to radian measure. Answer: $\frac{2\pi}{3}$ rad.

5. Convert $\frac{3\pi}{4}$ to degree measure. Answer: 135°

6. Convert $-\frac{16\pi}{3}$ radians to degree measure. Answer: -960°

7. Convert $\frac{3\pi}{2}$ radians to degree measure. Answer: 270^0

8. Convert $\frac{5}{12}\pi$ radians to degree measure. Answer: 75^0

9. Convert -12π radians to degree measure. Answer: -2160^0

10. Convert -120^0 degree measure to radians. Answer: $-\frac{2}{3}\pi$

11. Convert $-\frac{5}{2}\pi$ radians to degree measure. Answer: 450^0

12. Convert $\frac{2}{3}\pi$ radians to degree measure. Answer: 120^0

13. Convert $\frac{7}{4}\pi$ radians to degree measure. Answer: 315^0

Section 12.2

1. Evaluate $\sin(-\frac{\pi}{2})$. Answer: - 1

2. Evaluate $\cos(-5\pi)$. Answer: -1

3. Evaluate $\sin\frac{13\pi}{6}$. Answer: $\frac{1}{2}$

4. Evaluate $\cos\frac{9\pi}{4}$. Answer: $\frac{\sqrt{2}}{2}$

5. Evaluate $\sin\left(-\frac{5\pi}{3}\right)$. Answer: $\frac{\sqrt{3}}{2}$

6. Evaluate $\sec\frac{5\pi}{3}$. Answer: 2

7. Evaluate $\csc\frac{13\pi}{4}$. Answer: $-\sqrt{2}$

8. Evaluate $\tan\frac{31\pi}{6}$. Answer: $\frac{\sqrt{3}}{3}$

9. Evaluate $\cot\frac{13\pi}{3}$. Answer: $\frac{\sqrt{3}}{3}$

10. Evaluate $\tan\frac{2}{3}\pi$. Answer: $-\sqrt{3}$

11. Find all values of θ in the interval $[0, 2\pi]$ that satisfy $\cos\theta = -\frac{1}{2}$.

    Answer: $\frac{2\pi}{3}$ and $\frac{4\pi}{3}$

12. Find all values of θ in the interval $[0, 2\pi]$ that satisfy $2\sin\theta = 1$.

    Answer: $\frac{\pi}{6}$ and $\frac{5\pi}{6}$

13. Find all values of θ in the interval $[0, 2\pi]$ that satisfy $3\tan\theta = \sqrt{3}$.

Answer: $\frac{\pi}{6}$ and $\frac{7\pi}{6}$

14. Find all values of θ in the interval $[0, 2\pi]$ that satisfy $\cot\theta = -1$.

Answer: $\frac{3\pi}{4}$ and $\frac{7\pi}{4}$

15. Verify the identity $(1-\sin\theta)(1+\sin\theta) = \frac{1}{\sec^2\theta}$.

16. Verify the identity $\frac{\cos\theta}{1-\sin\theta} = \frac{1+\sin\theta}{\cos\theta}$.

17. Verify the identity $\frac{1+\cos\theta}{\sin\theta} + \frac{\sin\theta}{1+\cos\theta} = 2\csc\theta$

18. Verify the identity $\cos\theta + \cos\theta\cot^2\theta = \cot\theta\csc\theta$.

19. Verify the identity $\sin\theta \cdot \sec\theta = \tan\theta$.

20. Solve the equation $\tan x - \sqrt{3} = 0$ in the interval $[0, 2\pi]$.

Answer: $\frac{\pi}{3}$ and $\frac{4\pi}{3}$

21. Solve the equation $\sin^2 x + \sin x = 0$ in the interval $[0, 2\pi]$.

Answer: 0, π, 2π, and $\frac{3\pi}{2}$

22. Graph the function $f(x) = \sin(x + \frac{\pi}{4})$.

Answer:

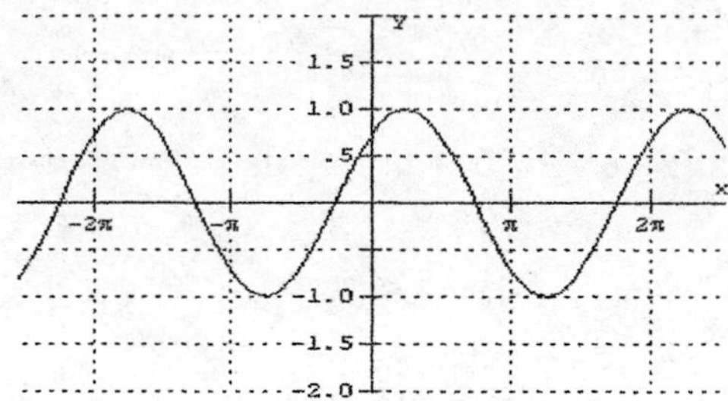

23. Graph the function $f(x) = 3\sin(x + \frac{\pi}{4})$.

Answer:

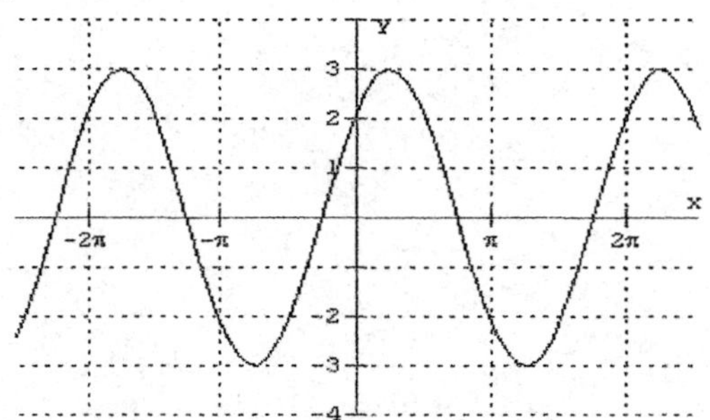

24. Graph the function $f(x) = 3\sin(x + \frac{\pi}{4}) + 2$.

Answer:

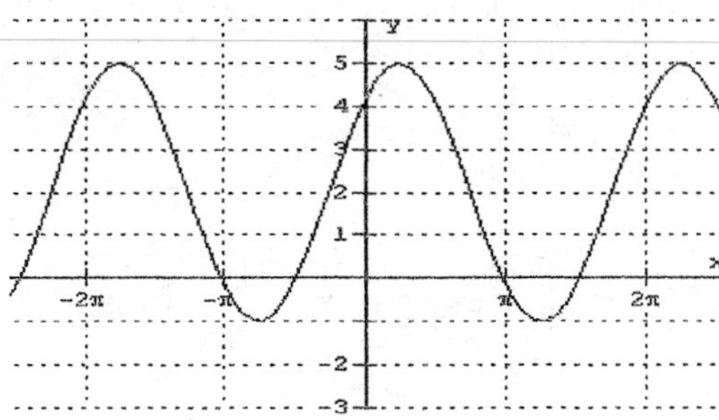

Section 12.3

1. Find the derivative of $f(x) = \sin 5x$.
   Answer: $5\cos 5x$

2. Find the derivative of $f(x) = \sin 2x + 3\cos 4x$.

   Answer: $2\cos 2x - 12\sin 4x$

3. Find the derivative of $f(x) = 2\sec 3x + 4\cot 2x$.

   Answer: $6\sec 3x \tan 3x - 8\csc^2 2x$

4. Find the derivative of $f(x) = \sin(5x - 10)$.

   Answer: $5\cos(5x - 10)$

5. Find the derivative of $f(x) = \cos(5x^2 - 10x + 12)$.

   Answer: $f(x) = -10(x-1)\sin(5x^2 - 10x + 12)$

6. Find the derivative of $f(x) = \tan(2x + 6)$.

   Answer: $2\sec^2(2x+6)$

7. Find $f'(x)$ if $f(x) = x^2 \sin 2x$.

   Answer: $2x(\sin 2x + x\cos 2x)$

8. Find the derivative of the function $f(x) = e^{\sin x + 1}$.

   Answer: $(\cos x)e^{\sin x + 1}$

9. Find the derivative of the function $f(x) = \ln(\sin x + \cos 2x)$.

   Answer: $\dfrac{\cos x - 2\sin 2x}{\sin x + \cos 2x}$.

10. Find $f'(x)$ if $f(x)=\dfrac{\sin 2x}{1+x}$.

Answer: $\dfrac{2(1+x)\cos 2x-\sin 2x}{(1+x)^2}$

11. Find $f'(x)$ if $f(x)=\dfrac{\sin x}{5+\cos x}$.

Answer: $f'(x)=\dfrac{5\cos x+1}{(5+\cos x)^2}$

12. Find $f'(x)$ if $f(x)=(x+4)(5-\sin 7x)$.

Answer: $f'(x)=(5-\sin 7x)+(x+4)(-7\cos 7x)$

13. Find $f'(x)$ if $f(x)=\cos^2 x$.

Answer: $\dot{f}(x)=-2\sin x\cos x=-\sin 2x$

14. Find the derivative of $f(x)=\sin^2(2x+3)$.

Answer: $4\sin(2x+3)\cos(2x+3)$

15. Find the derivative of $f(x)=\sec x\tan x$.

Answer: $\sec x(\sec^2 x+\tan^2 x)$.

16. Find the derivative of $f(x)=\dfrac{\sec x}{1+\tan x}$.

Answer: $\dfrac{\sec x(\tan x-1)}{(1+\tan x)^2}$

17. Find an equation of the tangent line to the graph of $f(x)=\tan x$ at the point $(\frac{\pi}{4},1)$.

Answer: $y=2x+1-\frac{\pi}{2}$

18. Find the equation of the tangent line to the graph of $f(x)=\sin x+x$ at $x=\dfrac{\pi}{2}$.

Answer: $y=x+1$

19. Find the equation of the tangent line to the graph of $f(x) = \sin x - x$ at $x = \dfrac{\pi}{2}$.

Answer: $y = -x + 1$

20. Find the intervals where $f(x) = \sin^2 2x$ for x in $[0, \pi]$ is increasing and where it is decreasing.

Answer: Increasing on $(0, \frac{\pi}{4}) \cup (\frac{\pi}{2}, \frac{3\pi}{4})$; decreasing on $(\frac{\pi}{4}, \frac{\pi}{2}) \cup (\frac{3\pi}{4}, \pi)$

21. Find the derivative of $f(x) = \ln(\sin x + 12)$.

Answer: $f'(x) = \dfrac{\cos x}{\sin x + 12}$

22. Find the derivative of $f(x) = \tan(e^{2x} - 4x + 3)$.

Answer: $f'(x) = (2e^{2x} - 4)\sec^2(e^{2x} - 4x + 3)$

23. Find the derivative of $f(x) = \cot(e^{2x} - 4x + 3)$.

Answer: $f'(x) = -(2e^{2x} - 4)\csc^2(e^{2x} - 4x + 3)$

24. Find the intervals where $f(x) = \cos^3(2x)$ for x in $[0, \pi]$ is increasing and where it is decreasing.

Answer: Increasing on $\left(\dfrac{\pi}{2}, \pi\right)$ and decreasing on $\left(0, \dfrac{\pi}{2}\right)$.

25. Find the intervals where $f(x) = \tan^3(2x)$ for x in $[0, \pi]$ is increasing and where it is decreasing.

Answer: Increasing on $\left(0, \dfrac{\pi}{4}\right) \cup \left(\dfrac{\pi}{4}, \dfrac{3\pi}{4}\right) \cup \left(\dfrac{3\pi}{4}, \pi\right)$.

Section 12.4

1. Evaluate $\int (2x+\cos 2x)dx$. Answer: $x^2+\frac{1}{2}\sin 2x+C$

2. Evaluate $\int 2\sin(2x-7)dx$. Answer: $-\cos(2x-7)+C$

3. Evaluate $\int (2x-5)\cos(x^2-5x+\frac{1}{3})dx$. Answer: $\sin(x^2-5x+\frac{1}{3})+C$

4. Evaluate $\int (\cos x)e^{\sin x}dx$. Answer: $e^{\sin x}+C$

5. Evaluate $\int \frac{\sin\sqrt{x}}{\sqrt{x}}dx$. Answer: $-2\cos\sqrt{x}+C$

6. Evaluate $\int 3x\sec^2 x^2 dx$. Answer: $\frac{3}{2}\tan x^2+C$

7. Evaluate $\int (\cos^2 x+1)\sin x\, dx$. Answer: $-\frac{1}{3}\cos^3 x-\cos x+C$

8. Evaluate $\int \sin^5 3t\cos 3t\, dt$. Answer: $\frac{1}{18}\sin^6 3t+C$

9. Evaluate $\int_0^{\pi/4} 3\sin 2x dx$. Answer: 1.5

10. Evaluate $\int_{-3\pi/4}^{-\pi/4} \cos x\sin x\, dx$. Answer: 0

11. Evaluate $\int_0^{\pi/4} \tan^{3/2} x\sec^2 x\, dx$. Answer: 0.4

12. Evaluate $\int_0^{\pi/2} \frac{\sin x}{1+\cos x}dx$. Answer: $\ln 2$

13. Evaluate $\int \frac{\sin(\ln x)}{x}dx$. Answer: $-\cos(\ln x)+C$

14. Evaluate $\int \frac{\cos x}{\sqrt{6+\sin x}}dx$. Answer: $2\sqrt{(6+\sin x)}+C$

15. Evaluate $\int (\sin x)^{\frac{1}{2}}(\cos x)dx$. Answer: $\frac{2}{3}(\sin x)^{\frac{3}{2}}+C$

16. Evaluate $\int (\sec^2 x)\sqrt{1+\tan x}dx$. Answer: $\frac{2}{3}(1+\tan x)^{\frac{3}{2}}+C$

17. Find the average value (to the nearest hundredth) of the function $f(x)=x\sin x^2$ between $x=0$ and $x=\frac{\pi}{2}$.

Answer: 0.55.

18. Find the average value (to the nearest hundredth) of the function $f(x)=(2x+5)\cos(x^2+5x)$ between $x=0$ and $x=1$.

Answer: 0.2794

19. Find the area of the region under the graph of $f(x)=\sec^2 3x$ from $x=\frac{\pi}{12}$ to $x=\frac{\pi}{9}$.

Answer: $\frac{1}{3}(\sqrt{3}-1)$

20. Find the average value of $f(x)=2x\cos(x^2)$ over the interval $[0,\sqrt{\pi}]$.
Answer: 0

21. Evaluate $\int x\sec^2 x\,dx$. Answer: $x\tan x+\ln|\cos x|+C$

22. Evaluate $\int_0^{\pi/2} x\sin 2x\,dx$. Answer: $\pi/4$

23. Evaluate $\int x\cos xdx$. Answer: $x\sin x+\cos x+C$

24. Evaluate $\int x\sin xdx$. Answer: $-x\cos x+\sin x+C$

25. Evaluate $-\int x^2\sin xdx$. Answer: $x^2\cos x-2(x\sin x+\cos x)+C$

26. Evaluate $\int_0^{\frac{\pi}{2}} x\sin xdx$. Answer: 1

Exam 12A

Name:
Instructor:
Section:

Write your work as neatly as possible.

1. Convert 240° to radian measure.

2. Evaluate $\cot\left(-\frac{\pi}{6}\right)$.

3. Find all values of θ in the interval $[0, 2\pi]$ that satisfy $\sin\theta = -\frac{\sqrt{3}}{2}$.

4. Verify the identity $1-2\sin^2\theta = 2\cos^2\theta - 1$.

5. Find the derivative of $f(x) = (x^2 + \cos 3x)^{3/2}$.

6. Find the slope of the tangent line to the graph of $f(x) = \dfrac{\sin x}{1+\cos x}$ at the point $\left(\frac{\pi}{3}, \frac{\sqrt{3}}{3}\right)$.

7. If $f(x) = x^2 \sin x$, find $f'\left(\frac{\pi}{2}\right)$.

8. Evaluate $\int (2x-9)\cos(x^2 - 9x + 11)dx$

9. Evaluate $\int \frac{1+\cos x}{x+\sin x} dx$

10. Find the area of the region under the graph of $f(x) = \tan^2 x \sec^2 x$ from $x = 0$ to $x = \frac{\pi}{4}$.

Exam 12B

Name:
Instructor:
Section:

Write your work as neatly as possible.

1. Convert $-\frac{3\pi}{4}$ radians to degree measure.

2. Evaluate $\sec\left(-\frac{11\pi}{4}\right)$.

3. Find all values of θ in the interval $[0,\pi]$ that satisfy $\cos 3\theta = 1$.

4. Verify the identity $\frac{1}{1+\cos\theta}+\frac{1}{1-\cos\theta}=2\csc^2\theta$.

5. Find the derivative of $f(x)=e^x \sin 2x$.

6. Find the rate of change of $f(t)=e^{-t}\cos 2t$ when $t=\pi$.

7. If $f(x)=\tan^3 x$, find $f'\left(\frac{\pi}{4}\right)$.

8. Evaluate $\int \tan x\, dx$.

9. Evaluate $\int_{\pi/6}^{\pi} \sin x \cos x\, dx$.

10. Find the average value of $f(x)=3x\cos(x^2)$ over the interval $[0,\sqrt{\pi}]$.

Exam 12C

Name:
Instructor:
Section:

Write your work as neatly as possible.

1. Convert $-\frac{8\pi}{3}$ radians to degree measure.

2. Evaluate $\cot\left(-\frac{\pi}{4}\right)$.

3. Find all values of θ in the interval $[0, 2\pi]$ that strictly satisfy $\tan\theta = -1$.

4. Verify the identity $\sec\theta - \cos\theta = \sin\theta\tan\theta$.

5. Find the derivative of $f(x) = xe^{\sin x}$.

6. Find the relative extrema of $f(x) = \cos x + \sqrt{3}\sin x$ on $[0, 2\pi]$.

7. How fast is $f(x) = \frac{\sin x}{x}$ changing when $x = \frac{\pi}{2}$?

8. Evaluate $\int \frac{\sin x}{\sqrt{1+2\cos x}}dx$.

9. Evaluate $\int_0^{\pi/2} \sqrt{\sin x}\cos x\,dx$.

10. Find the average value of $f(x) = x\sin(x^2 + \frac{\pi}{3})$ over the interval $[0, \sqrt{\pi}]$.

Exam 12D

Name:
Instructor:
Section:

Write your work as neatly as possible.

1. Convert 320° to radian measure.

2. Evaluate $\csc\left(\frac{7\pi}{2}\right)$.

3. Find all values of θ in the interval [0, 2] that satisfy $\sin \pi x = 1$.

4. Verify the identity $\tan\theta + \cot\theta = \csc\theta \sec\theta$.

5. Find the derivative of $f(x) = 3\sin x \cos 2x$.

6. Find an equation of the tangent line to the graph of $f(x) = \cos^2 x$ at the point $\left(\frac{\pi}{4}, \frac{1}{2}\right)$.

7. Find the rate of change of $f(x) = x\tan 3x$ when $x = \frac{\pi}{12}$.

8. Evaluate $\int 2\sin x \cos^2 x\, dx$.

9. Evaluate $\int_0^{\pi/4} (1 + \tan x)\sec^2 x\, dx$.

10. Find the average value of $f(x) = x\sin(x^2 - \frac{\pi}{3})$ over the interval $[0, \sqrt{\pi}]$.

Answers to Chapter 12 Exams

Exam 12A

1. $\frac{4\pi}{3}$ rad
2. $-\sqrt{3}$
3. $\frac{4\pi}{3}$ and $\frac{5\pi}{3}$
5. $\frac{3}{2}(2x-3\sin 3x)(x^2+\cos 3x)^{1/2}$
6. $\frac{2}{3}$
7. π
8. $\sin(x^2-9x+11)+C$
9. $\ln|x+\sin x|+C$
10. $\frac{1}{3}$

Exam 12B

1. $-135°$
2. $-\sqrt{2}$
3. 0 and $\frac{2\pi}{3}$
5. $e^x(\sin 2x+2\cos 2x)$
6. $-e^{-\pi}$
7. 6
8. $-\ln|\cos x|+C$
9. $-\frac{1}{8}$
10. 0

Exam 12C

1. $-480°$
2. -1
3. $\frac{3\pi}{4}$ and $\frac{7\pi}{4}$
5. $(1+x\cos x)e^{\sin x}$
6. $\left(\frac{\pi}{3},2\right)$ rel max;
   $\left(\frac{4\pi}{3},-2\right)$ rel min
7. $-\frac{4}{\pi^2}$
8. $-\sqrt{1+2\cos x}+C$
9. $\frac{2}{3}$
10. $\frac{\sqrt{\pi}}{2\pi}$

Exam 12D

1. $\frac{16\pi}{9}$ rad
2. -1
3. $\frac{1}{2}$
5. $3(\cos x\cos 2x-2\sin x\sin 2x)$
6. $y=-x+\frac{1}{2}+\frac{\pi}{4}$
7. $1+\frac{\pi}{2}$
8. $-\frac{2}{3}\cos^3 x+C$
9. $\frac{1}{2}$
10. $\frac{\sqrt{\pi}}{2\pi}$